Designing and Building Special Cars

Designing and Building Special Cars

André Jute

B. T. Batsford Ltd, London

For Kati and Huba
and
Mary Rose and Joe
and as always
Roz and Charles

© André Jute 1985
First published 1985
Reprinted 1986

ISBN 0 7134 0778 6
Typeset by Latimer Trend & Company Ltd, Plymouth
and printed in Great Britain by Anchor Brendon Ltd,
Tiptree, Essex
for the publishers
B. T. Batsford Ltd,
4 Fitzhardinge Street,
London W1H 0AH

Contents

Acknowledgment

I am grateful to the following individuals and institutions who provided information and illustrations for this book: Brighton Marina; Cambridge Public Library, Lion Yard; Caterham Car Sales; Cheetah Cars; Contemporary Classic Motor Car Company; Cork Public Library, Grand Parade; Ford; Gable Arc Welders; Huba Gall; GP Specialist Vehicles; Interstyl; Liddell and Horner; Marlin Engineering; Midas Cars; Oselli Engine Services; Quality Rod Parts; Joe Quigg; Replicar Imports; Revolution Wheels; Harry J. Sibley; ST Cars; State Library of South Australia; Strand Glassfibre; Sylva Autokits; Thoroughbred Cars; Total Performance; Triking Cars; Weiand; Wolfrace Wheels; John Woolfe Racing. The section by Arthur Mallock on pages 58–59 is reprinted by courtesy of *Cars & Car Conversions* who first published it in January 1983.

Introduction

This book contains all the knowledge you need to design and build your own car. Therefore it also contains all the knowledge required to judge the competence of design and suitability, for your purpose, of mass produced cars and all cars that are in some way *special*. This includes kit cars, modified cars, special interest vehicles, and cars of various ages – veteran, vintage, antique, classic – plus sports cars and all the way up to exotica. If you can design a car with confidence from the ground up, any alterations or other work that you carry out to an existing car will be done with much greater assurance.

The total of automobile knowledge would fill a very substantial library. This book covers the irreducible minimum required; my publisher and I were surprised to find it is so much, but any car is a complex artefact and the special car most of us would design for ourselves is the supreme artefact, so a good deal of knowledge in many diverse fields is necessary.

A lot of automobile knowledge is highly theoretical and requires substantial mathematical and scientific background, and ability to apply this rigorously in the higher reaches of the art, say in designing Formula One cars. Since this is not a book for professional

Figures 0.1, 0.2 and 0.3. Comfort, panache and brute force – cheap. The very popularity of these Fords counts against them with special car enthusiasts

0.2
0.3

Figure 0.4. This Caterham Super Seven has superior performance even from stock Ford engines, but many owners build it simply because it *looks* different.

designers or engineering graduates, I have ruthlessly weeded abstruse maths and replaced it wherever possible with rules of thumb or empirically observed shortcuts that require no more than junior high school maths – and work! In the same spirit, I have given all the useful versions of the various formulae instead of leaving the reader to struggle with algebraic transformations; there is also a table of cubes and cube roots. Wherever possible, I have shown how to make comparisons between materials, say, without having to know what the units mean, by the simple process of an analogy with a familiar material like mild steel. Where the point of a table is a comparison, I have left off the units. Where relevant, there are worked examples. In addition, I have preferred simple one-dimensional geometrical sketches to photographs with their plethora of confusing and irrelevant detail, especially in the discussions of suspension design where the geometry is *everything*. Furthermore, this book is arranged not into theoretically related "logical" sections but according to the flow of design of a car as normally encountered by the special car designer. This has led to a small amount of repetition – on the important subject of aerodynamics for instance – but allows you to keep the book beside your drawing board and work through it sequentially rather than paging back and forth.

If you observe reasonable safety margins, you should, with the aid of this book, be able to design anything from a replicar prevented by its aerodynamic drag from exceeding 100mph to a streamlined two-seater capable of 175mph. That will be good enough for most people, but if you want more, if for instance you want the two-seater autobahnfuhrer to be ultra-light, or if you want to build racers, you will have to look further. For space and cost reasons, I have confined myself here to the art of the special car as attainable through the skills and pockets of the majority of special car designers and builders. For those who want to go on to become formula car designers – or who read for interest – I have mentioned, in the text, the best book I know giving a general introduction to the subject under discussion.

The typical designer and builder of special cars is typical only in that he is an individualist, so I expect that virtually every reader will disagree with me at some stage – say, with my generally apparent view that form without function is abhorrent. But please do bear with my advice on safety-related matters: it's your life – but it could be another roaduser's as well.

A question I'm often asked, but which is really outside the scope of this book to answer in detail, is: "Can I

Figure 0.5. If you pine for a car you could never afford, a replica may be available for fitting to a Beetle chassis. This one is Replicar Imports' Ferrari 250LM lookalike.

Figure 0.6, Even if you could afford the real thing, your insurance company might insist you *drive* an exact copy, like this Cobra from Contemporary Classic Motor Car Company.

afford a special car?" The answer is almost invariably: "Yes, if you can afford an Econobox Lookalike Mark-nothing, you can afford a special car – and the special car could well be cheaper." There are two points to watch out for: while the special car may be either cheaper or more expensive than a bland tin box to acquire initially, insurance is almost always more expensive exactly because it is *special*; and the cost of upkeep of a special car may horrify you. Two examples of upkeep cost will suffice: the oil filter for my Bentley Mk VI special cost eight times as much as that for a Ford and had to be changed four times as often; when I had a Maserati engined Citroen SM, I had to drive 70 miles one way from where I lived to get the engine serviced properly and then 30 miles the other way to get the suspension seen to competently, a round trip of 200 miles and two days wasted waiting around, and earning nothing.

There is another cost to special cars which you may either describe as a hidden cost or as that facet of special cars that makes it possible for you to have a *different* car at all. Most of us don't reckon our own time spent as anything but a labour of love, and believe that a special car is possible *only* because we will do the work ourselves. Certainly, you can design a car as good as anything Ghia, Ital Design, Ogle or Pininfarina can do – but who could afford their labour charges for building it?

Designing and building your own car takes anywhere from one year until you finish.

Happy designing and building!

ANDRÉ JUTE
Bandon, Eire, 1985

Specifying Your Car

1 People and Comfort

The very first decision you must make when you start designing a car is how many people it must carry. Racing cars normally carry only the driver with space for no one else; certain racing cars were required by regulations to provide two seats and became wretched 1½ seaters. A replica Bugatti Type 35 should authentically have 1½ seats which is all there is space for across its 32-inch seat width. (When it was new, people were smaller.) Perhaps an ultra-economy special intended for commuting should have only one seat. An economy special with two seats should logically have them one behind the other to keep the car narrow and save the weight of the differential, as with the Peugeot Quadrilette which appeared after World War I and the Messerschmidt of the 1950s and 1960s.

This shows how complicated even so simple a decision as the seating capacity can be, because a motorcar is nothing but a drivable compromise. Three other design parameters (a fancy word for considerations) must be kept in mind while deciding how many people your ideal car should seat:

– the all-up weight will determine the acceleration and play a very big part in determining fuel consumption in normal use;
– the shape or aerodynamic profile and frontal area will determine top speed and help to determine touring and high speed fuel economy;
– all other things being equal, the more seating capacity, the more a car will cost to build.

The exact calculation of the tradeoff between weight and acceleration, and between aerodynamic efficiency and top speed, will be discussed later but for now it must be borne in mind that, for a given amount of torque from the engine, 0–60mph acceleration times will become longer with increased weight and shorter with decreased weight. Similarly, the car with lesser frontal area and greater efficiency of aerodynamic profile (and attention to detail) will go faster with the same engine than one that is high, wide, and bluff-fronted.

The easiest shape to fit people into is high, wide and square-fronted, the more so if you want to fit two side

Figure 1.1. Small, light and aerodynamically efficient, the Midas offers excellent performance from small engines and motorbike economy. The GRP monocoque is very stiff.

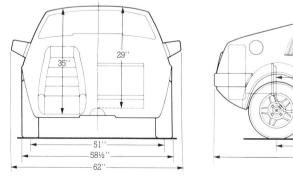
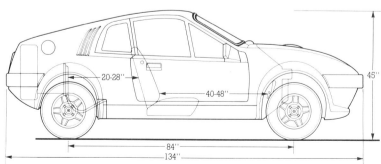

Figure 1.2. The electronic dash on the Probe III shows you everything I have against LEDs and LCDs. Round dials with white numerals on black background are better.

by side, or four in two pairs, even more so if everyone must have good elbow and head room.

Ask yourself the purpose of your special car. How many people will be in it over most of its use? It is a well-known fact that over 90% of car journeys are made with only the driver in the car; in the States figures as high as 98% have been reported. How long are typical journeys with the full complement of passengers ever likely to be? Even in normal use as an only car, will your special car ever have to carry the full complement for long distances? It strikes me that most people these days prefer to take their own car when they go out, even short distances, and only rarely do they take more than the immediate family touring.

The illuminating answers to these questions might lead you to decide on fewer seats – saving the weight of the seats and the luggage space and of course the general construction weight that each additional seat brings with it. Or you may decide that you don't need full leg and head room in seats that are likely to be used at most twice a year for a journey only a mile or two, or ten, long.

Now let's look at the various seating arrangements and their implications. Single seaters are suitable only for racers and economy/commuter specials; $1\frac{1}{2}$ seaters are justified only when building pre-War racer replicas or trying to cheat on post-War sports-racing regulations demanding two seats. That leaves everything from full two seaters to full nine seaters, after which you get into buses.

Two seats in tandem are so unsociable as to be justified only for economy specials and motorbikes.

Two plus two seating is an excellent compromise between the demands of low weight and frontal area and aerodynamic design on the one hand (and the resulting short wheelbase may be desirable from a roadholding and handling viewpoint), and very infrequent use for short journeys by three or four adults on the other. But more than ten minutes in the back seat of most modern 2+2 configurations is likely to give adults or teenagers an excellent impression of what the chicken in the egg feels like. If there is going to be inadequate leg room behind the driver's seat when it is as far forward as possible while still allowing for safe driving, it is better to leave that area "luggage only" and have a 2+1 with the +1 behind the passenger seat.

On the other hand, if the car will frequently have to carry three or four adults, don't design a 2+2, nor if your children are aged ten or more, as they'll grow out of those back seats before the car is built. There is nothing more frustrating than finding that a car over which you have slaved perhaps for several years is no good for its intended purpose for want of an inch of headroom and a half-inch of legroom.

It is a good idea to split the rear seat in +2 configurations – indeed in all coupes and hatchbacks and many sedans – so that a passenger and long or unwieldy parcels (golf clubs are notoriously awkward in any but the largest luggage compartments) may be carried at the same time.

Before we go on to three seaters, the uncompromising two seater still has much to recommend it as a car for a bachelor, a couple who've decided not to breed in the immediate future, or as a second car. The outright two seater can normally have anything from six to thirty inches less wheelbase which, in addition to a weight and perhaps an aerodynamic advantage, makes for a more nimble car and – if it isn't too low – a better commuter because it's faster through the traffic and easier to park in less space.

The three seater is a layout often overlooked. It is an excellent solution that has been applied to classic Panhards and to today's Matra Murena (and its predecessor, the Bagheera) as three full seats abreast, or, in various coachbuilt specials, as a single full seat set crosswise behind the two front seats and called an opera seat. The three-abreast solution is limited to mid-engined or front drive cars where the drive tunnel does not interfere. (Or rear engined cars of course – but that is a crude solution to the problem of positioning the drivetrain for any except beach buggies and other VW based specials, and the gearbox tunnel will definitely interfere with three-abreast seating here.) If you're building a vintage style with the propshaft under the floor, a bench seat might also offer three-

Figure 1.3. Don't let your car's interior damn it as an amateur effort – but don't burden a humble motor with too much interior. This Ghia city car strikes a happy medium.

abreast seating, but it will be a scrunch because the body, if authentic, will probably be less (much less in most cases) than 50 inches across the elbow line on the inside, and 51 inches on the seat is an absolute minimum space required to accommodate three modern adults. In 1914, coachbuilders reckoned on 16 inches minimum per person *on the seat* with another $4\frac{1}{2}$ inches or more across the elbow line, but people were smaller then. Two adults and a child *may* be comfortable on 48 inches if the child doesn't fidget.

A minimum lengthwise space for a seat with legroom for an adult in the rear is 30 inches from the back of the front seat to the back of the rear seat. This should allow for long-distance travel in reasonable comfort, though not luxury which starts at 32 inches

and reaches Jaguar or Mercedes 500SEL sumptuousness between 35 and 40 inches. On the other hand, if that same seat is turned sideways it will take up only 17–20 inches along the length of the car and offer a good deal more legroom; this solution was often applied to three seater coupes in the 1920s and 1930s. I cannot understand why the makers of mostly useless +2 seating arrangements do not revive this very intelligent configuration for cars like the Porsche 944 or the Jaguar XJS, the rear "seats" of which torture even children.

Normally, at this stage of design, I reckon 55 inches from the back of the driver's seat to the firewall, which just happens to be the distance I take up, complete with luxurious seat and space for pedal movement. To

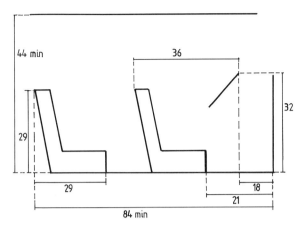

Figure 1.4. My personal minimum measurements for carrying four adults. You should take your own, starting perhaps with your existing car or a VW Beetle.

find out what suits you best, sit in a car in which you feel comfortable, adjust the seat – and the steering wheel, if possible – until you are comfortable. Then measure the distances as on Figure 1.4; you can make adjustments later for the space required by different pedal boxes, etc.

It is possible to find a few inches of length by seating driver and passengers on higher seats, so that their legs are more vertical, as in a truck seat. This will also bring the body more upright and extra headroom will have to be found. The same effect can be achieved by keeping the front of the seat high but hollowing the seat out under the bottom, bringing the knees closer to the chin. This only works for rear passengers and must not be overdone, not only because it would be difficult to get out of again, but because a seat too high at the front in relation to the bottom can be uncomfortable and can cut off blood circulation by pressure against the underside of the thighs. Lotus uses this approach in the back of their Elite and Excel, but if you are over 30 or even slightly broad of beam – or, more to the point, if your passengers will be – try it first before you copy the layout. The "bucket" made by the wheelarches and the drive tunnel can grasp one quite relentlessly. Another car you should look at – and one that is more easily available – is the ubiquitous VW Beetle: the relationship of seat and steering wheel and pedals in the front match those of the 1928 Ford Model A Roadster almost exactly.

In mid-engined three-abreast configurations, one could place the driver in the middle seat with the passengers on either side of him but moved backward some three to five inches to give him extra elbow room.

This is a logical place from a control and balance viewpoint and, since 90% of the time only the driver is in the car, is an additional safety factor in that the driver is further removed from any side impact. Setting the passenger back slightly is also something you should do if a two seater is for any reason, say because it is a period replica, any narrower than 38 inches inside from door to door.

Dickey seat configurations, whether +2 or +1, are too anti-social to consider seriously unless you live in California or Florida; elsewhere in the States and in Europe, that space in replicas is better saved for a decent-sized fuel tank and/or luggage. It is not for nothing that the English cabriolet was for a long time better known as a "foursome *sociable*".

When it comes to four seaters, don't waste your time drawing diamond patterns and other strange designs. The only configuration that works really well is the tried and proven one of driver and passenger in the front and two passengers in the rear. In a full four seater one must allow for the driver a length of about 55 inches and for the passenger behind him between 30 and 40 inches (preferably not less than 32 inches). Anything less than 30 inches in the rear is not a full four seater.

If the car is to be strictly a four seater, why not make the seats all the same as the driver's? Four fully adjustable bucket seats really do look luxurious. If the car is strictly a four seater, it may also be possible to have a lower roofline than for a five seater. Five seats, the fifth one normally in the back over the drive tunnel, usually need a slightly higher roofline to make space for the fifth passenger's head and the propshaft. An extra inch of headroom can mean as much as 60 square inches of frontal area to push through that invisible liquid, air: it all costs petrol.

Six seaters seem to have declined with the increased popularity of the floorshift and bucket seats; with stylists' increased awareness of the penalties of frontal area and the present foreseeable preponderance of RWD for the bigger cars wide enough to take three abreast, I really don't see the bench seat making a big come-back. In fact, many so-called five seaters are really only four seaters or 4+1 seaters: the luxurious and admirable Jaguar XJ sedans are normally described as 4/5 seaters, but the padding over the drive tunnel is too thin to allow a third passenger to take long journeys in the back and headroom is also less than in the two flanking seats.

Seven to nine seaters are limousines and mini-buses or the ingenious Swedish and French "familiale" station wagons. There's really not much to say about their design, except that, if you have three rows of seats, you should consider turning the middle one so

Table 1.1: The average man and his car.

These are my own average of the average figures from several sources. Though they may be of some use to designers working in the studios of the megalomanufacturers, building a car someone else will have to live with, they should be treated with the greatest suspicion by the special car builder. Rather than accepting them at face value, use them either as a table to generate your own offsets against or merely to check that you have considered all dimensions.

Transverse Dimensions

Elbow room, minimum, two people	40 in
Elbow room, moving, per person	25 in
Man's back, fully clothed	23 in
Comfortable seatback, shoulder level	22 in
Trunk, maximum width	19.5 in
Spread of knees, minimum	18 in
Spread of knees, comfortable	24 in
Seat centreline to side of car, optimum	14 in
Pedals, minimum width	3 in
Pedals, optimum width	4–5 in
Pedals, round, maximum diameter	4 in
Pedals, length, minimum	1 in
Pedals, optimum length	3 in
Pedals, minimum separation	2 in
Accelerator, width, minimum to optimum	3–4.5 in
Accelerator, optimum angle from heel to toe to right	10°
Horizontal visibility, minimum requirement	180°
Horizontal visibility, optimum	220°
Seat cushion, minimum width	19.5 in
Steering wheel, diameter, average	14–17 in
Steering wheel, rim thickness	1.75–2 in
Gear lever to steering wheel, optimum distance	2.5 in

Longitudinal dimensions

Length of seat on cushion	17 in
From seat backrest to nearest part of steering wheel, minimum	19 in
Front of seat to nearest part of pedal, minimum	12.5 in
Seat adjustment, fore and aft, minimum, in 1 in steps	6 in

that it faces the rearmost one. If you then seat only four people in the back, they can share the footwells quite reasonably. If you intend regularly seating three passengers abreast, it is best to have all the seats facing forward and paying the length-penalty for it. The Volvo design of five seats in front of a dog-guard plus a rear-facing bench seat behind the dog-guard is an intelligent solution to the problem of carrying mixed parties of adults and children. But bulk carriers are not what most of the readers of this book mean when they speak of special cars.

So far we have looked at what might be described as "normal" measurements across the length and breadth of a car. In the "normal" seating position, for "normal" adult headroom, you should allow a passenger cabin 42–46 inches high from the top of the carpet to the underside of the headlining (in convertibles, the underside of the support struts). We have seen that this requirement may be decreased for rear seat pas-

sengers by hollowing out the seat. For the driver, this is impossible and there are only two possibilities: lower the seat and put the driver in a semi-reclining position. The big Marcos, for instance, without reclining the driver too far, gets down to 42 inches overall height by lowering the seat right down onto the floor. This means that more legroom is required which is the main reason this solution is not applied to the rear seats. Lowering the driver's seat may also bring other ergonomic problems: in sleek cars the seat adjustability may be severely limited by the proximity of the top rail of the windscreen to the driver's forehead. Again the Marcos solution is ingenious: not only an adjustable steering wheel but an adjustable pedal box as well!

Watch that you don't go too low or the car will be difficult to drive in traffic. I think that the Marcos and Super Seven (née Lotus Seven) are right on the limit here. Any lower and the driver reclines so far that not only vision but control becomes impossible. When I

From seat backrest to nearest part of instrument panel, minimum	29 in
Accelerator, best length	9–10 in
Accelerator and footrest, angle from horizontal	28°
Accelerator, arc of depression, maximum	15°
Steering wheel overhang over front of seat cushion	5 in

Vertical dimensions

Seat cushion to underside of roof, minimum	42.5 in
Clearance above head, minimum	2 in
Seat cushion to top of head, tall person, sitting upright	40.5 in
Backrest height from cushion top, absolute minimum	18 in
Eye level above cushion top, average ⎰ incl. 2 in cushion	30–32 in
Chin level above cushion top, average ⎱ depression	27.5 in
Backrest height, from cushion top, optimum for rearward visibility	19.5 in
Steering wheel, lowest part, to floor, minimum	21 in
Steering wheel to seat cushion clearance, minimum	5 in
Vertical seat adjustment, desirable	4 in
Pedal stroke, maximum	4 in
Brake pedal higher than accelerator, maximum	4 in
Height of pedals (brake, clutch) above floor, optimum	6 in
Height of pedals above floor, absolute maximum (trucks!)	10 in
Hand, normal position on steering wheel, to foot on unpressed brake or clutch pedal, minimum (diagonally)	26 in
Angular displacement of hip joint, optimum	15°
Angular displacement of hip joint, maximum	25°
Angular displacement of knee joint, optimum	105°
Angular displacement of elbow operating controls and turning wheel, optimum	15°
Optimum zone for manipulating controls: between shoulder and elbow	??°
Angle between thigh and back in normal driving position	97–108°
Angle of backrest inclination, common	20°
Angle of vertical visibility, above horizontal eye line, optimum	15°
Angle of vertical visibility, below horizontal eye line, minimum to optimum to maximum (including instruments)	15–30–35°
Claustrophobia angle (between horizontal chin line and lowest sight line to road, i.e. highest point of dash or bonnet)	15°

Figure 1.5. The rally seat, left, has slots for racing harness but requires a tilting frame for use in two-door cars; the sports seat has a folding mechanism built in.

drove a Porsche to work, I used to get nightmares in which the most prominent feature was a huge wheel of a city bus towering over me with the driver another four feet up and unable to see my car or me down below hub-height. It is said that Sir William Lyons designed the window line of his Jaguars by the rule that no part of the seat should rise above the lower edge of the window. My rule for the height of low slung cars is that the roof should rise at least three inches above the window line of the average large car it is likely to meet in its travels.

Another problem with ultra low seats in a sports car with the engine up front is that the drive tunnel intrudes. In the TVR, for instance, it is a long reach *up* to the gear lever, but here the problem is partly caused

Figure 1.6. Porsches are fair game for kit car manufacturers and this one, from GP Specialist Vehicles, can easily be mistaken for the real thing – if you don't fit VW dials!

by the car having a backbone spaceframe chassis with the propshaft inside which is a good deal more bulky than a mere sheet metal or GRP sheath over the propshaft. You get used to it, of course, especially if you use it as an everyday car, but it is as well to consider this problem at the specification stage and certainly at the design stage.

You will notice that I give the measurements *I* normally work to rather than any notional "average." Those figures can also be misleading in that often they reflect minimum acceptable standards as defined by mass market manufacturers. An orthopedic consultant scotched a suggestion by his mass market Eurobox clients that he should design a seat without any adjustment (and therefore cheap) because they had market research that "proved" that the average buyer set the rake of his seatback at exactly 102° by saying "Everybody who's paid his money has the right to redesign my seat by turning one simple knob. *I* sit at 108 degrees." (The same man also told me, "A seat is designed by sitting in it." What a refreshingly sensible attitude.) If you're designing and building a car for yourself, it would be foolish not to take cognizance of the fact that *you* are *not* average. A variety of seats is normally available cheaply at scrapyards and wreckers or, if you know which aftermarket seats you will fit,

you can buy one before you start designing the car (and mount it on a pedestal for use at your drawing board until your car is built). Put the seat in the middle of some clear space and sit in it. A cardboard box weighted with a brick does duty as a pedal. A steering wheel from the wreckers on top of a broomstick completes the tableau. Now you get someone to measure from the top of your head to the floor and from the soles of your feet to the back of the seat. Add a *minimum* of two inches for headroom. Five inches for pedal movement is enough. Hold the wheel at a comfortable reach and angle and get a measurement across the elbows; add *at least* two inches and preferably four or five inches for elbow movement on the door side – the other elbow can use the space above the drive tunnel. This you treat as a first set of measurements because, as you design your car, compromises will have to be made here and there.

Gabriel Voisin, the aviator, aircraft constructor, lover, and builder of some of the most superbly efficient and potent cars of the inter-War years, compared a car without space for luggage to "a weapon without ammunition." The ideal here is that each passenger should have a full size suitcase, each female passenger should have a vanity case, and each male passenger should have either a camera case or a

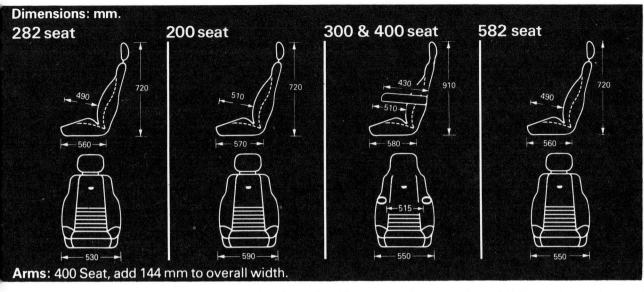

Dimensions: mm.

282 seat — 490, 720, 560, 530

200 seat — 510, 720, 570, 590

300 & 400 seat — 430, 910, 510, 580, 515, 550

582 seat — 490, 720, 560, 550

Arms: 400 Seat, add 144 mm to overall width.

Figure 1.7. Seat measurements are good and well but the only way to select a seat is to *sit* in it – get a money-back guarantee if you buy seats by mail-order.

briefcase. A suitcase is normally 26 inches long by 20 inches wide by a minimum of 6 inches deep. Softsided suitcases bulge out to about 10 inches. A decent-sized vanity case or case for two cameras and assorted lenses is $12 \times 9 \times 6$ inches; a "standard" briefcase is 17 inches long by 12 inches wide by 2–4 inches deep. Most people who travel by air also own shoulder bags and these are nominally $12 \times 12 \times 6$ inches but very quickly bulge out to $14 \times 14 \times 8$–9 inches. If you cannot fit the

shoulder bags as well as the other luggage, it may be an idea to design the luggage space so that the shoulder bags will fit in the place of the vanity/camera/briefcase combination. Or you can design and construct your own luggage to fit the shape of the available space.

We now know how many people must be seated, in how much comfort and with what luggage. We have a box of certain dimensions; now is the time to decide on its shape.

Figure 1.8. William Towns's ingenious Mini-based Hustler started out as an all-wood car but customer-resistance soon caused Towns to add modular metal and GRP versions.

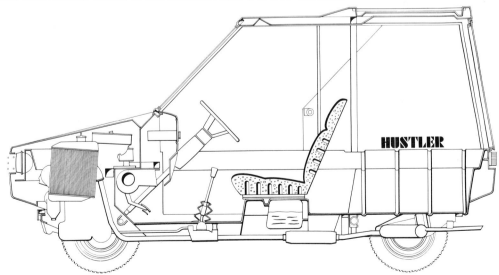

HUSTLER

2 Style and Impact

After you've decided how many passengers you are going to seat, comes the pleasurable decision of the style of the car. In fact, most of us know first what the car will look like and then we compromise a little with appearance for the sake of function. A drawing board is a great aid in defining the impossible. For instance, it should take no more than a weekend with pencil and paper to convince you that a fastback tail on a full four seater must either sacrifice rear headroom or be longer than necessary in the wheelbase and therefore less nimble. Another example: the long-bonnet vintage replica will require a wheelbase longer by up to 20 inches than a modern style with the same passenger capacity, and it will sacrifice top speed against the similarly engined but more aerodynamically efficient modern design. It will also be less economical with fuel in the higher speed ranges and even more so at top speed.

As with the decision about the number of passengers and their luggage, styling conventions cost in lost space, in additional weight and in decreased aerodynamic efficiency, all of which translates into more

Figure 2.1. The Escort/Lynx engine/transmission/final drive pack is a natural for mid-engined specials. This Ghia version is the granddaddy of them all and uses the autobox.

money. The list of sacrifices made for the sake of style goes on: beware that you don't have to drop the front suspension to change a plug – the beauty will pall before the skinned knuckles have healed, to paraphrase Sir Henry Royce. That is not to say that any car is perfect, only that in some the compromises are more bearable than in others. Everybody knows that the Lotus cars of the 1950s and 1960s were rather prone to fall apart with or without provocation (door pulls attached to nothing but the cardboard that gave the padding its shape!), but I have yet to meet an owner who will admit anything more damning than that their Lotus is "perhaps a little fragile if you don't know how to handle a thoroughbred"; they are more impressed by its handling, economy and its sheer exhilaration. Yet, objectively, it is cramped, noisy and – dare I say it? – consistently unreliable. However, your dream car may be an Elan with all the bugs ironed out. The question is, Can you do it? I think the answer is, Nearly, or, Almost. There are a great many new materials and techniques that will allow you to design and build your latterday Elan almost as light as Colin Chapman's and with guaranteed reliability. Alternatively, you can build as light as Chapman and with more reliability but not the ultimate you can achieve

by sacrificing a little of the lightweight agility. To achieve both you're likely to pay dearly. What we're looking at is a three-way compromise: weight vs reliability vs cost. You can choose to be on the advantageous side of two attributes only by making sacrifices in the third.

Another obvious example of compromise is the monocoque or unit construction convertible which, even with additional and often heavy bracing, is almost never as stiff torsionally as the saloon from which it was derived. This applies even to convertibles sitting on separate chassis but is not so important unless the body is supposed to enhance the stiffness of the chassis. What is sacrificed in the monocoque convertible, besides torsional stiffness and weight, is the aerodynamic smoothness of the saloon. The next time you're belting along in your ragtop, spare a look for the blonde in the next seat: which way is her hair blowing? Is that the direction the wind should be blowing over a speeding car? That explains why convertibles are always faster (and more economical on petrol) with the top up. The integral rollbar is not just a styling device: many present-day convertibles cannot have it removed without collapsing the first time you drive over a cigarette butt.

Figure 2.2. If you're thinking small, light and fast, don't overlook three-wheelers. Just standing still, this Triking looks fast enough to grow hair on your chest.

The compromise does not end just within the confines of the car itself. You must also consider your skills as a constructor (or the cost of sending the work out to a specialist) and your materials preferences. As an example, if you want to work in aluminium (aluminum) and you lack panel beating skills, you are virtually limited to vintage replicas, military replicas and utilities. I have no stomach for military replicas or utilities, but I've designed a number of vintage replicas for myself and others because, with careful design, they can be constructed of flat sheets given single curvatures only; it is also possible to make a cheap mould for GRP construction by bending hardboard but again complex curves are not possible. All these compromises really boil down to design considerations rather than specifications of the car but it is well to keep in mind that the two have to interact.

The list of styles you can choose literally has no end, and any list I make is bound to be incomplete. Specials break down into two non-controversial classes: replicars and new designs. Replicars can cover brand new "veterans", vintage and post-vintage replicas, sports racing replicas and cars like Vegantune's Elan-but-better. I suppose anyone who now builds a leadsled or lowrider is building a replicar, as those styles are really identified with the 1950s and 1960s. There's a spate of VW-based Lambo Countach lookalikes and they're replicars of a car still in production. The Caterham Super Seven, built under license from Lotus, could be called a replicar in so far as the last Seven Lotus built was a Series IV (strange flat-back rear mudguards) which Caterham dropped very smartly to return to the Series III (round rear mudguards). Note that I class as replicars even cars that are intended only to evoke an era or style of motoring even if they do not copy a specific model; Americans know these as nostalgicars. A brand new design is a great deal more difficult to define or find. The only recent new design that I can think of is William Towns's Hustler, which is the modular car the Ford Motor Company and others have been promising for years but so far not delivered. Before that the last genuinely new design was Alec Issigonis's Mini and before that the hatchback pioneered by Citroen in – wait for it – 1934; at the same time he pioneered mass market front wheel drive. Before that, Levassor's systémè Panhard and now we're almost back with Daimler and Benz at the dawn of motoring. Genuinely innovative design, as opposed to logical and even clever development of existing standards, will write your name in lights but it is more

Figure 2.3. A Lotus racer by any other name, the Caterham Super Seven is worth its high price for lightweight Colin Chapman design. Caterham are licensed by Lotus to build it.

than most special car builders can hope for. The special car builders who made it into manufacturedom didn't want to reinvent the wheel: they were just looking for ways of making it spin faster. With the notable exception of Ettore Bugatti, who was an artist, the great designers were all specialists – and even Bugatti had his blind spots, vide his valve-cooling arrangements. Bentley was an engine designer of genius but his chassis betray his railway-shed upbringing. Chapman was a chassis designer who never designed an engine in his life and for a hobby practised miserliness on each fraction of a gramme of weight. Maurice Olley, the father of independent front suspension, designed and tested suspensions all his life, first for Rolls-Royce, then for General Motors. The great Professor Porsche designed some of the most marvellous engines ever but could, unless prevented by his assistant Rabe, commit the most elementary suspension blunders. Even such men could not manage all-round excellence.

Stylists and body shapers are a lesser class of men – though the prima donnas among them are not likely to admit it – and we can quite reasonably aspire to competing with them and even bettering them. Beauty is in the eye of the beholder, and since your special car will come out of your own pocket, there is only one beholder that counts: you. While you may start off with less experience and perhaps less talent than a Giugiaro, he labours under one huge disadvantage that you do not: he designs not to please himself but to a commission from a megalocommittee or on spec to impress such a committee enough to buy the design from him. He must therefore take account of the preferences and quirks of the members of the committee (and their internal power-struggles) as well as what is likely to happen in the market place six, seven or ten years hence when the design hits the streets.

Nobody chooses your own compromises, but certain styles do limit your choices severely. The scale of your vintage replica is determined, quite literally and without exception, by the size of the wheels you decide to fit and the largest size (diameter) tires suited to your performance parameters. This is why Glenn Pray's beautiful and persuasive Auburn replica is not full size and why Brooks Stevens's Excalibur looks odd. The British builder of a largish vintage replica is virtually limited to choosing 15-inch wheels and 70% profile tires because any other combination will give him either a smaller diameter or will limit him to cross-ply tires that do not have the ultimate handling capabili-

Figure 2.4. The curse of mid-and rear-engined special cars is often a slack gearlever. This Ford autobox for the Escort has a bypass giving 93% efficiency at high speeds.

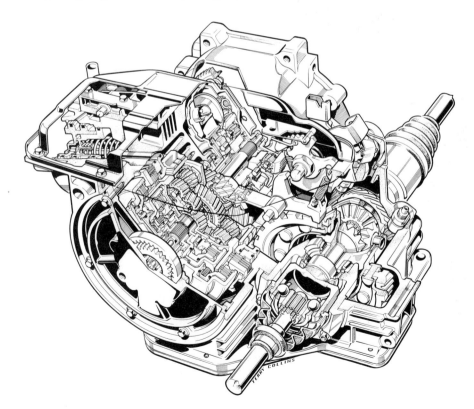

Figure 2.5. The Seven is an instant club racer and this is reflected in the two important gauges – tacho and oil pressure – placed directly in the driver's sightline.

Figure 2.6. When you get your ergonomics and your aesthetics as neatly integrated as in this Probe IV, you can relax and start counting your 'Best Interior' prizes.

ties. However, on 15-inch wheels fitted with 235 × 70 tires, you can go all the way up to a megalomaniac 142-inch wheelbase (like on the Panther de Ville) and still by dint of careful design make everything look right. On the other hand, if you start with a Bentley MkVI chassis which is high off the ground, and fit the most cost-effective wire-wheels from the same Jaguar that the wheels for the purpose-built special came from, it looks all wrong because of the additional height of the Bentley which normally has 16-inch wheels. So your choices are: Stick with the 16-inch Bentley wheels and cross-ply tires which are not so good for racing, fit ultra-low profile tires available in 16-inch sizes, which looks wrong, switch to 15-inch wheels which are attractive because they are easily available in wire patterns and take available radials but which also looks wrong, lower the Bentley chassis radically (difficult and expensive to do right), or chuck the Bentley chassis out and design your own to be low enough to suit the 15-inch wheels that take the tires from the corner garage and still look right.

Lil' John Buttera says, "If it looks right, it is right." For my current project, a vintage style twin screen torpedo on a 134-inch wheelbase, I'm choosing 205/70 × 15-inch tires on the grounds that it's what will come with the wheels I'm using and that replacements are cheap because its the standard tire for the Jaguar saloon.

If for any reason – say you already have a set of 14-inch magnesium wheels that you want to keep – you use smaller wheels, the whole of a vintage replicar must be scaled down or it will look wrong. At the other extreme, if you're trying to get the nose of a mid-engined Countach eater down low enough to see over from a reclining position, you might try to swop those 14-inch wheels for 13-inchers. On a car like that it is, I think, permissible to have larger wheels at the rear than the front and you may in any event, once the car is built, have to set up the handling by changing the wheel sizes. I have yet to see a Mini-based kit car or special that doesn't benefit by going to 13-inch wheels both front and rear.

Offroaders should be high off the ground. Nothing looks more ridiculous than a set of all-terrain knobblies on a car with its tailpipe only a cat's whisker above instant self-destruction.

Sports cars should be low, but not lower than three inches above the window line of larger cars. Until recently, received wisdom was that a sports car was by definition narrow. This no longer applies; some sports cars have become wider to improve the general comfort of driver and passengers, others are wide for structural reasons, such as the TVR mentioned in the previous chapter. The one sports car of recent years

specifically and consciously designed to be narrow is the Midas whose designer was aiming for the least possible frontal area which would then reflect in the highest possible performance and economy from a given small engine. For the moment, you can specify the width of your car as elbow room for two plus the width of the drive tunnel plus the thickness of the two doors. For European use the overall width of any kind of car should not exceed 70 inches, with 66 inches a far nimbler width and 72 inches an absolute outside limit which I would not like to take into the lanes and byways. For Stateside use, cars up to 74 inches wide are acceptable. But remember, if the width adds nothing to your comfort or the performance of the car, you're paying good money to push unproductive space through the air. Overhangs over tires should be small – an inch maximum – but you must observe the legal requirement that the tires not protrude beyond the bodywork above hub-height. On vintage replicars two inches of overhang helps modern tires look a little slimmer.

Front and rear overhangs should be kept to a minimum consistent with the desired wheelbase, passenger and luggage capacity, and chosen style. A vintage replicar really should have no overhang beyond the quite modest sweep of the rear mudguard. A sports car handles best with a wheel at each corner and the engine well back, though this may conflict with the highly theoretical desired radius of gyration which has to do with the way the car vibrates on its springs when

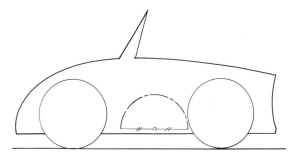

Figure 2.7. The radius of gyration is the arc in which the sprung mass of the car could be said to be concentrated while still oscillating at the same frequency as the body.

it hits a bump (see page 66). In general, as most enthusiasts know, having the engine well back will give better braking and handling and roadholding. Large overhangs and weights outside the four corners defined by the wheels will almost always affect the handling detrimentally. Note, however, that in existing chassis the weight is very often placed where it is to balance another weight. For instance, cutting the rear of some pre-War Talbot chassis off behind the quarter-elliptical spring mounting affects the handling adversely because it results in a new and unfavourable weight distribution. A newer example: I know the incompetent manufacturer of VW-based kit cars instantly simply by where he sites the spare wheel, the battery and the fuel tank. Unless other arrangements have been made to change the weight distribution, VW kit car manufacturers would do well to print in their manuals a prominent warning to buyers not to move the spare wheel. Going back to the time of the Talbots mentioned above, you may find that many of the real cars from the period handle better with the fashionable sidemounted spare wheels removed from the wheel-wells in the mudguards to the back, and virtually all replicars will be improved in the same way by moving the spare wheel rearward. As will be seen from Figure 10.11 (see page 120) the car I'm designing right now has twin sidemounted spares but that isn't because I don't practice what I preach: it is because the all-ali Rover V8 I intend using weighs only 360 lb all up and the Salisbury diff at the back comes to hefty 200 plus lb once the inboard discs and shafts and wishbones are on it and the fuel tank with 20 Imperial gallons will be slung behind it. My original specification read "twin sidemounted spares, luggage box to open down to bumper height", but even so I will test it with the sidemounts in place before I go to the expense of making the mudguards with wheel wells, just in case I have to move the wheels to the back. First though, I will see if I cannot get away by just removing one sidemount altogether, leaving the one on the kerbside to balance the weight of the driver for the majority of unaccompanied trips.

It is difficult to make a full four seater lower than 50 inches and virtually impossible to make it habitable under 48 inches high without having an extremely long wheelbase. Wheelbases shorter than about 84 to 88 inches tend to make the car susceptible to sneeze-steering, especially when coupled to the high ratio racks the exponents of the ultra-nippy often fit: it's like driving an early Porsche in a 60 mph crosswind that changes direction every few seconds. That leads us directly to roadholding, handling and performance.

Before we go to performance specification, let me reassure you. If by now you feel you have to keep so many things in mind – things you shouldn't do, things you cannot do, things you must do, what will have which effect on what else – that you need a computer, don't worry. Once we start actually designing your car rather than just talking about what it should be like, everything falls into place almost automatically. And what makes it fall into place with that practised touch is this disciplined, logical approach: How many people and what luggage? What style? What sacrifices must I make for space and style? What performance? What will all that cost in compromise elsewhere?

Figure 2.8. The Ford Model B coupe (pronounced 'coop') or Deuce is, in the opinion of many, *the* classic hotrod and the author is happy to concur.

3 How Fast and How Well?

Most of us can quote at least two performance parameters of whatever car we presently drive: top speed in miles per hour and 0–60mph acceleration in seconds. Motorbikers and drag racers often prefer to quote an elapsed time through the quarter mile in seconds and a terminal speed at the end of the quarter mile in mph. Suspension engineers will give you an earful of polar moments of inertia and transient response times and lateral gees (g for gravity). Even the least technically minded enthusiast can also tell you whether his car corners well and whether it rolls (leans over) a lot while cornering hard.

This is only a very small sample of a babel of technicalities that can soon overwhelm the novice designer. But, before he starts putting his car on a drawing board, he must know how fast he wants it to go and how fast he wants it to accelerate in order to allow space for a suitable sized engine. And he must have some idea of how he wants it to handle so that the various masses (bodies with weight) can be disposed of in the most advantageous manner. The answer is not to let yourself be snowed under by technicalities. Choose three or four simple parameters, specify in some consistent way (so that you can compare across various competing designs you may make) what you want in each attribute and forget the rest until it raises its head at a logical point in the progress of the design. You can then study each complication in isolation before

Figure 3.1. Cars must go, they must corner, and they must stop. How well they do all these things is up to the designer. Set your sights high and you can't go seriously wrong.

returning to make adjustments for its interaction with facets of the design you dealt with earlier. I've been at this a long time and still do it that way. The only caveat is that you must finish the design on the drawing board absolutely and not leave any niggling little problems to be worked out "in the metal": they never do work out and this kind of "workshop-think" is probably responsible for more half-finished, abandoned projects than straightforward incompetence.

Normally I select only four parameters of performance at the specification stage. You can of course read through the rest of the book and choose other parameters more important to you.

How fast do I want the car to go? Or, what must its top speed be? This one's quite simple. You pick a figure. An ultra-economy special does not need a top speed over 55mph; if it's on an ultra-short wheelbase, it shouldn't have a top speed over 35mph. A high-off-the-ground veteran or antique replica is best governed to 20mph. Vintage replicars should be able to do the genuine ton with three-wheelers being capable of 80mph; I realize these figures were only dreams between the two World Wars but they are easily achievable with modern materials, techniques, and knowledge. A modern-shaped sports car should be able to touch the ton with an engine around 1 litre (61 cubic inches) and 120mph with a 2-litre engine. 2.8 litres or over should give 130mph: if you can't match

Figures 3.2 and 3.3. Compact, powerful, cheap and common, the Ford V6 engines in carburettor 135BHP and fuel injected 150BHP versions are very popular with special builders.

3.3

or better the German Ford Capri even when freed from the restraints its designers laboured under, you shouldn't be designing and building your own. The sports or sports-racing replica types, often with 1950s style bodies like the AC Ace (Cobra) should for the same engine output manage something between 10 and 20mph slower. I'm now talking about cars for everyday road use, with appropriate gearing; many owners will find a 130mph top speed academic and prefer to gear for traffic, sacrificing top speed for acceleration. If you're building a modern streamline sports car with an AJ6 or V12 Jag or a big Ford or Chev V8 – and if your suspension, brakes and general engineering arrangements are up to it – you could aim over the 150mph mark but this could easily cost enough to make it viable to buy a pre-loved Jaguar XJS or to borrow some more money and buy a good used Ferrari or Aston.

Another way of determining top speed is to choose your engine first. Perhaps you already have an engine. Perhaps you have special knowledge of or had good experience with a certain engine. Perhaps you want a generally available engine with a choice of either hotrod or economy goodies in case you change your mind later. Perhaps you want to experiment with diesel or LPG or steam. Perhaps you want an all-ali engine for low weight: it is normally possible to achieve for most engines with a range of performance packages available a good range of BHP and torque outputs. You will have to sacrifice some engine flexibility at the higher specific outputs and, at the extreme, very narrow powerbands will make the car a curse to drive long after the novelty of massive power under those infrequent perfect conditions has palled; under these circumstances it is always better, in an existing car, to go to a different – normally bigger – engine.

If you're designing for yourself from the ground up, you can choose your compromises to a different priority. You may choose to trade off a few weighty comforts for more mph from the same number of horses. Every thousand pounds of weight takes at least 14bhp to drive at 130mph. You could elect to work very hard on your aerodynamic profile and detailing to reduce drag and so make the same horses drive the car faster. You will be rewarded with a higher speed and better economy for the hours spent over the drawing board fitting the exhaust pipe into the prop tunnel to lower the floor and then rearranging the seating in order to lower the roofline an inch to reduce the frontal area by a full square foot (which gives a saving of around 5%). So, you can use the engine you have and still choose a speed anywhere within reason by making compromises elsewhere.

The point about compromises, here as elsewhere, is that they could actually be an improvement! One of the most comfortable car seats I have ever sat in consisted of a bent tube frame with a webbing of leather straps and absolutely no padding; it was in a Ferrari Daytona and the reason nobody has ever copied it is probably because it doesn't *look* luxurious. Yet it is luxurious – and light, and a space-saver. Another lightweight yet comfortable seat, from a less obvious source, is the one fitted to the Fiat Panda. Convince yourself that the pejorative sense of "compromise" does not apply to motor car design and you will soon come to see that the challenge of solving the conflicting demands of man and machine by the most cost-effective and often pleasure-enhancing compromise is the great attraction of special cars.

How fast must the car accelerate from standstill to 60mph? If you are young or you often have to match your car against others at traffic lights, the specified acceleration will be of much more interest. Even if your main driving is out of town, you will still be interested in acceleration, though of a slightly different kind.

Acceleration from standstill to 60mph is a function of only two factors: weight and torque. We shall return to the mathematics of torque vs weight = acceleration in the next chapter and the technical ins and outs of torque will be explained in the chapter on engines. For now it is enough to know that torque is a *twisting movement* – like turning a wheel – of a force times a distance; it is not time-dependent (like horsepower, which is a rate of doing work). We all know that one has to exert more force to move a heavy object than to move a light one the same distance, or that the same force will move a light object further than a heavy one. If you use a tennis racket to hit a tennis ball and a

soccer ball, the tennis ball as the lighter object will travel much further in the same time.

Theoretically, air drag and other small factors (such as the inertial forces of the oil in the sump!) can affect acceleration times. In practice though, for our purposes, if you can put the power on the ground – which you should be able to do after reading the chapters on suspension design – you need only worry about one thing if you want to go faster: weight. An optimal weight distribution will help tremendously but in almost all but out-and-out purpose-designed dragsters, other considerations such as seating will take precedence.

So, unless you want to breathe on your engine for more torque or unless you want to go to more cubic inches which will also deliver more foot pounds of torque, you must look to weight reduction to achieve your specified acceleration from standstill to 60mph. With an existing car you can slim only so far before you transgress safety standards, but designing from the ground up opens vistas of materials and methods that often cost no more than equivalent mild steel except in that they are labour intensive – something the mass market men care about but irrelevant to you. It is for instance possible to design a GRP car quite incompetently and still have it weigh only 60–70% as much as a similarly designed mild steel monocoque or unit construction: both cars will offer the same tensile strength and stiffness; in fact, since the GRP car will have been designed by tensile stiffness, it will be superior to the steel body in tensile strength. A design that makes adequate use of the special properties of GRP, such as the facility for local thickening and reinforcement, should not weigh more than half as much as a steel body of equal strength. Carbon fiber, Kevlar and developing technologies can make further savings, but first exhaust the possibilities of GRP. Wood is another much underrated construction material but I think it suffers from a psychological barrier. Don't forget that the first very successful Marcos racers had wooden chassis and that the metal chassis was introduced only in 1969 and then because Jem Marsh found he could get them made cheaper! Nobody who looked after his wooden-chassised Marcos correctly ever experienced a chassis failure. William Towns's Hustler also started out as an all-wood car before being joined by its steel-and-GRP clones.

At what level should you set your acceleration requirement? With the exception of ultra-economy specials and cars with engines under 1.5 litres (90cid), I think all specials should be able to do 0–60mph in less than 10 seconds. Anything over 12 seconds is a disgrace, even for Mini-engined specials. Any car with sporting pretensions and an engine over 2.0 litres

Figure 3.4. The Mini-Marcos grew up to manufacturedom as the Midas. Really good special cars get to be kit cars and then go into series production. Hurrah for Harold Dermott!

should manage 0–60mph in 8.5 seconds or less. I know this is yet a long way off Super Seven performance but the Super Seven is in a class of its own and is in this context better viewed as a racer made slightly civilized than a stripped down sports car.

If you want to match Porsche turbos in the 5-second bracket and you're willing to sacrifice almost all comforts (but not superlative roadholding) for that aim, you would be better off buying the fully developed Super Seven than trying to roll your own – because that's literally what you'll be doing, rolling, if you shave that extra ounce of weight in the wrong place. The Super Seven comes with engines up to a twin-cam 150bhp but Caterham lists a complete car minus engine and gearbox. If I lived in the States and 0–60 under 5 seconds was my dream, I'd buy this and brew my own engine: the Pinto drops straight in and other engines can be shoehorned in but consult the folk at Caterham before you commit any major cut-and-shut surgery. When you get to this level of performance per pound of all-up weight, the integrity of the chassis is *everything*; if it isn't sound, the best engine in the world is only good enough to kill you a little faster.

Caterham have sold over a thousand of their Lotus-licensed Super Seven and it *is* a Colin Chapman design, so it's guaranteed to be both light and strong. There's another way of mixing it with the Porsche Turbos, by tweaking a monster motor in a Camaro, but I've always considered cars that offer straight line performance of such an elevated order without the ability to turn corners reassuringly to be an aberration. If you're building your own from the ground up and you're going for the big motor that'll pull the weight to 60mph in the lower brackets, it costs no more in time, effort or parts to give the car decent cornering capabilities as well – in fact, fitting a complete Jag front suspension and steering subframe could be considerably cheaper than a "trick" chromed tube front.

Passing is another kind of acceleration that is important for cars used much outside city limits. This is usually listed in motoring magazine tests as the time taken to accelerate, in various gears, over 20 mile per hour segments, e.g.: 3rd gear – 50–70mph 5.8sec, 60–80mph 8.1sec, 70–90mph 11sec. The roads you drive on, your normal speeds and what kind of a driver you are determines which brackets are important to you and what time bracket will be acceptable. I'm an impatient driver who will normally pass in very short spaces from close up behind the car I'm passing and most of my driving is done on roads where motorists drive at less than 50mph so my interest is the 50–70mph bracket. On the Continent, I like touring at about 80–85mph and for that, since traffic there normally cruises at about 70mph in the fast lane, I'm interested in the 70–90 and the 80–100 brackets. These passing times are an important safety consideration and for that reason alone I think that it could be stated as a general rule that all special cars – excepting only ultra-economy specials and the very small-engined – should be able to accelerate from 60–90mph in no more time than they took from 0–60mph. This is easier said than done. The Mercedes 500SEC coupe cannot manage it, nor the Corvette Z51 but the Aston Martin V8 manages handsomely – at the cost of a horrifying fuel thirst. None of these cars are actually slow to 60mph; it's just that two of them don't meet the next criterion and the one that does compromises economy to do it. To give you an idea of how difficult a criterion it is to meet if you must have economy as well (which implies quite "tall" gears), one of the really good cars of our time, the Porsche 944, takes nearly three times as long to reach 100mph as it does to reach 60mph; of course, with a reasonably light right foot, it will return 30mph. Once you get into this class of car – and the cost of equivalent specials – the only justification for tackling the job at all is that you will make some signal advance in two or more parameters simultaneously: for instance, design a car with all of the Aston's performance and better fuel economy than the Porsche, or a car with a performance edge on the Aston and the same economy as the Porsche.

Still, on a more modest scale, choosing your gearing so that the 0–60mph and the 60–90mph times are the same will be worth more in peace of mind than the saving in petrol. It is also worth sacrificing a few miles per hour of top speed: you will be performing passing manoeuvers a great deal more often than you will ever travel at top speed.

Passing performance is also torque-dependent but in these ranges a couple of additional questions have to be answered. The exact amount of torque available is important, i.e. the margin for acceleration. In this regard the big engine will score every day over the small one, because cubes and torque are directly related. Secondly, unless you want to swap cogs all the time, even for routine passing manoeuvers, the spread of torque – the operating band of the engine within which there is useful torque – should be as wide as possible. Here too big engines score over small. Thirdly, your gear ratios must be matched to your

engine's torque characteristics and this is where multi-geared small engines can make up some of the ground they lose to big engines.

All the same, if you're economy minded, the best 60–90mph times will in each case be achieved by the lighter car, so compromise on the weight before you slot in a bigger engine. I have often heard it said by experts that the really relevant aerodynamic drag starts over 90mph in that, for instance, the aerodynamic drag of the wheels is negligible until you go over 90mph but mostly this applies to utilitarian vehicles rather than fat tackies, which must by definition have a larger frontal area and therefore more drag. I feel that a good aerodynamic profile and good aerodynamic detailing may pay off in a fraction of a second off the 60–90mph time.

The final criterion I usually specify at this sage of the design of a car is its desired lateral acceleration. This describes the highest constant speed a car can achieve around a circle of a certain diameter and is expressed as fractions of an acceleration of one gravity, abbreviated g. It's a fancy way of describing cornering power objectively. To make an accurate measurement, one needs access to a skidpad because otherwise you're likely to roll a lot of cars; on the skidpad the car just slides away harmlessly. I had access to a skidpad for a couple of years, but frankly, don't miss it now. To use such a thing properly, as does *Road and Track* for their road tests, one also needs sophisticated instruments. It is in fact far more useful to say, simply, My car must corner as well as the latest Corvette, or the Jaguar sedan; you choose your own standard. As you will see, after designing an ideal suspension, in most cases we will use the nearest proprietary suspension parts with only minor modifications for reasons of cost, convenience, safety and security. So, if you choose the Jaguar as your reference standard, don't be too surprised if your ideal suspension design looks quite closely like a Jaguar design. All you have to do after that is watch your car's weight distribution, something you were going to do anyway.

And that is my list of criteria to consider at this stage of specification. Your list may be different. I know from experience that a car that corners right can be set up to have acceptable performance on other aspects of the ride, roadholding and handling package and that a car that doesn't corner right and can't be made to corner right isn't worth having.

The question of the engine position arises again when you specify the roadholding/handling/ride package. Rear-engined cars are bad. Mid-engined cars handle beautifully but you will of course have to sacrifice payload capability. Front-engined cars with the engine set well back seem to me the best compro-

Figure 3.5. The Alfasud has a good drivetrain but a distressing tendency to rust – the ideal combination for a special. This Cheetah prototype could use a bit more headroom.

mise. The handling characteristics of front and rear wheel drive cars also differ and there are problems with putting more than about 200bph through driven wheels that are also used for steering the car.

One question I don't normally consider for my own cars because my total annual mileage never exceeds 7000–8000 miles, but which you may want to attend to is fuel economy. It is quite easy to show theoretically that extra weight costs extra fuel and that, over the average annual mileage, weight is the sole determinant of consumption. This may well be true for the every-day car but for the special that must also offer economy you should, after you've thrown out all the surplus appurtenances from the inside and dipped it into an acid bath to thin the body, also slim it from the outside by ensuring a good aerodynamic profile and (terribly important, this) attention to every detail that could possibly disturb the airflow over the car. The reason for this is that most specials will see quite a bit more high speed motoring than the family car, so the consumption-mix will be different and the extra "aero-dynamic mpg" may just be the one that breaks the 40mpg or the 50mpg or even the 100mpg barrier. Low rolling resistance tires may also offer you useful fractions of mpg.

But note that the lowest powered version of an engine is not necessarily the most economical, nor is the smallest cubic version of the engine the most economical. All things considered – meaning that we take it for granted that the engine puts out all the power you require but no redundant surplus – the most economical engine is the one that makes the best use of a given amount of fuel, delivering more power for the same fuel or delivering the same power for less fuel. If you don't keep your foot in the floorboards all the time, you may surprise yourself by finding that your quite highly tuned engine offers markedly better fuel economy than the base model from which you developed it. The high specific output engine is simply more efficient.

Table 3.1: The smallest engine isn't necessarily the best choice! These government test figures for Ford Sierras with various engine sizes prove the point. Even if you argue that with a five-speed box the smallest engine would compare better, the 2.0 litre engine is better than the 1.6 litre at both constant speed tests. Only if most of your mileage is going to be urban is the 1.3 attractive from an economy viewpoint.

Saloon models	Government test figures (mpg)			Max speed (mph)
	Constant 56mph	Constant 75mph	Urban cycle	
1.3 4-speed	44.8	35.8	30.7	94
1.6 5-speed	47.9	36.7	28.0	103
2.0 5-speed	49.6	38.2	26.9	115
2.3 V6 5-speed	44.8	35.3	23.3	118

35

One final consideration: I, and many others, will, on aesthetic grounds, normally prefer the light and the small in whatever is under consideration, including engines, whence my high regard for the all-ali Rover V8 née Buick engine. But there is a practical reason for choosing this engine if you want lots of torque with economy and that is that it offers demonstrably more of everything the British enthusiast wants per pound of weight than any other engine. We won't go quite as far as the aeroplane designers who rank engines in order of pounds per horsepower but the special car designer should consider horsepower per pound.

Engine sizes are externally not critically wide apart except for the most bizarre swaps, like trying to put a 7.2-litre Chrysler hemi into the space occupied by a 1-litre engine; 38 inches along the length of the car should allow you to fit any four or V8 except the very largest and Jaguar sixes have been fitted into as little as 40 inches along the length of the car, but for heat dissipation I should allow 44 inches, which will then also take a V12 if you should suddenly come into an inheritance. These figures include space for radiator and fan; on my current project I'm allowing 40 inches for the Rover V8, fan and radiator which includes ample space to change the fanbelt without removing the radiator. The Ford Model B of 1932, and its replicas, offer only 32 inches from the firewall to the grille and we've all seen some pretty big engines sitting in there with very little or no firewall relief but that cuts it very fine. Table 3.2 tells you the size of some of the bigger engines. All four-cylinders known to me will fit where a Rover V8 works (though normally an enthusiast would see it the other way round) but watch the width of the V8s when fitting them to a narrow car with McPherson strut suspension.

Now we are ready to put the whole car on paper.

Table 3.2: Engine sizes. A typical engine swap is to fling out an in-line four and replace it with a V8 or V6. At first sight, the most immediate problem is that the V8s are all longer than a four but in practice that length is easily found by re-siting the radiator and perhaps relieving the firewall a modest amount; a far greater problem, especially with McPherson struts, is normally encountered in trying to accommodate the more expansive widthwise spread of a V8.

| Engine | Measurements in inches | | | Weight (lb) |
	High	Long	Wide	
Chevrolet 350	27	28	26	570
Ford 351	29	29	25	550
Chrysler Hemi	31	32	29	690
Rover-Buick 215	29	30	26	360
Ford V6 3 litre	21	25	24	430
Typical in-line four cylinder	30	25	24	300

Designing and Building Your Car

4 The Whole Car

The first part of drawing-board work is also the most exciting: drawing the car in profile, front, rear, and plan views. You need a common soft pencil, a soft rubber, a ruler, graph paper and some cellotape to stick the paper to the kitchen table. Once you've determined the scale you want to work to, you're sure to find a round item somewhere in the kitchen that you can use for drawing perfect circles for wheels. If you want to splash out you can buy a cheap student's drawing board, set square, adjustable plastic triangle, a proper 0.2 or 0.3 mm drafting pencil, french curves (very useful, these), compass, and protractor. What kind of graph paper you buy depends on the scale you want to work to. Professionals design on plain paper but it's an enormous hassle taking measurements every time you want to draw a line if you aren't used to it; I taught myself to do it and then went back to graph paper because I found that fabricators and welders I work with prefer it. I like to use A3 graph paper (about 16 × 12 inches), divided into blocks 1 mm square, with harder divisions 10 mm and 20 mm square; this paper I then use to the scale of 2 mm = 1 inch, a scale that lets me fit two cars up to 17 feet long to a single page at approximately one-thirteenth scale. Graph paper marked in tenths and eighths of an inch is also generally available and allows scales of one-tenth, one-fifth, one eighth, and one-quarter. Using graph paper also gives you a readymade grid when you want to

Figure 4.1. Perspective drawings of your car are a waste of time. Paul Moorhouse thought this drawing of his Marlin good enough. The Marlin is a best selling kit car.

38

transfer your design fullsize to the garage floor and wall. Any machining work you're going to send out with a drawing will be done quicker and cheaper and with less chance of going wrong if you make your drawing full size and take care to write every relevant dimension on it; I also always explain what I want very carefully to the actual operator.

First, draw a line to represent the road. On this mark off the wheelbase, leaving enough space front and rear for the overhangs; mark the axle centre lines with an X. Next mark on the roadline the position of the bulkhead. From this towards the rear axle line measure the space you're allowing for the driver plus seat thickness plus pedal movement, say 55 inches. From the back of the driver's seat to the rear axle should be the space you allow for rear seat passengers plus an allowance for the axle and/or inboard brakes to operate; this is usually less than their full lengthwise space requirement because the seat will normally slope so that the bottom clears the axle or inboard brakes while the top of the seat hangs over these essential parts of the drivetrain. Note two things about "the back of the seat", i.e. the rearmost part of the seat at the top of the backrest: space for the rear passengers' legs is found by the slant of the front seats towards the floor and for their feet underneath the front seats. With the exception of Bentley MkVI specials which start high off the ground anyway, I try never to seat any passengers behind the rear axle line because, after you allow space for the independent suspension from, say, a Jaguar, it is virtually impossible to have a low roofline. If you're going to seat passengers over the rear axle, your car is likely to be over 60 inches high. If you allow 1 inch along the length of the car at seattop level for the vertical movement of a live rear axle or $2\frac{1}{2}$ inches' clearance for inboard disc brakes on independent rear suspension designs, seatbacks raked 5 inches from top to bottom should clear 11-inch inboard discs. You can refine the design later.

Now make little ticks on the roadline to indicate where the front and rear extremities of the car will fall and you're ready to go higher up your car. Draw a line parallel to the roadline and above it to indicate your desired ground clearance (5–8 inches for most cars) and another horizontal line to indicate the overall height of the car, i.e. where the roofline will fall.

Now comes the tricky part. What we want to mark is a point through or outside of which the windscreen line must pass to allow space for the steering wheel, the driver's knuckles and some clearance. For me this point is normally 35 inches from the back of the seat and 33 inches above the floor (assuming I use Volvo seats). This point I mark with a dot and draw a circle around it in ink. It once cost me a lot of money, time

and wasted materials to resite a windscreen. Another point you must mark at this stage is the driver's eye level and position. It is useful to specify this in terms of the knuckle clearance point – for me $22\frac{1}{2}$ inches behind and $3\frac{1}{2}$–5 inches above depending on how low the car must be – so that you always move both at the same time and don't end up with a windscreen top-rail in your forehead or directly in your line of sight. The back of the rear passenger's head will normally be safe if you don't bring the top rail of the rear window further forward than 5 inches from the back of his seat – reduce this figure for thin seats.

One final decision: what will the height of the elbow or window line be? This is determined by the style of car you're drawing, vintage cars having a lesser glass area than modern cars. Draw this line lightly.

Now you can start drawing your car between the borders you've now outlined. First, draw the general outline of the car, not worrying overly much about where you will put doors and so on because you will soon find that you have to do it over and over to get it right. This is called design iteration and in special cars the words have (or should have unless you're rich) a very special meaning. Mass market and even low volume car producers use the phrase to mean a cycle where a component goes from designers to prototypers to test and development engineers to production engineers (and their associated cost accountants) and back to designers an infinite number of times until it is absolutely right, i.e. until it will do the job adequately for the least possible cost. This is an enormously costly process but the amount it costs on each unit is infinitesimal because it will be produced in hundreds of thousands or even millions. The special car builder does not normally want to test one example of something to destruction but to design something once, build it right, and have it do the job for the life of the car – in my view, the best special cars are designed to be permanent and last forever. Working backwards, the component won't do the job even adequately unless it is built right and it can't be built right unless it is properly designed. Building something twice costs twice, whereas, since the special car builder doesn't reckon his own time, painstaking design costs nothing at all. Design iteration for the special car builder therefore means exploring all avenues at his drawing board and ironing out the glitches right there on paper.

This applies to the overall design of the car even more than to the detail. Every detail of a car can be spot on but if the overall appearance shouts "Amateur!", it wasn't worth the effort. It is not uncommon for me to use up ten sheets of paper – twenty drawings – on the profile of a design already almost settled, simply redrawing the curve of the waistline over and

Figures 4.2 and 4.3. Bentley Mk VI and R-type specials are the *ne plus ultra* of nostalgicars. They offer surprisingly modern performance and brakes but are expensive.

over again, each time fractionally deeper or shallower, because the smallest things can make a difference. Other people make tracings but I usually do the whole thing over and, with practice, you'll soon find it goes very quickly indeed. Certainly, if you add as much as an inch to the wheelbase, you must redraw everything and not just trust to imagination because, unless you're hugely experienced, it is almost impossible to grasp what a very big difference quite small alterations can make. Illustrate this for yourself on your own design, or cut a picture of the Corvette out of a magazine and change the angle of the rubber strip along the side slightly by drawing on it with a felt pen and see what a difference it makes. That strip on the Corvette rises less than two inches from front to rear ... yet I think it *makes* a design that is otherwise very clever and subtle but, for all of that, only a development of the 1982 Corvette shape.

The shape and width of doors are likely to give the novice designer a good amount of trouble even at this stage, and a great deal more when later he has to design their construction details. On a strict two seater, the doors should open from the back corner of the seat to about 12 inches in front of the forward edge of the seat, a distance of about 41 inches. On two-door four seaters you should take the door width up to the front edge of the rear seat if, in the process, that doesn't make the door wider than 50 inches. In four-door cars the centre pillar should rise from the point where the front seat base meets its backrest but this often conflicts with the visual masses of the two doors so created. The split line between the front and rear doors can be curved to allow rear passengers room to get their feet in and out.

It is important to draw everything that will be on the car, because add-ons generally ruin a design that looked clean and unfussed without them. Spoilers, bumpers, outside mirrors, fuel tank cap or flap, rubbing strips, exhaust if it's going to show beneath the car, windscreen wipers, radio antenna (can you hide it in the windscreen?), extensions to cover protruding wheels, power bulges, air in and outlets, anti-static and anti-lightning chains, door handles and catches, external burglar alarm keyhole, everything! If you don't show it, you won't know it a distracting element and once your car is built, it's going to cost money and time and temper to change it.

There's no point whatsoever in offering you an art-school lecture on form, mass and balance: you're reading this book because you have decent taste and the practicalities involved in automobile aesthetics can only be learnt with a pencil and a piece of paper. However, I can share a few tips with you without presuming to prescribe taste. "If it looks right, it is right." It's your car, so, if you want to make sacrifices

for the sake of appearances, do it! Several times, I've chosen practicality and function above elegance and been bitterly unhappy about it ever afterward. A quick way of checking whether a design is really right, is to turn the paper around and hold it up to the light: "wrong" lines seem to thrust themselves at you better that way. Get a few thickish felt pens and some copying paper (or bank typewriter paper) and copy the main lines and details like door handles and see if the whole still lives for you. Next photocopy (xerox) your finished designs and use colouring pencils to colour it and then see if it's still right. I always use bright yellow and black for the body with a light blue for chrome parts: this combination highlights "wrong" masses like nothing else. Switch the colours in the different blocks and see which masses now jump out to hit you in the eye. Finally, copy your finished design on a clean sheet of paper.

After the profile, you must draw the front and rear views of the car to the same scale and validate them as you did the profile. Then a plan view of the car as seen from directly overhead. When you have all these on clean sheets of paper, xerox them all and use them to draw in the seats and moving parts of the car and its controls (steering wheel, gear lever, pedals, handbrake). Once you have done all this, check against your specification: is there space for all the people you want to carry? The required amount of legroom, headroom, hiproom, elbow room, luggage space, engine space, service space? If all are present and correct, mark the final sheets "version 1" or some other way of distinguishing them from the drawings to come – because you will iterate this design several times more.

Let's now jump several steps from the beautiful shell you have designed – albeit with *space* for people and drivetrain – to a point where you have also designed a chassis and chosen an engine which must mount to it and done many other clever things, like designing a suspension. As we already know, all these things will interrelate and, despite the appearance our disciplined approach here gives, nothing about an automobile is designed or used in isolation. At that stage you are going to have to redesign the details, and sometimes the overall shape, of your special car quite radically: say your design is for a biggish vintage replica, then you will have to fit a biggish ladder frame into the same space as people's feet, or find somewhere else to put their feet, or have a higher car. This is generally not a big deal and you'll probably be so practised by then that the whole affair will take only a couple of hours. But another problem arises and this can be quite frustrating – or you can see it as a brand new challenge of an even higher order than those you will then have met.

Figures 4.4 and 4.5. Small frontdrive cars normally have the engine, gearbox and final drive in unit and complete in its own subframe – a special builder's dream.

In the chapters dealing with the specification, we took informed guesses about things like all-up weight and power requirements and tyre sizes, derived mainly by comparison to existing cars; we emphasized that every decision had a cost somewhere else, for instance that additional weight would cost in higher fuel consumption and slower acceleration times and longer exposures when passing other traffic. But, as you get deeper and deeper into the design of your car, the factors behind these trade-offs start to emerge and when the cost is specified in exactly how much of another desirable attribute you have to sacrifice, you may decide to alter the specification rather than to pay the price. Each and every time this happens, you have to return to this point, which is why the mathematics of the various trade-offs are included here rather than anywhere else. Having read the figures, you might even decide to respecify your car right here and now.

Trade-offs

A motor car works only as the sum of its constituted parts. Some of the constituted parts are abstracts (roadholding, say, or comfort) and can be quite subjective but even so they are generally effected in the hardware in a way that leads to quantification of useful comparative measures that, in addition, can be shown to interrelate with each other. Figure 4.6 shows how the specification of the car, the hardware and the abstracts interrelate. The picture is of course grossly over-simplified and you can break each little module up into many others but it shows the main streams of the argument we want to consider here.

We have decided we want to carry a certain number of passengers in a certain comfort and with given luggage in a certain style of body. We have decided that the engine should be of such power that it can carry them at a given top speed, can accelerate the car

from 0–60mph and from 60–90mph in a predetermined number of seconds. We already know that frictional resistance against the air and the road will determine the top speed for a given engine output in brake horse power, and that the weight of the car will be the sole determinant of the acceleration for a given amount of torque. We also know that certain styles of body, and certain details of fixtures on the body, cause greater frictional resistance and that greater weight will also cause greater resistance against the road surface. More passengers and more comfort almost always mean more weight.

How many brake horsepower will you need from your engine to drive your car at the desired speed? First, how many horses will do nothing but overcome aerodynamic drag?

$$\text{Drag horsepower} = \frac{C_x A v^3}{146,600}$$

where C_x is a dimensionless drag coefficient,
    A is the frontal area, sq ft
    v is airspeed, mph

which is of course no good to anybody without some figures to put to the formula. Starting with the one we desire: v is the speed you want the car to go through still air (i.e. with no wind – a head-on wind should be added and a tailwind subtracted), say 130mph, and is multiplied by itself three times to get $v^3 = 130 \times 130 \times 130 = 2,197,000$. A is the frontal area in square feet, for modern cars about 80–85% of their width × height (for nostalgicars say 70%) and, since car measurements are normally given in inches, calculated thus

$$A = (0.85)\frac{54 \times 66}{144} \text{ sq ft}$$
$$= 21.43 \text{ sq ft}$$

$$\text{or } A = (0.7)\frac{54 \times 60}{144}$$
$$= 17.33 \text{ sq ft}$$

C_x or C_d as Americans are likely to know it can be

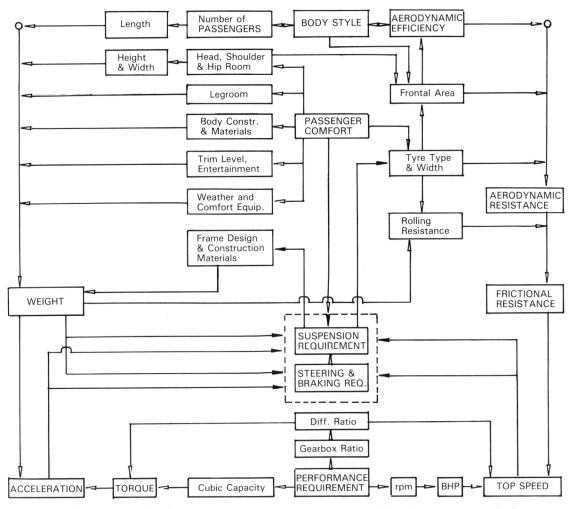

Figure 4.6. This is a simplified chart of the order and interrelationship of the decisions you make in designing your car but it serves to show why, once the passenger space, style and performance requirements are specified, detailed mechanical design starts with the suspension.

fairly accurately calculated by coastdown method *after the car is built* or determined with perfect accuracy by subjecting a full-sized very accurate model to a wind tunnel. Both these methods are too costly for the special builder who wants to build only once. Fortunately it is not difficult to guess at a good value for C_d and even quite large errors will not throw the calculations out much as the largest component, especially at the higher speeds, is the *cube* of the speed. Vintage replicars have a C_d (with the top and windows or side-screens up) of around 0.7–0.75. The 1950s style sports racer should fall somewhere in the 0.5–0.6 range and E-Types and suchlike in the 0.4–0.5 range. Modern cars quite easily achieve C_d figures of 0.3–0.4. Look for

a comparison with something close to your car from the Table 4.1. This aerodynamic drag can break down into components such as profile drag, the most important at about 60% of total drag; drag due to excrescences like trim mouldings, door handles and ornaments, about 15% of all drag; about 12% cooling system drag; with the rest divided between induced drag and frictional resistance. It's that first 87% you want to look at when you make comparisons: the car's shape and attention to the detail of conducting the air over and through and under the car. Let's say for the moment your design is a square rigged vintage replicar and choose $C_d = 0.75$ and plug the figures into our equation:

Table 4.1: Low drag results from attention to detail rather than apparently slippery shapes.

Car	Cd
Audi 100	0.30
Citroen GSA X3	0.32
Mercedes Benz 190	0.33
Fiat Uno ES	0.33
Ford Sierra	0.34
Porsche 944	0.35
Mercedes Benz S-Class	0.36
Rover SDI Vitesse	0.36
Citroen CX	0.37
BMW 3-Series	0.38
VW Polo	0.38
MG Metro	0.39
Volvo 760 GLE	0.40
Porsche 928	0.41
VW Microbus	0.42
Citroen 2CV	0.51
Lotus (Caterham) Super Seven	0.65

$$\text{Drag horsepower} = \frac{0.75 \times 17.33 \times 2,197,000}{146,600}$$
$$= 195\text{bhp}$$

to which we must still add to overcome road friction 14bhp per 1000 lb of the car's weight and losses in the drivetrain as these are flywheel bhp as observed on a dynamometer. Of course, we don't have a dyno either . . . There's a shortcut. It is probable that aerodynamic drag accounts for half of all resistance to motion at speeds as low as 45mph; it is certain that over 60mph aerodynamic drag represents the major resistance. The power required to overcome the road-resistance rises very approximately as the square of the speed; the power required to overcome the air-resistance rises as the cube of the speed, so that over about 90–100mph, while the curve of the rolling resistance increases its slope, the brake horse power required to overcome this resistance (while absolutely larger) becomes a very small part of the total power requirement. These factors and direct observation has led Colin Campbell to suggest in his evergreen *The Sports Car: Its design and performance* (Robert Bentley, Cambridge, Mass., various editions since 1954) that the bhp to overcome aerodynamic drag is about 70 per cent of the net bhp available at the flywheel. If we then plug this into our calculation for aerodynamic drag, we get:

$$\text{BHP}_v = \frac{C_x A v^3}{146,600 \times 0.7}$$

or a requirement, for our example above, of 279bhp to drive the specified car at 130mph.

But what if the engine you intend using self-destructs over 240bhp and in fact isn't pleasant over 220bhp and beyond 200bhp isn't a bargain any more? That is why I chose this example. Trying to make vintage replicas go much over the ton is a megalomaniac ambition. A more realistic top speed would be 100mph when the bhp requirement immediately falls to 127bhp or 110mph for which the requirement rises to 169bhp.

At this stage it may strike you that you could build a sleek modern projectile with an 0.375 C_d with little more than half the power, since the modern car would for the same height × width have a higher 0.8 or 0.85 conversion factor than the replicar; in fact, since you could probably bring the modern car down to at least 50 inches and perhaps less, you could go 130mph with less than half the power the replicar needs. And since every one of those horses drinks petrol . . . play around with the formula for a while before you make any important decisions. Those aerodynamic mpg will appear over every kind of use to which you put the car but less so at low speeds than at high and preferably constant speeds as compared to a car less aerodynamically efficient.

If you're into economy specials you should read *Fuel Economy of the Gasoline Engine* (D. R. Blackmore and A. Thomas, eds., Wiley, New York, 1977). The alternative formula below tells you how many horses you need to drive an economy car:

$$\text{BHP}_v = \frac{v}{375}\left(C_r W + 0.0026 C_d A v^2 + GW + FW\right)$$

where BHP_v is the bhp required at the rear wheels for the speed, v

v	is the speed desired, mph
C_r	is the coefficient of rolling resistance
W	is the vehicle weight, lb
C_d	is the coefficient of aerodynamic drag
A	is the frontal area, sq ft
G	is the road gradient expressed as a fraction
F	is the acceleration, a fraction of one gravity

C_r you can take for radial tyres at 0.014 or 14 lb per 1000 of vehicle weight, crossply tyres at 0.019 or 19 lb per 1000 of vehicle weight. On a level road there is of course no gradient. That bit about acceleration in fractions of g is very useful for testing your guesses about C_d when you use the coastdown method which will be described in a later chapter – and if you also know that

g (one gravity acceleration) = 32.2 ft/second^2

Figures 4.7 and 4.8. The city car is, considering the times we live in, a much neglected avenue for, perhaps, *your* talents. This Ghia Trio has three-abreast seating.

and

$$\frac{\text{present speed} - \text{previous speed (mph)}}{\text{time (seconds)}}$$
$$= \text{average acceleration in miles/second}^2$$

(read "miles per second per second").

These are genuine DIN horses, not shadow horses from a Madison Avenue nightmare. If you're using an engine from the muscle period of American cars, divide the Campbell formula's result by another 0.875 or you might be disappointed with the end result. The newer SAE horses are stronger but I would still divide by 0.925 to be certain. If you dyno your new engine, always do it with all ancillaries that will be in the car in place on the engine and *driven*; otherwise multiply the end result by 0.875 to get the gennie horses you'll get at the flywheel with the engine installed.

Here's a formula, used by drag racers, that tells how fast your car will go at the end of a quarter mile from a standing start:

$$V_{qr.m} = 225 \left[\frac{bhp}{W} \right]^{0.318}$$

where $V_{qr.m}$ is the terminal velocity mph at the end of 440 yards
bhp is the dyno flywheel horsepower
W is the weight of the car in lb

This formula can be rewritten to tell you how many horses you need to give the car some desired speed at the end of a quarter mile:

$$BHP = W \left[\frac{V_{qr.m}}{225} \right]^{3.1447}$$

with $V_{qr.m}$ as the speed you want the car to be going after 440 yards.

Because the amount of torque produced by a given engine is mathematically related to horsepower and the engine's speed, we normally ask, How fast will a car of this weight accelerate, given so much torque? Turning again to the invaluable Colin Campbell, we find he offers this formula for determining how fast a car will reach 60mph from standstill:

$$t_{0-60} = \left[\frac{2W}{T} \right]^{0.6}$$

where W is the weight of the car in lb
T is the maximum net engine torque in ft lb

which gives pretty good results. For those of you who

can't be bothered with logarithms, a rule of thumb used by an ancient who used to truck my racing engines to and from the dyno people gives excellent results and can be quantified as follows:

$$t_{0-60} = \frac{11 \times W}{20 \times T}$$

where W is the weight in lb
T is the torque in ft lb

or, to save calculation time on the electronic abacus:

$$t_{0-60} = 0.55 \left(\frac{W}{T} \right)$$

which is the one I use myself since I don't have a calculator with logs. (Most hardware stores and tool-stores sell a little booklet with bolt and nut comparisons, cos, sin and tan calculations and log tables that you can carry around in your top pocket. Mine was published by Zeus Precision Charts and is invaluable for determining next-best drill sizes as well.)

You don't need to be Einstein to see that there is a perfectly direct relationship between acceleration and weight for a given amount of torque. If you have 200 ft lb of torque you can propel a 2000 lb car from standstill to 60mph in 5.5 seconds. If the torque remains constant and the weight increases to 3000 lb, 0–60mph will take 8.25 seconds and, if you have "only" 200 ft lb of torque to push your average 3800 lbs Camaro from standstill to 60mph, you'll have no less than ten-and-a-half seconds to write away for hotrod goodies. As a rule of thumb, an independent rear suspension and really good, wide rubber is worth between a second and a second-and-a-half off the times so calculated. If you have a big engine – $3\frac{1}{2}$ litres and over – with a good autobox, subtract another half-a-second unless the torque spread and gearing is such that there would be no change with a manual box. With small engines and autoboxes, add two or three seconds and pray it's enough – or find a five-speeder. You can of course choose your gearing so that a given engine will be operating right on its torque peak all the way to 60mph, and aid and abet this with a rear axle ratio so low (that's a high numerical number, 4.8:1 rather than 2.88:1, say) you chew up a set of tyres every time you prove the acceleration but such a car is likely to be unpleasant and tiring to drive at touring speeds, in fact anywhere except on a drag strip. So, if you want acceleration, look first to weight, then at ways of getting more torque from your engine.

Turning to economy, let us say that you've pared the weight right down and have made every last possible effort to lessen road drag and air drag. Now you want a few more miles from the same engine or from a different engine. To compare different versions of the same engine or to compare different engines, we use the bmep or brake mean effective pressure which tells us how much combustion pressure in pounds per square inch the engine develops (averaged over all four strokes, but don't let that worry you now):

$$bmep = \frac{bhp \times 13000}{Capacity \times rpm}$$

where bhp   is the net flywheel horsepower
    capacity is the cubic capacity in litres
          (61 cubic inches = 1 litre)
    rpm   is the rpm at which peak torque
          occurs

A. Graham Bell, a racer and tuner whose *Performance Tuning in Theory and Practice: Four Strokes* (Haynes/ Foulis, 1981) is a standard reference for engine tuners, reckons a well-developed road engine should run 165–185psi against the normal showroom floor bmep of 130–145.

The point of interest to the special builder is that the bmep allows him to compare the efficiency of engines regardless of cubes or operating rpm. Using the bmep will prevent the novice from falling into the all too common trap of buying a motor that has a lot of horses because it turns unnaturally high rpm but has no more torque and therefore will do no more work than a cheaper and more pleasant engine. For special builders interested in economy, the more efficient engine, i.e. the one with the higher bmep, will be the better choice in the same application – if you can resist using its greater efficiency to give greater performance! One way of checking this is with bsfc or brake specific fuel consumption, which tells you how well the engine uses its fuel but has the problem that it requires figures most of us don't have, viz how many lbs of fuel the engine consumed in an hour of steady running at the rpm at which it produced such and such bhp (choose the rpm for touring or all-out performance or whatever you like). But, if you buy your tuning kit from one of the bigger manufacturers, they will be able to look the figures up in their dyno records of the tests they performed on the equipment; torque and bsfc are the two parameters experienced dyno operators use to optimize an engine's efficiency, so very careful records are kept. The figures then plug straight in to the formula:

$$BSFC = \frac{\text{fuel consumption in pounds per hour}}{\text{bhp produced}}$$
$$= \text{lbs of fuel per horsepower-hour}$$

The thing you must watch here is to compare like with like: don't compare full throttle operation on one engine with part-throttle operation on another. The lower the bsfc, the more economical the engine will be at that rpm. If you know the bsfc over a range of rpm operation, you can choose your gears so that they suit your intended usage at the best economy level: this is the reason for 5th gear overdrives that have a lower top speed than the 4th gear in the same box.

Where to start?

Given the number of passengers, their desired comfort level, their luggage requirement, the desired top speed and acceleration, and at least comparative cornering/ roadholding/handling/ride parameters – and having just designed the outer shell of the car – where do we start with the grubby bits? Or, depending on your viewpoint, the most interesting part? Figure 4.9 shows the normal order in which I construct a vintage replica, leaving out such steps as stripping down again for final painting. But just a moment's thought will convince you that one cannot buy bits and pieces until you know which bits and pieces you will need, nor can you build a chassis until you know which suspension you want to hang on it, etc. A look back at Figure 4.6 shows us that all the choices we make, and their results, react with each other. But all the physical and abstract functions that make a car a mechanism rather than a sculpture react through the suspension and the steering and the brakes to and from the road. It is for this reason that, having decided the overall function and form of the car, we start the detail design with the suspension, after which we will turn to the chassis and drivetrain and then the body and trim.

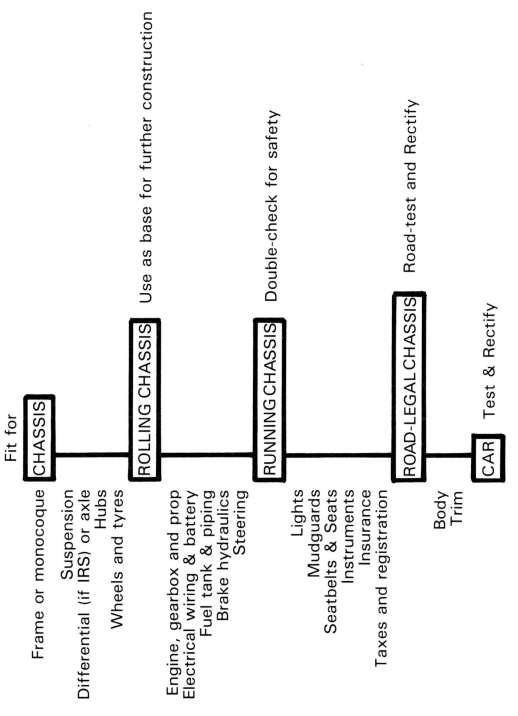

Make, buy, rebuild or build

Base car and/or bits

Fit for

CHASSIS

Frame or monocoque
Suspension
Differential (if IRS) or axle
Hubs
Wheels and tyres

ROLLING CHASSIS — Use as base for further construction

Engine, gearbox and prop
Electrical wiring & battery
Fuel tank & piping
Brake hydraulics
Steering

RUNNING CHASSIS — Double-check for safety

Lights
Mudguards
Seatbelts & Seats
Instruments
Insurance
Taxes and registration

ROAD-LEGAL CHASSIS — Road-test and Rectify

Body
Trim

CAR — Test & Rectify

Figure 4.9. The logical order of construction of a special car bears little relation to the sequence of specification and design. For instance, you cannot design the frame until you have designed the suspension and chosen the drivetrain.

5 Suspension: Principles

"The purpose of the suspension is to keep the wheels on the car," says one writer who shall remain nameless. No, the purpose of the suspension is first and foremost to keep the tires in permanent and firm contact with the road with the tire square or nearly square to the road surface under all operating conditions. This is necessary so that the car may be driven and steered: a wheel that is turning in thin air cannot drive the car forward nor steer it in the desired direction. Secondly, and almost as important, the suspension isolates the passengers from the irregularities of the road. With perfect roads, no suspension would be required – or so we are sometimes told. This is not right because the suspension has the further function of stabilizing or using to the greatest possible advantage the weight transfers brought about by cornering, accelerating or braking.

The suspension consists of the tire, the wheel itself, the upright (or hub carrier or spindle), the spring and damper and the linkages to the chassis and, in the case of independent suspension, part of the drive shafts which often form locating linkages. In all cases it is convenient to think of outboard brakes as forming part of the suspension in that they make up an important weight element outboard of the chassis. In the cases of beam or swing axles the whole or a good part of the axle must also be counted in with the suspension. This might horrify the purists but it prevents the special car builder from neglecting to consider weight that may well make the difference between a car that is sweet-riding and handling or not.

Consider a car standing on its suspension on a flat and level surface; it can move in three ways. First, you can press hard in the centre of the bonnet (hood) or of the bootlid (trunk) and the car will then *pitch* forwards and backwards along its length like a seesaw. Now get someone to help you and press both corners on the same side, front and rear: the car will *roll* around some longitudinal axis, with one side going down on the springs and the other side rising on the springs. Next,

get all your friends and let half of them push against the mudguard near the front of the car and the other half against the rear mudguard on the other side of the car: the car will *yaw* around an imaginary spike driven through the roof into the road. It will also be noticed that the tires *slip* over the surface of the road. If you now drive the car, you can further determine whether it goes around corners well, whether it goes where you steer it, how quickly it changes direction to your command, whether it changes direction due to some outside factor (wind, bad road surface), whether and how quickly it returns to a stable position or line after a manoeuvre. All of these, and other, parameters of a car's behavior relate, through the suspension design, to the weight of the car and the distribution of that weight.

If you are starting a design from scratch, and given that the major masses are distributed according to some predetermined function (as discussed in the previous chapters), you will then have to compromise between your various ride, roadholding and handling criteria in order to design the optimum suspension. "Optimum" means only the most suitable for your purpose; there is no such thing as a perfect all-purpose suspension that will meet everyone's ideal. If the compromise then leads to an unacceptable or unsafe suspension design, you must return to the pre-design specification stage and compromise with the function until a weight distribution is achieved that will allow you to design the appropriate suspension. In practice this does not happen often to the special car builder unless he is designing something quite extreme (a 9 seater with a 12 ft turning circle, say) or unless he's designing a racer *and* he drives so well that he can extract that last razor's gleam of balance; it is not difficult to find production cars with their weight dangerously distributed or with incompetent suspension design made lethal by peculiar weight distribution. In this regard, it must be noted that an engine behind the rear axle is not automatically a bad thing –

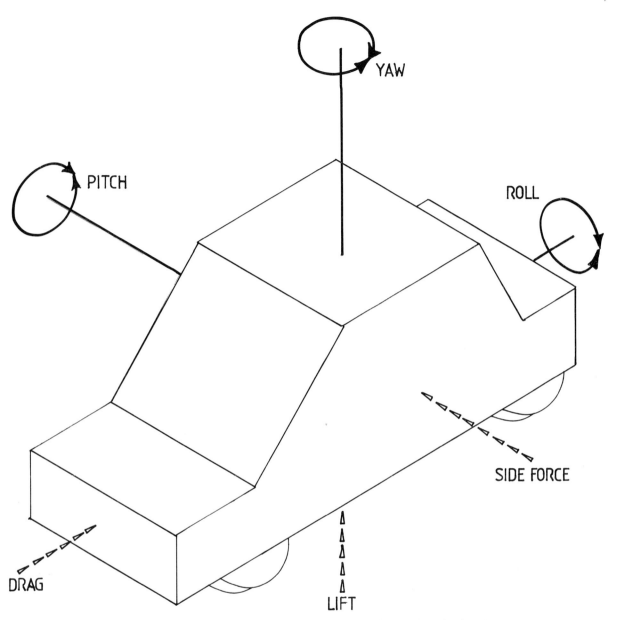

Figure 5.1. The primary motions of and forces on a car, much simplified and neglecting the engine's forward propulsion and the downforce of air over the car in motion.

competent design can give it whatever handling is desired, vide Porsche – but it doesn't make things easier for the designer, especially if he is new to the game. The reason for the misconception that all rear-engined cars oversteer terminally is simply that all the original rear-engined cars had swing axle suspensions which are subject to extreme camber variations.

Everything in and about a car weighs something, even the air that presses on it from above and below: the study of aerodynamics is aimed at reducing this weight or redistributing it to benefit traction for acceleration or cornering, or to increase directional stability. The actual amount of weight has, as we have seen already, a decided influence on acceleration and economy and a smaller content in the determination of top speed. The greater the mass to be sprung, the greater the suspension requirement for optimizing the various desired parameters, with the exception that many designers find it easier to give a heavy car a good ride than a light one. Greater weight will in itself

51

Figure 5.2. Light alloy wheels can save unsprung weight but it is normal to go up a size or two when changing wheels so that you get better traction for the same weight.

require heavier suspension linkages, bigger wheels and tires, a heavier design of upright and hub, and more effective brakes which may mean bigger or ventilated (double) disks or a greater number of calipers or all three; all of these things increase the unsprung weight which in turn also magnifies the suspension requirement in that it is more difficult to control a high unsprung weight than a low one. The unsprung weight therefore differs from the sprung weight in that there are no circumstances in which greater weight is more advantageous than less. (Always assuming that you have not been so foolish as to pare the suspension weight down to the extent that engineering integrity – and your safety – is endangered.) The greater the sprung weight, the more weight will be transferred in roll (for a given roll centre and centre of gravity) and therefore the greater the demands made on the designer in drawing his suspension.

All in all, low overall weight is desirable and low unsprung weight is essential for any kind of a car.

Whatever the weight is, the sprung weight will be subject to the pitch, roll and yaw movements of the car. Aspects of each are usually subsumed into the discussion of factors influencing weight transfer under the collective title "roll" and what remains will be discussed under the miscellaneous items comprising the other factors of chassis behaviour. This weight is concentrated through a point called the Centre of Gravity (CoG) and *rolls* about the car's *roll axis*, which runs between the front and rear *roll centres*. This is not as imaginary as it seems – it's what makes one car break 12 sec over the quarter while another stands idly smoking its tires; it's what makes one car corner on rails while another digs in and falls over or slides off into the ditch. This roll is resisted by the springs (and by the dampers and other frictional forces) so that we describe a *roll resistance*.

The CoG is not necessarily symmetrical over the width of the car; in a sports car, unless the engine is offset, the CoG will always be on the driver's side when he is alone in the car. California hot-rod builder Jerry Kugel offset the small-block Ford V8 in his

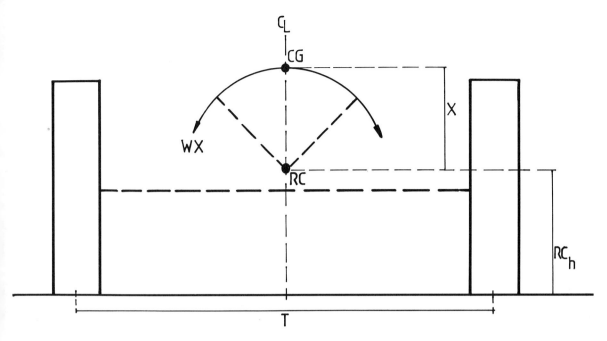

Figure 5.3. The roll moment is the car's weight multiplied by the distance of the Centre of Gravity above the mean Roll Centre height. *Some* distance is desirable on road cars to give warning of when handling limits are approached.

deuce roadster by 1 inch. It is worth having a good look at the engine, because the starter, alternator, inlet and outlet manifolds and oil filter may all stick out and offer unbalancing forces. The amount of force will be the distance of the offset from the centreline multiplied by the weight, so the further away, the more force. This applies to every other aspect of the car as well.

As one cannot determine the centre of gravity until the whole car is designed, why don't we do the suspension last? The answer is that you set an ideal height for the CoG and try to design accordingly; your guesses will improve with practice. It should also be noted that the CoG should not simply be at any point along a line stretching the length of the car a certain height above the ground: there are distinct and important reasons for placing it not too far forward and not too far rearward, to which we shall come later, which relate to the directional stability of the car and its drivability.

It is essential to choose your roll centres as a pair, front and rear, as the distribution of weight transferred depends on the slope of the axis between them and its mean distance *below* the CoG. If the roll axis passes above the CoG, the car will roll *inwards* on corners. The less the mean distance of the roll axis from the CoG, the less the car will roll. If the CoG were to lie on the mean roll axis, the car would not roll; it was this

coincidence that gave the SS100 and the low-chassis Invicta their reputations for swapping ends without warning. But we cannot say that, to reduce weight transfer, we should raise the roll centres towards the CoG (see panel, pages 58–59). We only reduce *roll* by raising the roll axis.

A complication here is that certain kinds of suspension linkages carry with them roll centres fixed to within very narrow limits: parallel, equal length wishbones, for instance, always have their roll centre at ground level, while axles located by twin longitudinal leaf springs (Hotchkiss drive) have their roll centre at the height of the spring anchorages to the axle where they can obviously be moved very little above and below hub height by fixing the axle to the other side of the springs or using blocks.

Suppose you start with a blank sheet and have unlimited funds so that you can design the ideal suspension without having to economize by using any proprietary parts at all. Where would you then put your roll centres? If you're designing a big five seater with an overall height of 54 inches, it is extremely likely that your car's centre of gravity will be about 18–23 inches above the ground. If it's your first design and you can get the CoG down to 16 inches on such a big car, you're doing very well. Go over 23 inches high and you'll want to look closely at whether mass

53

Figure 5.4. The Marlin is a mudplugger with style, being originally designed as a trials car. There are two versions, one with Triumph front suspension, the other all Marina.

production designs aren't superior. On sports cars you should be able to get the CoG down to hub height, easily so if you're using the same 26-inch diameter tires I am assuming for both these examples. For the big car I would choose, initially, roll centres of 4 and 5 inches above the ground, front and rear; for the sports car around 3 and 4 inches front and rear. (If I knew the sports car would have to have a live axle and get driven enthusiastically, I'd probably still choose 3 inches and 4 inches front and rear.) I would also design the linkages to be adjustable and I would in any case resign myself to redrawing the lot around new roll centres when the other masses have been placed exactly and the distributed weight of the chassis can be reckoned in and all the fine adjustments can be made.

The total weight that will be transferred from the inner to the outer wheels in a corner is

$$\frac{WH}{T}g$$

where W is the weight, lb
H is the height of the CoG above the ground, inches
T is the track, inches
g is the cornering rate, fraction of 1

The track is the distance from the centre of one tire's contact patch to the centre of the contact patch of the opposite tire; add the two tracks together and divide by two if they're not the same. Only the most incompetent amateur designs will have g below 0.6 and only the most brilliant above 0.9. Note that the amount of weight transferred depends on the height of the CoG and the width of the track and the weight (the amount of cornering force you are *able* to generate also depends on these) and you must change these rather than the roll centre heights or the spring rates if you want more or less weight transferred from the inner to the outer wheels. What you can arrange by choosing varying roll centres and resistance rates is to transfer more weight

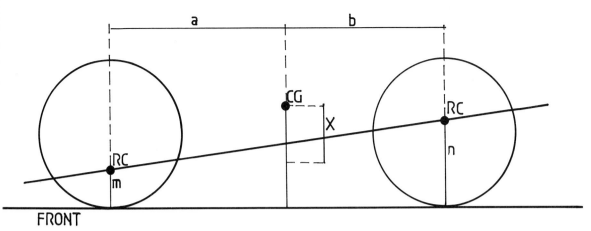

Figure 5.5. The Centre of Gravity lies above the *mean* height of the axis between the front and rear Roll Centres by the distance X. The greater X, the greater the roll moment.

at one end than at the other and this is where the chassis designer comes into his own. To repeat, the *total* weight transfer is determined by the position of the CoG, and the track and mass of the car; the *disposition* of this transfer between front and rear is up to you. How you arrange for the weight to be transferred depends on where you want more effort from the tire, in the steering or in the traction.

The mean height of the roll axis is

$$\left(\frac{bm + an}{a + b} \right)$$

and the CoG is above the mean height of the roll axis by X which is calculated as

$$X = H - \frac{bm + an}{a + b}$$

where X   is the distance the CoG is higher than the mean roll axis

   H   is the height of the CoG above the ground

   m   is the front roll centre height

   n   is the rear roll centre height

   a   is the horizontal distance from the front axle centreline to a transverse plane through the CoG

   b   is the horizontal distance from the rear axle centreline to a transverse plane through the CoG

The roll moment of the sprung mass about the roll axis can then be seen to be WX if you should manage to corner at 1g. This is not all, with independent wishbone suspensions the wheels themselves have an additional roll moment determined by the unsprung weight, the rolling radius of the wheels and the height of the roll centres at each end. Costin and Phipps calculate this as (for a cornering force of g)

$$W_f(r_f - m) + W_r(r_r - n)$$

where W_f is the front unsprung weight

   W_r is the rear unsprung weight

   r_f is the rolling radius of the front wheel

   r_r is the rolling radius of the rear wheel

and under the assumption that the CoGs of the unsprung weights are at the height of the rolling radius of the wheels (not quite the same as hub height but that is the shortcut I always take).

If we set this independent overturning moment of the wheels at Y, the total roll moment becomes WX + Y and it can easily be seen that large and heavy wheels or other suspension parts can have a detrimental effect, magnified by low roll centres. How is all this roll movement resisted?

Through the springs, is the part answer though they are not the sole determinant of the roll resistance, as Arthur Mallock shows on pages 58–59. Nor, even when all the other determinants are taken into consideration, can we just take the spring's resistive qualities at face value. There is a lever arm principle involved and "wheel rates" as well as spring rates; I usually eliminate the problem by tackling the subsidiary calculations first and just plugging the answers into the main formula.

Because some of the required inputs for these calculations are often only available to the metric standard, we now have to change gait. For those of you who, like me, are happier with imperial measurements, here are some conversion factors:

Spring rate and wheel rate, N/mm, multiply by 5.71 to find lbf/in.

Roll stiffness, Nm/deg, multiply by 0.73756 to find lbft/deg.

Length, inches, multiply by 0.0254 to find meters (m).

The spring rate of a leaf spring is

$$\frac{b \times n \times t^2 \times 4 \times E}{L^3} \text{N/mm}$$

where b is the width of the spring blade (m)

n is the number of blades

t is the thickness of the blade (m)

E is the modulus of elasticity

L is the distance between the eyes of the spring when laden

E, the modulus of elasticity, modified to allow for internal friction, may generally, for steel springs, be taken as $159 \times 10^6 \text{kN/m}^2$ (this measures pressure and kN/m^2 multiplied by 0.145 gives lbf/in^2), and the eye-to-eye distance of a transverse installation as on the Model T Ford is usually 32.5 inches plus or minus a bit depending on your shackle arrangements; when calculating for Hotchkiss drive (longitudinal leaf springs), this easily available 32.5 length makes a convenient starting point.

For a torsion bar the spring rate for the deflection at the end of a lever is given by

$$\frac{G \times 3.1416 \times d^4}{32 \times e^2 \times 1} \text{N/mm}$$

where G is the modulus of rigidity

d is the diameter of the torsion bar (m)

e is the length of the lever (m)

l is the length of the torsion bar (m)

G, the modulus of rigidity may, in the absence of specific information and as a first approximation, be taken as $78.5 \times 10^6 \text{kN/m}^2$. Note that *l* is taken as the *effective* length of the torsion bar so that, where it is installed as an anti-roll bar, you should plug only *half* the length of the bar into the calculation. That the diameter of the torsion bar is raised to the fourth power is worth a moment's consideration: it accounts for the fact that we specify changes in the thickness of torsion bars in minute fractions of an inch.

For a coil spring (more properly called a helical spring), the spring rate is given by

$$\frac{G \times d^4}{8 \times n \times D^3} \text{N/mm}$$

where G is the modulus of rigidity (say 81.5×10^6)

d is the wire diameter (m)

n is the number of free coils (total coils minus 1.5–2 coils used to provide abutment)

D is the mean coil diameter (m)

Figure 5.6. To determine the wheel rate of a beam axle, you must know the dimensions from the axle centre to the spring mount centre and the tyre contact patch centre.

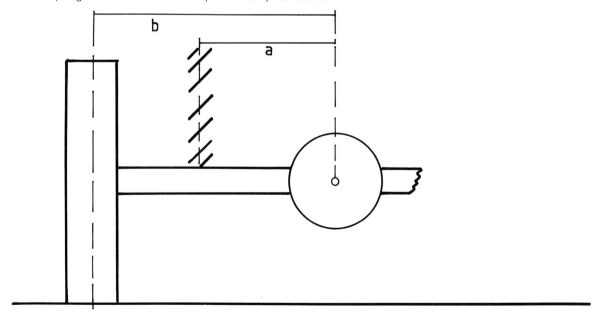

We can now calculate the roll stiffness of a beam axle as

$$C_s \times s^2 \times 0.08729 \, \text{N m/deg}$$

where C_s is the spring rate (N/mm)
    s   is the distance between the spring mountings (m)

and its wheel rate, which is not the same as spring rate but depends on the separation of the springs relative to the track, as

$$C_w = C_s \times (a^2/b^2) \, \text{N/mm}$$

where C_w is the wheel rate (often, confusingly, known as the "spring rate at the wheel")
    a & b   are the distances shown in Figure 5.6 measured in meters

The effective leverage of a swing arm or other single suspension arm is similar and the wheel rate formula the same, except that the distances a and b are measured not from the centreline of the axle but from the inboard pivot of the suspension link on which the spring rests (Figure 5.7).

Before we can calculate the roll stiffness of double wishbone suspension, the wheel rate must first be found:

$$C_w = \frac{C_s \times a^2 \times c^2}{b^2 \times d^2} \, \text{N/mm}$$

where C_s is the spring rate a, b, c and d are as illustrated in Figure 5.8 which can then be plugged into

Roll stiffness, independent suspension
$$= C_w \times t^2 \times 0.08729 \, \text{N m/deg}$$

where t is the track in meters measured from centre to centre of the tire contact patches.

Playing around with the formulae by plugging in different values will soon convince you that, while roll resistance may be increased by fitting stiffer springs (higher spring rate), more is to be gained by moving from a solid axle to independent suspension, by widening the spring base if possible, and best of all, once all other remedies have been exhausted, by widening the track.

Now look at the panel which conveniently brings together all the threads into a comprehensible whole and offers authoritative examples of uncommon lucidity.

Figure 5.7. To determine the wheel rate of semi-trailing arm and swing axle suspensions, the dimensions are taken from the inboard pivot of the assembly, not the axle centreline.

Figure 5.8. Determining the wheel rate with double wishbone independent suspension requires the notional pivot of the instantaneous link centre to be calculated (or drawn) first.

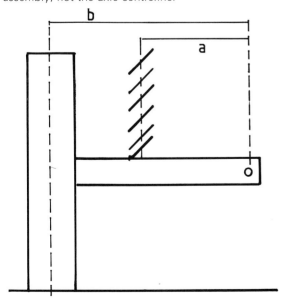

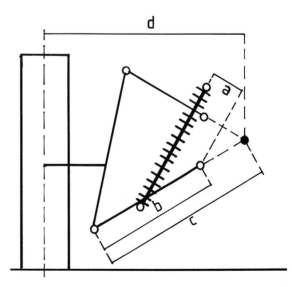

Arthur Mallock has been Godfather to three generations of club racers and his own racer (which he sells to all-comers) has in continuous development reached Mark 25; many's the top designer and driver who had his knowledge handfed by the Major. Mallock's style and examples are inimitable as he expounds the effect of roll centre height on weight transfer:

The fundamentals of modern suspension theory were established by Maurice Olley before the war and recounted in laymen's terms by Donald Bastow in a series of five articles in *Motor* in 1944. The main conclusion was that cart suspension was fundamentally a poor solution because the front spring base was inevitably narrower than the rear, so that even with stiffer front suspension (bad for pitch reduction) the rear weight transfer was more marked than the front, which gave the worst type of oversteer.

Bastow suggested that the solution was to use independent front suspension which automatically gave a spring base equal to the track. Remember again the lever arm squared factor: with a typical front track-to-spring-base ratio of 2.25, this on its own would increase roll stiffness as much as five times.

Bastow further pointed out that most independent front suspension systems had a very low roll centre, but not until the last article, some two months after the others appeared, was it really made clear that a low roll centre itself reduced weight transfer. Thus was born the myth which led to The Great Mistake.

First published in 1961, Racing and Sports car chassis design by Costin and Phipps soon became The Bible for all embryo designers and has remained so, almost, to this day. A problem with The Bible is that it has to be believed, so that when the text claimed, in two places, that lowering a roll centre transfers more weight, this became an accepted fact and was repeated time and time again in various publications, and in print by four current formula car designers.

As with Bastow, the truth came at the end, where calculations at the back of Costin and Phipps showed exactly the reverse.

How can such things be? Surely if the roll centre is lowered, roll will be increased, springs will be compressed more and hence greater weight will be transferred? All correct, except the last sentence. The anomaly is that weight is transferred in two ways: partly by roll through the springs and partly directly through the roll centres.

One example will show the truth. Suppose the centre of gravity coincides with the roll axis. (Not impossible, the Jaguar SS100 came pretty close.) There will then be no roll; the springs will not be compressed and changing their rate till the cows come home

will not make the slightest difference to weight transfer.

The calculations in the appendix of Costin and Phipps are pretty formidable, but by making some approximations, such as ignoring unsprung masses and some simplifications, such as assuming a symmetrical car and a one G cornering rate, we should be able to get the picture.

Some revision first: At 1G cornering rate, centrifugal force is equal to weight and the overturning couple is this multiplied by the centre of gravity height, H. If both front and rear tracks are the same, T, then the total weight transfer is

$$\frac{WH}{T}$$

Putting in a few figures; say W=1000 lb, T=48 in. and H=12 in. then

$$\frac{WH}{T} = \frac{1000 \times 12}{48} = 250 \, lb.$$

Total weight on the two outer wheels is now 750 lb and on the two inners 250 lb.

Playing with roll stiffness and roll centres can never change this relationship, but it *can* concentrate

SPRING FREQUENCY AND STATIC DEFLECTION

Working with the spring rate is all right for weight transfer calculations but for comparisons between cars of different weights, and when faced with spring information given as frequency in Hertz (Hz; medical-type data relating frequency to passenger comfort stretches back to Dr Frederick Lanchester at the dawn of the internal combustion era), the novice designer is often tempted to throw up his hands in horror and not

bother. For the mathematically inclined, I recommend the brief but excellent discussion in Campbell's book, which also contains the theoretical justification for my earlier unsupported statement that the ratio of unsprung to sprung weight should be as low as possible.

The practical designer would, however, do well to think of the *static deflection* of a spring with a weight on it instead of wheel rate – which is independent of weight. The static deflection is simply the difference in the length of the spring between the normally loaded

the weight transfer at one end or the other.

The simplified front weight transfer formula is:

$$\frac{Wm}{2T}+\frac{WX}{T}\left(\frac{Rf}{Rr+Rf}\right)$$

where m=front roll centre height
X=distance of C of G above mean roll centre height (so WX is the roll moment)
Rf=front roll resistance
Rr=rear roll resistance.

The first term

$$\frac{Wm}{2T}$$

is the weight transferred via the roll centre and the second term is that, via the springs. A few examples will perhaps help you get the feel of it.

The simplest case is when the front and rear roll resistance are the same, so that

$$\frac{Rf}{Rr+Rf}$$

becomes $\frac{1}{2}$. If the front and rear roll centres are the same, then the car is completely symmetrical and intuition would tell us that front weight transfer would be half the total.

If roll centres are at 12 in. then X=0 and the second term becomes zero and first term

$\frac{Wm}{2T}$ becomes $\frac{1000 \times 12}{2 \times 48}=125\,lb.$

If we drop both roll centres to ground level the first term becomes zero, X becomes 12 in. and

$$\frac{Wm}{2T}\left(+\frac{WX}{T}\right)\left(\frac{1}{2}\right)$$

becomes 125 lb.

If both roll centres are at 6 in. then X and m are both 6 in. and

$\frac{Wm}{2T}+\frac{WX}{2T}$ becomes

$$\frac{1000 \times 6}{2 \times 48}+\frac{1000 \times 6}{2 \times 48}$$

still 125 lb.

How dull, nothing so far seems to have made any difference. The exciting bit comes when the roll centres differ front to rear.

Suppose we are racing an IOTA 500cc Formula Three car, or a low slung beach buggy, a Formula Vee or even an Auto Union P Wagon. The front roll centre is close to zero and the rear close to centre of gravity height. In this case m=0 and X=6 in. so that

$$\frac{Wm}{2T}+\frac{WX}{2T} \text{ becomes}$$

$$0+\frac{1000 \times 6}{2 \times 48}=62.5\,lb.$$

As the total transfer was 250 lb, the rear is therefore 187.5 lb, now three times as much as the front. Not at all good ... bags of wheelspin and fistfuls of opposite lock!

So why do we not simply fit a stiff front anti-roll bar?

Well, it's true that a modest improvement can be so achieved, but it is very much a law of diminishing returns. If we go over the top and make the front roll stiffness 1000 times greater than the rear, then

$$\frac{Rf}{Rr+Rf} \text{ becomes } \frac{1000}{1001}$$

call it 1 and the formula becomes

$$0+\frac{1000 \times 6 \times 1}{48}=125\,lb.$$

A more practical solution is to interconnect rear suspension sides so that Rr become zero and

$$\frac{Rf}{Rf+Rr}$$

is still 1, but even with these extreme measures, we have still only managed to equalize front and rear weight transfer, whereas for good traction we need greater change at the front.

condition and the totally unloaded condition and can be found empirically for an existing car by measuring the length of the spring at the normal ride height, jacking the car up until the weight is just off the spring, and measuring again.* Thus a 100 lb spring deflected 1 inch by a 100 lb load will ride as softly as a 600 lb spring deflected 1 inch by a 600 lb load. The practical application of this is that the required wheel movement (i.e. suspension travel and wheelarch clearance) is normally about twice the static deflection. If you double the spring rate, you will halve the static deflection. Table 5.1 converts various frequencies directly to static deflections. The static deflection D = mass/spring rate. The natural frequency can be found from the static deflection by

$$\frac{30}{\sqrt{D}} \text{ cycles/min}$$

*If there is a lever in between, measure the static deflection *at the wheel*. A convenient way of determining the SD is by measuring the *vertical distance* between some point on the hub and a point on the body before and after jacking. A dressmaker's hemming measure comes in handy here.

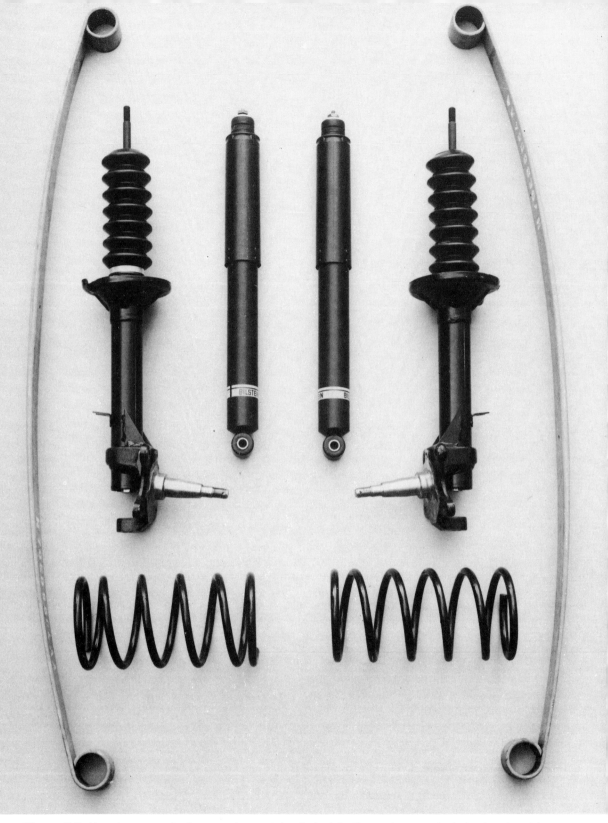

Figure 5.9. Uprating a standard suspension puts back the bite the cost accountants took out and is essential for high-powered special cars using common proprietary parts.

where D is the static deflection (m). While grand prix designers may work with static deflections of 1 inch and less, only the hardest sprung (and usually least competently designed) small sports cars will have SDs of less than 3 inches. For a modest sized car, aim for 4.5 inches and better still, for 5.5 inches and a frequency between 80 and 90 cycles. The bigger the car, the higher the SD you should aim for and the lower the frequency. A big car should have an SD of at least 7 inches and up to 11 inches with natural frequency between 55 and 70 cycles/min. On only the most advanced suspensions can competent roadholding and handling be reconciled with SDs over 11 inches and natural frequencies under 55 cycles/min. This is because it is extremely difficult to arrange linkages that will control the wheel satisfactorily over the long travel soft springs need towards full bump to avoid crashing through (bottoming out) and jarring the occupants; in low cars, the extra-long springs or dampers may also be difficult to fit in.

The most comfortable ride/roadholding compromise is given by long-travel, soft springs firmly damped. Here again it can be seen that designing large cars to the highest criteria is easier than meeting the same desired parameters in a small car.

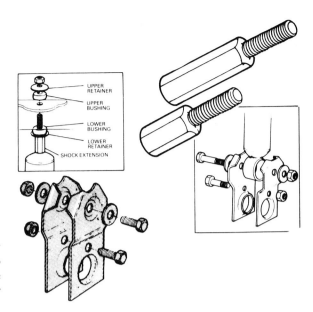

Figure 5.10. It is best to find dampers that fit your suspension design exactly but, if you can't, extension kits to tailor stock dampers are available for both eye and pin shocks.

Table 5.1 Static deflection and spring frequency	
Frequency (Hz)	Static deflection at wheel (inches)
3.133	1
2.216	2
1.566	4
0.783	8

DAMPERS (SHOCK ABSORBERS)

The first leaf-sprung cars were damped by nothing but inter-leaf friction; later, friction discs between two levers, one attached to the axle, the other to the chassis, were used; still later, hydraulic dampers operated by levers came into vogue. Both lever types had the advantage that the levers could be used for positive axle or wheel control if desired as, for instance in the Bentley MkVI/R and R-R Silver Dawn where the upper wishbone of the independent front suspension also operates the damper, and the lever from the live rear axle to the damper does double duty as a radius arm to position the axle longitudinally against spring windup caused by braking or acceleration. The modern telescopic damper (sometimes surrounded by

the coil spring) cannot, except in the special case of the McPherson strut and its near-copies, be used as a positional linkage because it is liable to bend; making it stiff enough to suit as a link will make it much heavier and so increase the unsprung weight.

The ideal dampers should exert very little force on bump and on rebound should compromise between allowing the car to transverse small road irregularities without any harshness and the stiffness required to control bump-induced oscillations so that the car does not wallow. Note that dampers will also resist the weight transfer as the car leans when cornering and that excessively stiff dampers can interfere with the car's cornering prowess. Again, one must compromise.

WHEELBASE AND TRACK

If you design from the ground up without restrictions as to proprietary parts – or if the choice of proprietary parts is wide enough, you may take advantage of two axiomatic tenets of car designers. First, long wheelbases travel in a straight line with the minimum of twitching which calls for correction and have a more comfortable ride than a car of the same design but on a shorter wheelbase. Secondly, wide tracks offer optimum cornering power, the more so with short wheelbases.

The wheelbase is designed by the style and required

carrying capacity of the car, keeping in mind the greater construction and operation costs of longer cars. The use to which the car will be put should also be considered in that the turning circle, given the same maximum wheel lock, is directly related to the length of the wheelbase:

$$\text{Minimum turning radius} = \frac{W}{\sin L}$$

where W is the wheelbase
L is the maximum lock angle of the *outside* wheel

which, as can be seen easily by filling in various values for W while keeping L constant, also implies that the longer wheelbase car will corner less nimbly.

The track should be designed by the optimum cornering power required, the seating and drivetrain requirement across the car (and in nostalgicars sometimes space for running boards), and the types of roads the car will be used on. It was once axiomatic that a sports car should be narrow – mainly a function of old English lanes – but this is no longer so and the Lotus, always a touchstone of advanced design, is now decidedly *wide*. Proprietary parts need not be too much of a hindrance to achieving the ideal track: track rods and rack and pinion steering racks are available in a huge variety of widths and can, in extremis, be altered; rear axle shafts or linkages are as easily lengthened as shortened (though the less common extension operation might be more costly); the number of proprietary front subframes match the number of rack and pinion assemblies of various widths; beam front axles can be made to any width.

CENTRE OF PRESSURE

The high speed directional stability of cars on long wheelbases is in part due to the CoP, or Centre of Pressure, on such designs usually falling well behind the CoG. The CoP is that point, calculated on the side elevation (as a first approximation), through which all air pressures on the car are concentrated. Whatever the size of your car, it is essential that this point lies well behind the CoG; if it lies in front, the car will be aerodynamically unstable and perhaps dangerous. This is a particular problem if aerodynamically optimized cars in that the sum of *all* the forces of air pressure on the car (rather than just the approximation of the side elevation) is rather difficult to calculate even in the static position and these forces alter in a non-linear way once the car starts moving. Air pressure in front of the CoP will be positive, behind it negative. The problem arises when, as speed increases, the positive air pressures in front of the CoP increases

faster than the negative pressures behind it and the CoP consequently moves forward, perhaps past the centre of gravity, leading to a condition where any deviation from the desired course brought about by an external event (a bump in the road) or by driver insensitivity, instead of being subject to the normal self-righting forces of the previous condition (CoP behind CoG), is aggravated by a turning moment acting through the centre of gravity. Attempts to alleviate this undesirable handling characteristic through altering the suspension settings to provide more understeering forces from the tires will only lead to unacceptably heavy steering at low speeds.

The remedy is really a problem of body design (and we shall return to it) but, if your car will exceed 100mph, calculate the centre of pressure in relation to the centre of gravity with the greatest of care; for front-engined cars that will exceed 120mph, estate shapes or fastbacks with high Kamm tails usually answer to the problem.

TIRES AND WHEELS

Though we have had much to say about springs and linkages to them, the tire is the primary suspension medium. The tire, with its wheel, also make up the major part of the weight that is *unsuspended* by the springs and it is for this reason that designers have consistently progressed to smaller wheels and tires. As we have discussed, wheel and tire sizes may be determined by the style of car or the requirement for traction, but you should be aware that the increased weight of bigger wheels and tires will impose a higher requirement on your design.

Note also that for the tire to act as expected and required, the wheel itself must be stiff. Wire wheels are notoriously not stiff and suffer a weight disadvantage as well. The common steel wheel has a better stiffness/weight ratio, while properly designed cast or forged wheels in light alloy or magnesium have the best stiffness/weight ratio. Changing from steel wheels to alloy wheels of the same size will normally effect a weight saving (all unsprung weight, remember) of 30% but if, as is usual, steel wheels are replaced by aftermarket wheels and tires one size up, the weight saving is reduced to about 10%. That is still worth having but greater increases in wheel and tire size must be considered very carefully in the certain knowledge that they will *add* unsprung weight.

The designer will initially ask two questions about the tires he specifies, after ascertaining that they will carry the design weight at the desired speed with a decent safety margin. These two questions are: Will the tires give a comfortable ride? and Will the tires give

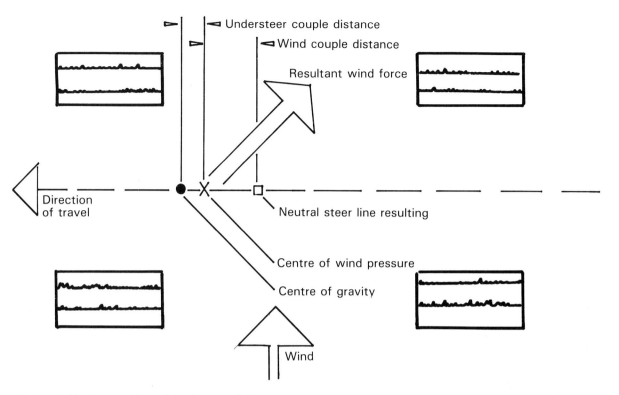

Direction of travel

Understeer couple distance

Wind couple distance

Resultant wind force

Neutral steer line resulting

Centre of wind pressure

Centre of gravity

Wind

Figure 5.11. The position of the Centre of (Aerodynamic) Pressure in relation to the CoG influences the car's behaviour in crosswinds. The CoP and CoG should *not* coincide because the result will be a car with fatally unpredictable handling.

the desired roadholding and handling characteristics? Neither question is as simple as its brevity might suggest. Comfort is not just a matter of soft ride on a good road but of damping out disturbances, not making excessive noise, having enough lateral stiffness so that the car doesn't "sway" and a great many other small and large factors. Roadholding and handling of various tire casing, tread and compound designs involves perhaps the most intricate of all aspects of automobile design; it is no accident that some of the brightest automotive brains of our time work for the tire companies.

The megamanufacturers solve the problem of tire selection for a new car or variant by extensive trial and error methods. The one-off designer cannot afford several or several hundred sets of tires. He must proceed by analogy and common sense. If another car of similar size and weight and performance to yours uses a certain tire (size, make, type), there is your starting point. If you want Rolls-Royce ride in a car powerful enough to rule cross-ply tires right out or ultra-speed tires with ultra-refined ride qualities that don't impair the roadholding and handling (as fitted to

Bristols), the Avon company will welcome you. On the other hand, if you want the ultimate in cornering power and don't care that you have to compromise the ride to achieve it, look at the Pirelli P7s on a Porsche. If you're going to do much wet-weather work, Dunlop is renowned for excellent wet-weather tires and Goodyear's racing experience has paid off there too. Michelin tires, in all their guises, are well known for surviving very high mileages.

Some general guidelines may be appropriate. Radial tires normally score higher with users on all parameters except low speed ride and ease of parking (important if you don't have power-assisted steering) than cross-ply tires. Ultra-low profile tires are likely to be noisier than their 70% aspect ratio fellows and their ride harsher because of the increased stiffness of their sidewalls which do, however, compensate by offering greater powers of roadholding and traction and, in most cases, better handling.

If your special car is economy oriented, you should keep the tires as narrow as is consistent with acceptable handling; special low rolling resistance tires may be the way to go.

Explanatory Notes

OFFSET – this is the measurement between the wheel mounting face and the centre line of the wheel. It may be either:

1) negative – in which case the wheel is termed inset.
2) positive – in which case the wheel is termed outset.
3) zero – when the centre line of the wheel and the hub mounting face correspond.

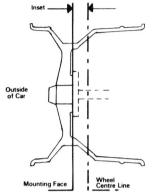

Inset is calculated by measuring in from the hub face to the wheel centre line

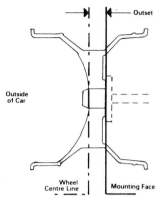

Outset is calculated by measuring out from the hub face to the wheel centre line

'C' DIMENSION

The 'C' Dimension is the measurement from the wheel mounting face to the edge of the inside rim.

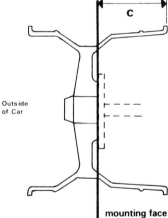

PITCH CIRCLE DIAMETER (PCD)

This is the diameter of the circle that passes through the centre of all four or five studs.

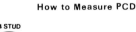

Figure 5.12. Measurements you must know before going out to buy aftermarket wheels. These illustrations are included in the very complete Revolution Wheels literature.

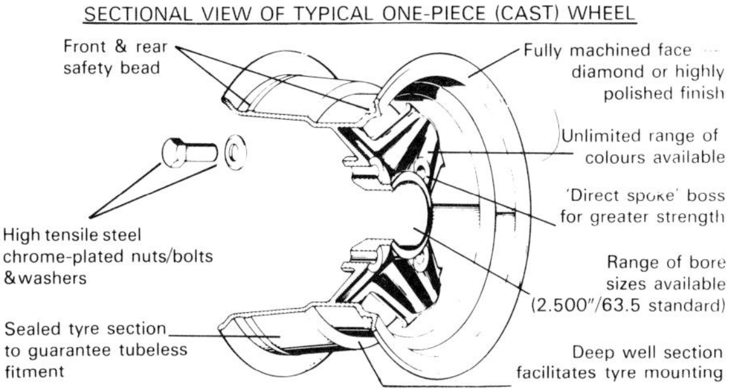

SECTIONAL VIEW OF TYPICAL ONE-PIECE (CAST) WHEEL

Front & rear safety bead

Fully machined face diamond or highly polished finish

Unlimited range of colours available

'Direct spoke' boss for greater strength

High tensile steel chrome-plated nuts/bolts & washers

Range of bore sizes available (2.500"/63.5 standard)

Sealed tyre section to guarantee tubeless fitment

Deep well section facilitates tyre mounting

Figure 5.13. Light alloy wheel construction. Be sure to buy only wheels of reputable manufacture.

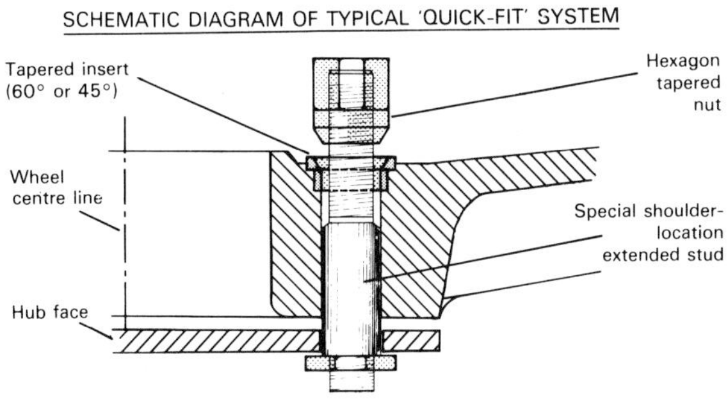

SCHEMATIC DIAGRAM OF TYPICAL 'QUICK-FIT' SYSTEM

Tapered insert (60° or 45°)

Hexagon tapered nut

Wheel centre line

Special shoulder-location extended stud

Hub face

Figure 5.14. Nuts for racers.

Figure 5.15. The primary suspension medium, the most important, most complicated, and least understood component of a car, the tyre's behaviour is totally and maddeningly non-linear.

ROADHOLDING AND HANDLING

To oversimplify matters, we might define roadholding as the maximum speed at which a car will travel around a circle of a given radius (as discussed earlier) plus its ability to keep driving and steering wheels in contact with the road surface regardless of irregularities. Handling would then cover the car's response and responsiveness to transient inputs from the road, aerodynamic pressures, and the driver by way of steering wheel, brakes, gearbox and accelerator; other inputs could include varying load condition of more or fewer passengers, a full or an empty tank, luggage distribution; variable conditions (as opposed to *events*) such as adjustable suspension mountings will also change the handling characteristics.

Roadholding will be good or bad as a consequence of the weight transfers we have been arranging. There are other factors, such as the size of the tire's contact patch with the road and the stiffness of the tire sidewalls, but dispose these as you will, they will avail naught if the total weight transfer and its division between the front and the rear wheels is awkward. Good roadholding results from a low centre of gravity, a wide track, a long wheelbase, long soft springs with stiff dampers, suspension linkages designed to keep the wheel upright or nearly so at all times, a low ratio of unsprung to sprung weight, tires with great radial compliance but little laterally — all of which we have discussed — plus provision against the weight transfers occasioned by braking and acceleration upsetting the roadholding (anti-squat and anti-dive, dealt with later). Finally, air pressure on the car changes with the direction of the wind, with the car's speed, and with its yaw, pitch and roll angles; air pressure is therefore another variable, shifting weight and influencing roadholding.

It has been said that the car with perfect roadholding would always go where the driver points it, and would therefore leave no scope for handling — "handling" being what the driver does with brain, seat of pants, hands and feet (mostly feet) to make the car proceed in the desired direction regardless of where it is pointed.

Handling phenomena can be made accessible without involved mathematics or computers by simply asking in each instance whether the slip angle of the tires at the front is greater than, equal to, or smaller than the slip angle of the tires at the back.

The slip angle is the angle between the direction in which the wheel is pointed and the path it actually follows. The divergence is caused by the deflection of the tire, which accounts for the desire to have tire sidewalls as stiff as possible consonant with comfortable ride. "Slip" is a piece of automotive jargon even

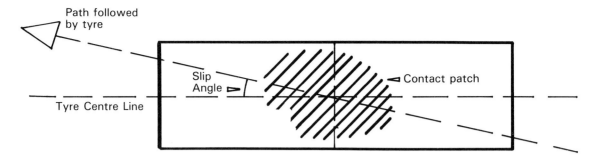

Figure 5.16. The slip angle of the tyre lies between the direction it is actually travelling in and the direction it is pointed in. The contact patch is often irregular.

more inaccurate than most: there is *no* slipping, sliding, skidding – rather the rubber *creeps* onto a new course. The slip angle will vary with the loads on the tire in each of the three planes and – to the fury of the mathematical modellers – is so non-linear that it varies several times even within the same manoeuvre and on all four wheels from front to back and even side to side.

If the front and rear slip angles are the same, resulting roughly speaking (remembering the non-linearity of cause and effect) from deflections of the same magnitude, the divergent path will be straight. If the front and rear slip angles differ, the divergent path will be curved. If the path is curved, the changed centrifugal forces now brought into play will deflect the tire further still, which will result in an increased slip angle which will curve the divergent path further still (or less in some cases), which will again change the centrifugal forces – and so on. The greater the cornering power of a given tire, the smaller the slip angles will become. Thus, if the cornering power at the front is less, resulting in a larger slip angle than at the rear, the car will "understeer". If the cornering power at the rear is less, resulting in a larger slip angle than at the front, the car will "oversteer". An understeering car will run wide of a corner and an oversteering one turn too tightly into the corner in relation to where the wheels are pointed. A neutral steering car (front and rear cornering power and therefore slip angles the same) will negotiate the corner without need for corrective action to steering or accelerator.

It is a commonplace that understeering cars are safer than oversteering ones, except in experienced hands, but this is an over-simplification. Understeering cars can run out of road too, though it is true they will not spin like a terminal oversteerer. The safest car is that which has the neutral steer line. It is difficult to arrange under all conditions, given the migration of the centre of pressure and the non-linearity of tire responses, and mass market designers play safe by building in substantial understeer.

The most important contribution the designer makes to handling is in drawing suspension linkages that keep the wheel upright at all times. There are tires that with up to 3° of negative camber exhibit an increase in cornering power. *There are no tires of which the cornering power is improved by positive camber, nor any conditions of roadholding or handling under which positive camber does not degrade performance.* Unless your chosen tires specifically call for some degree of negative camber which is not to be exceeded, you should design for zero camber or, if that is not possible because of some imposed compromise, a maximum of 1/2° negative camber.* Note that the steering geometry can reduce the camber angle in opposite lock when a large castor angle is used and that, even in normal steering, a large castor angle will increase the negative camber of the important outer wheel in a corner. Camber, castor and toe-in are all affected by spring deflections as can be seen in Figure 5.17.

A handling phenomenon, pitching, cannot like most of the others be solved mainly through suspension choices but relates more directly to the wheelbase and the longitudinal disposition of the masses around the centre of gravity. It is desirable, to avoid resonance pitching and heterodyning of harmonic motions which can lead to the car flinging itself into the air, that the front and rear masses of the car be so arranged that the period in pitch is as near as possible to that in bounce. The period in pitch depends on the radius of gyration, which is the radius about the CoG at which the sprung mass could be considered to be concentrated in an arc while still oscillating at the same frequency as the actual body. For the theory of this, I refer you to

---

*Mass production cars are set up with a small degree of positive camber to make them less sensitive to small road irregularities and crosswinds under the assumption that this will not degrade cornering power to the extent that their purchasers are qualified to notice.

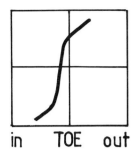 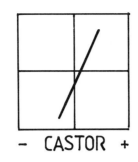 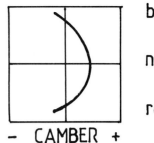

in   TOE   out   −   CASTOR   +   −   CAMBER   +

Figure 5.17. Toe, castor and camber settings are *not* immutable but nominal settings specified at normal ride height. In motion they vary according to the length and angle of links.

Campbell; the practical designer will have to accept that the desired end is achieved when the CoG is placed symmetrically with respect to the axle centre-lines, i.e. precisely halfway along the wheelbase. It is partly to achieve the desired radius of gyration (and partly to make space for passengers) that designers during the 1930s started moving the engine forward.

The radius of gyration may conflict with desired characteristics in the third plane. Movements about the yaw axis of the car are influenced by the polar moment of inertia: If the weight is concentrated mainly in the middle of the car, it will have a *low polar moment of inertia*, will be quick to yaw, i.e. change direction, and will be quick to recover. If the weight is mainly at the ends of the car (or even outside the axles) and there are big overhangs, the car will have a *high polar moment of inertia* which will ensure that it will be diverted from a given course only by the input of a larger force than a car with a low polar moment of inertia, and that it will be slower to recover or require more force. A low polar moment of inertia is eminently desirable if a car is to have light and responsive handling. Yes, I know all about those Porsches, such as the 911, even the 928 and 944 with the engine out front and the gearbox in the rear axle but they are the exception that proves the rule; in any event, while their handling has the responsiveness one expects from a Porsche, the steering of the 944 is undoubtedly *heavy*.

The axes about which the car rolls, pitches and yaws do not necessarily intersect.

ROLL, PITCH, YAW, WEIGHT AND SLIP ANGLE

This is the most important chapter in this book and perhaps the most difficult to comprehend but comprehend it you must if you want to design your own car.

To summarize: The suspension geometry determines the axis between the front and rear instantaneous roll centres around which the car rolls. The lateral weight transfer is determined by the height of the centre of gravity of the total mass of the car in relation to the track width; the division of this transfer between the front and the rear tires is determined by the distance of the centre of gravity of the sprung mass above the instantaneous roll centres. Longitudinal weight transfer in braking or acceleration is a function of the relation of the centre of gravity of the total mass to the wheelbase length. The car will pitch around the centre of gravity of the sprung mass but will yaw around the centre of gravity of the total mass. All of these weights either as initial loadings or as transfers will act through the tires to the road, deflecting the tires according to their cornering power and causing greater or lesser slip angles which then reflect in the roadholding and handling of the car. All of this is complicated by two important considerations: these points and axes are not static but may "wander" dynamically when the car is moving under the influence both of the weight transfers we try to control and of extraneous factors such as aerodynamics; tire response is non-linear under almost all relevant operating conditions.

Once you have some understanding of these complex interrelationships, you can proceed to choose the *kind* of suspension that would best suit your car.

6 Suspension: Choice

Given the non-linearity of tire response, a centre of gravity that in roll can run around like a marble let loose in a jar (taking the pitch and yaw axes with it wherever it goes), and roll centres wandering dynamically from the moment the car moves off, it is not surprising that there are a huge number of different suspension designs. What all these designs have in common is that they represent a compromise between cost, roadholding, handling and comfort, any number of which might have individually conflicting parameters. Many special car builders also want the suspension to look good, so they will consider appearance, perhaps before function – which accounts for the continued popularity of front beam axles under hot rods, for instance, and for the use of transverse leaf springs on these axles. If the special car builder is using proprietary parts bought second hand, the price differential between various designs is usually not large; it he has to have parts made up, the labour content is usually such that advanced designs cost no more – and sometimes less – than the most basic design (a front beam axle could easily cost more to manufacture than four wishbones). Appearance is a matter of personal taste. Most kinds of suspension –

Figure 6.1. The roll centre migrates between bump stops. Limiting spurious vertical movements conflicts with the desire for passenger comfort by long spring travel.

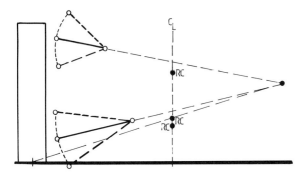

and all the ones in common use today – may be tweaked to give a comfortable ride, though some may have to sacrifice considerable performance to do so, for instance transverse springs on beam axles front and rear cause the car to sway alarmingly at anything over very moderate speed. That leaves roadholding and handling as the parameters to judge which suspension system is best suited to a particular purpose. Since handling is the correction of the deficiencies in roadholding, let us consider roadholding by itself for a moment.

Which suspension will give the best roadholding? The one which offers optimal wheel control under all operating conditions. If we can then define "optimal", we have a standard of judgement. The problem is that the suspension through defining the roll centres in relation to the CoG, determines the weight transfer, which in turn influences how much control is required. The suspension interfaces with the various factors we want to consider at so many points that analysis becomes impossible without the aid of a computer capable of considering seven or more free variables; books on the theory of the subject can grow pretty thick and obscure. What the special car designer needs is a short cut.

We know from the discussion in the previous chapter that it is desirable for maximum cornering power to keep the wheel upright or give it a very modest negative camber. Let this then be our first criterion, that the suspension should in roll keep the wheel upright when viewed from the front. As we shall see, some suspension systems manage to do this but, as the wheel moves up and down, allows the axle centreline to describe an arc when seen from the side of the car; the wheel moves vertically in a straight line when seen from the front but in a curve when seen from the side. Since the effect with this kind of suspension, when one side of the car goes down on the springs and the other goes up, is that the wheelbase changes, rear wheel steering results: an unexpected, uncontrolled

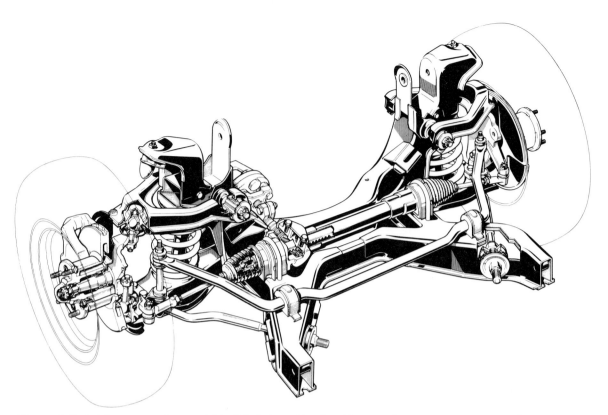

Figure 6.2. Subframes are the special builder's best friends, either to take exact measurements from or because they mount suspension, steering and brakes conveniently.

force, not good for roadholding. So, our ideal suspension will move the wheel vertically in both directions or as near as possible.

Having chosen your ideal suspension in this chapter, and designed it in the next, you will have to return, in the spirit of automotive compromise, and make sure there are no side effects: these are listed here too.

CONFUSING NOMENCLATURE

We have beam axles, live axles, dead axles and independent suspensions. A beam axle (sometimes called "solid" though it is almost always hollow *and* split in two) is one where there is a more or less rigid interconnection between the wheels: the wheels are therefore *non*-independent. A live axle is driven. A dead axle is one that is not driven (the rear axle of a front-drive car) but can be either independent or solid (hollow but *not* split in two). An independent suspension is best defined as one where the spring on one side may be compressed without changing the camber of the wheel on the other side of the car; there is no rigid interconnection between the wheels (except, sometimes, the anti-roll bar). You may sometimes hear

people speak carelessly of the "axle" of an independently sprung car, by which they will mean the complete suspension linkages, often complete with spring and damper, attached to their subframe (which in turn is then attached to the body); the rear subframe cage of any Jaguar from the S-type forward and the front subframe cage of modern Mustangs and Cortinas are examples. In all this the chassis or body of the car doesn't count as a "more or less rigid interconnection": the connection must be directly between the wheels on the other side of the springs from the chassis and body (or subframe).

In addition, the very word suspension is a misnomer: it applies to something hanging from a spring while we use it to indicate a car resting on top of springs. Furthermore, what we are dealing with in this chapter, while called suspension design, actually has nothing to do with the springs that suspend the car (except where they are used to position the axle or wheel, a minority of cases) but may be far more accurately described as wheel or axle control *linkage design*. In virtually every design discussed below the linkage attachment points are critical to within very narrow limits for any set of desired roadholding and comfort criteria whereas, for the same effect, the springs may (in most cases) be mounted in any spaces not required for the positive location links.

POSITIVE LOCATION LINKAGES

The novice sometimes finds it confusing that designers and texts mention positive location devices primarily in connection with beam axles – and then he finds them used in independent suspensions as well! A positive location link is simply one that limits the movement of an axle or another link (and therefore the wheel or wheels) to the vertical plane – or attempts to do so to a greater extent than whatever else is already fitted – and so prevent slewing of the axle (or toe-in of the wheels in independent designs). Positive location devices are always so arranged that they take out loads in compression or tension and never in bending, because bending would change the length of the link and betray its purpose. Longitudinal positive links are radius rods, torque tubes and A-frames. Transverse positive links are the Panhard rod (simply a transverse radius rod), the Watt linkage cribbed from steam engines, the sliding block sometimes found on De Dion suspensions, and the links of an independent suspension. Notice though that, while I have given the direction of primary stiffness of these linkages, many of them will also have benefit in the other direction, some merely from the solidity of their pivotal mounting, others by design or serendipidy; for instance, splayed wishbones are easily made equally stiff in both directions. Others may be turned through 90° to function in the other direction, like the Watt linkage found in the fore and aft direction under the pre-SDI Rover 2000 and 3500, one Watt system to each side of the axle.

Two points about positive links. The longer they are, the greater their radius about their pivot on the body or chassis and consequently the flatter their arc at the axle or wheel end and therefore the nearer they will come to moving the wheel up and down vertically, which is our ideal. Secondly, no structure of practical use about an automobile is stronger than the triangle, none more easily turned into a mechanism (i.e. a piece of equipment that *folds up* when enough pressure is applied to one of its joints) than a rectangle. If it is not possible to triangulate a linkage, at least angle the sides as steeply as possible to turn it into a trapezoid.

ANTI-ROLL BARS

These are often abbreviated simply as roll bars. A roll bar is a rod that lies transversely across the car and is cranked at each side with the ends attached directly or through a distancing link to the suspension linkages or

axle. On beam axles it is possible to attach the transverse section to the axle and the cranked arms to the body, as on the Cortina Mk III. Where the ends of the bar are attached to the suspension linkages there is, except in some special cases where the roll bar is used as a positive location link in addition to its other duties, no need to attach the transverse part to the body or subframe – it can just hang in mid-air; more normal practice is to attach it to body or subframe by two loose rubber bushes.

If both wheels bump, both ends of the roll bar will move upwards and the transverse section will simply rotate in mid-air or its mountings. It has no effect either in two-wheel rebound conditions. But, when the car is going around a corner, with weight being transferred so that the outside wheel rises in relation to the body (bump) and the inside wheel falls in relation to the body (rebound), then one end of the bar will be twisted up and one end down and the transverse part will act exactly like a torsion bar: a spring adding its rate to that of the "road" springs. Note that the anti-roll bar, by interconnecting the wheels, causes them to cease to be truly independent, the more so as the limit is approached where there is no further suspension travel; that is to say, the effect of an anti-roll bar is relative, varying from nothing to adding its total rate very effectively to the road springs' rate.

What then is its purpose? That flows from the effect of the roll bar: it alters the spring rate only in roll, i.e. its effect is on the roll resistance without affecting the spring rate under other conditions. It allows us to fit long, soft springs without suffering blancmange roadholding as payment for the good ride and without using up valuable suspension travel. It allows us to choose a low roll centre – advantages include minimum disturbance in bump and from lateral inputs – without the disadvantages associated with low roll centres: large roll angles and big camber changes; a roll bar raises the roll centre of the end at which it is fitted only under those conditions when it is most beneficial (except in single wheel bump and rebound). A roll bar fitted at the front only (common on mass production cars with live rear axles and independent front suspensions) transfers weight from the inside rear wheel to the outside front wheel and, by increasing the slip angle at the front, creates or increases understeer. Bars at both ends are normally required when you want to limit the roll angle without going to "hard" springs. Remember when choosing the ratio of bars front to rear, and when choosing a single roll bar, that the stiffness increases as the fourth power of the bar's diameter but that its effective length is only half the total length, the total length being the transverse section (not including the cranked arms' length).

Do not be misled into seeing the roll bar as the cure for suspension geometry solecisms; it should be designed-in from the start.

SPACE CONSIDERATIONS

Many of the linkages we will consider have limited application for reasons of space. It is irrelevant, for instance, that wide-based wishbones take up a great deal of lateral and longitudinal space when used at the rear of a single seater racing car; on a 5 seater saloon car the same wide-based wishbones at the rear would add appreciably to the wheelbase, weight, construction and operating costs, etc.

Alternatively, a certain design may require structures of a high degree of stiffness outside the wheelbase where its weight may be undesirable or construction complicated and costly; examples are trailing links at the front, such as used on the VW Beetle and Porsche 356, and the radius rods controlling the movement of the rear axle of the Pegaso which were arranged in a triangle with its apex in the very tail of the car (wonderfully positive but complicated and costly).

The reason for the different suspension systems often found on the front and rear of production cars is almost always, where cost is not the deciding factor, one of space, rather than that the engineers do not wish or cannot make any part of the body as stiff as is necessary; present production cars are about four times as stiff as supposedly advanced spaceframes in the lower classes of racing, such as Formula Ford. Since the special car builder, who does not normally work with unit constructions welded together in sheet metal, cannot take the stiffness of his chassis or car for granted, and will have to work very hard to make it stiff, the wary novice will avoid those designs that take suspension loads too far outside the wheelbase.

BEAM-AXLE SUSPENSIONS

With a beam the two wheels are connected side to side. When both wheels are in bump or rebound at the same time, the wheels will stay upright, viewed from the front. In single wheel bump, or when one wheel falls into a pothole, the camber of the other wheel is inevitably also changed as the axle tilts. During cornering, unless the wheel on the opposite end of the axle lifts (easily corrected by fitting a roll bar or changing the front/rear spring rate ratio), the outer wheel will be kept upright or at its present degree of camber. This is of course highly desirable but a price has to be paid: when one wheel goes over a bump, the whole axle (and the car with it) is displaced sideways. This stagecoach effect (I'm indebted to Arthur Mallock for this telling

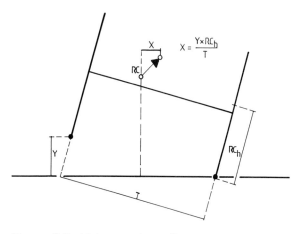

Figure 6.3. All beam axles suffer to some extent from the stagecoach effect: the lower the roll centre and the wider the track, the smaller the sideways hop in relation to the height of the disturbance in the road causing it.

phrase), known to rallyistes as bump scrub, is quantified quite simply as:

$$X = \frac{Y}{T/R_c} \text{ or } X = \frac{Y \times R_c}{T}$$

where X   is the distance the car will be displaced sideways
      Y   is the height of the bump
      T   is the track dimension
      R_c is the height of the roll centre above the ground

so that T/R_c is the track to roll centre ratio; which makes it perfectly clear that where the track and the roll centre height are the same dimension, the car will be displaced sideways by the total height of the bump; the lower the roll centre, the smaller the lateral disturbance.

Transverse leaf spring

A beam axle may be suspended on a transverse leaf spring (a single spring or a group of springs clamped together) shackled at each end of the axle and fixed to the chassis in the centre. The roll centre will be at the height of the body mounting to the spring. It is obvious that the single mounting will allow the body to sway from side to side and the axle to twist underneath the car. About the swaying of the body there is nothing you can do except slow down around the corners. The rotation of the axle in the horizontal plane can be

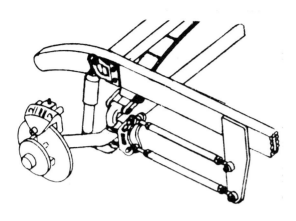

The spring may be arranged to mount to the front of the axle, above it, or behind it; your supplier will configure it to your heart's desire and will also set the kingpin inclination to suit your spindles (Anglia 4°, Chevrolet 5°, Ford 9°). Radius rods (parallel bars to hot rodders) may be attached through rubber bushes, track rod ends, or racing style rose joints. Rear radius rods are normally led forward (in which case they are said to be *trailing* the axle behind them) unlike front radius rods which normally extend behind the axle (described as *leading*) to take braking and accelerating reaction.

Hotchkiss drive

This design, still used at the rear on many cars, was popular at both ends of almost all cars until the advent of independent front suspension in the 1930s. It is simple, cheap, and more than moderately effective. In its most unadorned form, it consists simply of two longitudinal leaf springs to which the axle is clamped halfway; the springs are attached to the chassis or body at their forward ends on a pivot and at the rear end on a shackle to allow for length variation as the spring flexes under load. The springs locate the axle both longitudinally and transversely. In many early installations there was not even a damper, interleaf friction providing more than enough damping!

Figure 6.4. Hotrodder's heaven: the 'traditional' hotrod setup of beam axle, transverse spring, and parallel bars. It's hard on ride and handling but looks clean.

controlled by radius rods. When axles were forged in the shape of an I (seen as a section through the axle), two single radius rods angled inwards towards their pivoted mounting on a crossbar under the front of the engine could be used – and were, on the Model T. If space considerations prevent the use of a single inward-angled roll bar to a side, an I-section beam axle transversely suspended can be positively controlled by split wishbones (see figure 11.1, page 121: "split" wishbones are *joined* at their rear end) running back from the axle at a small or no inward inclination, depending on the lock clearance required for the wheel when steered, to the outside of the chassis. The modern tubular beam axle has greater torsional resistance than the I-beam – which twisted to allow for Henry's geometric solecisms – and will wreck split wishbones in no time at all. Two radius rods per side are therefore used, usually set parallel to each other and at some angle or coincidence pleasingly complimentary to the chassis or body lines; the best geometry is achieved when the bars are parallel to each other and to the ground as well at normal ride height. To avoid bump steer as well as bump scrub, you must arrange the steering geometry so that it neither fights the suspension geometry nor introduces spurious forces. This is best done by mounting your steering box on the same bracket that accepts the rear end of one pair of radius rods, making the steering arm as nearly the same length as the radius rods as possible, running it forward parallel to the radius rods and centrally between them, and arranging that the steering arm to drop- (Pitman-) arm pivot falls as nearly as possible on a line between the two radius arm rear pivots.

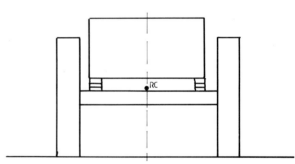

Figure 6.5. Hotchkiss drive consists of a beam axle with two fore and aft leaf springs attached as near as possible to the wheels. The roll centre is where the springs are attached to the axle: the springs provide lateral location.

The roll centre with Hotchkiss drive is at the level of the spring mounting to the axle and can be varied by moving the axle above or below the spring and interposing blocks. The "smile" in front beam axles is there partly to obtain a lower roll centre at the front and partly to obtain frame clearance so that the car can be lowered.

Lateral sway on the springs is nowhere near as large as with a transverse spring. It is usually very small and positive lateral location only becomes necessary at quite immoderate rates of lateral acceleration; Panhard rods, Watt linkages, A-frames, in fact all the normal lateral links, may be fitted.

Much more worrying is the tendency of longitudinal leaf springs to wind up under acceleration or braking, causing the spring to bend into an S on one side, which moves the axle mounting on that side and thus alters the wheelbase on one side only: the result is rear wheel steering (and some discomforting front wheel side effects to aggravate the already unfavourable unsprung weight of braked, steering beam axles). The cure is radius rods, as with the transverse leaf spring described above. The longer the rods are, the flatter the arc of swing they impart to the axle and therefore the least change in the wheelbase. By angling them inwards towards the centreline of the car so that they meet on the centreline, useful length can often be found, and any tendency towards binding because of the torsional stiffness of the axle negated. The ladder bars often seen under dragsters and Camaros with monster powerplants are simply beefed-up radius rods in their workings. The so-called anti-tramp bar (or snubber) is a bar attached to the chassis with its other end underneath the spring at the axle mounting; this is supposed to keep the spring straight but the special car designer will need its doubtful benefit only if he has been so careless as to leave himself absolutely no space to fit a more efficacious positive control link. The torque tube, enclosing the propeller shaft, bolted to the differential and pivoted at its forward end, is a somewhat expensive possibility; Ferrari once favoured it.

Radius rods on Hotchkiss suspended front beam axles should preferably be led forward to take brake reaction. Telescopic dampers cannot be used as positive links but, if you use a lever arm damper instead, the arm can be arranged to double as a positive locational link.

It is possible (as in the case of the Dutch Daf better known for its infinitely variable belt-driven transmission) to suspend a De Dion axle on twin longitudinal leaf springs but a bit pointless for a car favoured with a high power to weight ratio when so many other links offer themselves.

Other leaf spring systems

There is a vast number of other leaf spring configurations which I cannot recommend to special car designers, nor believe that they would want.

However, there are two systems which, though not necessarily to be recommended for new construction, can still be seen giving yeoman service under elderly cars still road-usable.

Cantilever suspension, an early Rolls-Royce favourite, consists of a half-elliptical spring clamped at one end to the axle, at its middle to the chassis, with the other end attached to the chassis by a shackle or between rollers. The purpose of this arrangement is to reduce unsprung weight. Lateral location of the axle is better than would be guessed at a quick glance.

Quarter-elliptical suspension is, as the name suggests, achieved by one-half of a semi-ellipse. One end of the spring is clamped to the axle, the other to the chassis. Reversed-quarter elliptics, favoured by the great Ettore Bugatti, have the *thin* end clamped to the chassis and the *thick* end to the axle. Quarter-elliptics save both sprung and unsprung weight and affect the unsprung/sprung weight ratio favourably when compared with either Hotchkiss drive or cantilever suspension; this is because the deleted half of the spring made up a greater part of the unsprung weight than of the sprung weight. However, unless a quarter-elliptic is abnormally long, the ride is very harsh.

With both cantilevers and quarter-elliptics it may be possible to save the weight of the chassis either rearwards or forwards beyond the spring mounting but this aim is often compromised by the need to mount dampers, petrol tanks, the body, lights, bumpers, even the number plate; at the forward end of the car the radiator and its water needs solid mountings and the engine too cannot rest in thin air.

In any event, overall weight saving was very unlikely to be the reason for specifying quarter-elliptics; several veteran car racers ruined the handling of their Talbots by sawing off the rear frame behind the quarter-elliptic chassis mounts which altered the weight *distribution* deleteriously.

Coil springs, dampers and bushes

A coil spring is a helically wound torsion bar. Consideration of its form should make it obvious that it will not offer the axle positive location in any of the desired directions. The telescopic damper is, by design, not rigid; the design is also such that, even if the two telescoping sections were joined rigidly into a single extended bar, it would probably bend under quite small load. It is possible to make a damper able to telescope and yet resistant enough to bending to use it as a positive location link but only at several multiples of its present cost.

Co-axial helical spring and damper units (colloquially "coil-overs") offer economics in mounting numbers and complications and weight. Some coil-over designs have the bumpstops built in – another weight saving and, for hot-rodders, a contribution to a "clean", uncluttered appearance.

Figure 6.6. Kits that take all the mechanicals from a single source offer special car builders one-stop convenience. Both the Merlin TF and a version of the Jago B use all-Cortina mechanicals, including engines (not illustrated).

Coil-sprung suspensions can be stayed by four links with two splayed, two links and an A-bracket, four parallel links and a Panhard rod, four parallel links and a Watt linkage, a torque tube and one or more links either angled or parallel per side.

In each case the roll centre is at the mounting to the axle of the lateral control arm or arms, but the primary considerations governing choice between these in mass market designs (next to cost) are that some of them are more difficult than others to insulate from the passenger cabin in respect of noise and that one in particular, the A-frame, can wear out bushes abnormally fast and become subject to increased servicing. The special car builder will want to weigh each for the purity of its geometry and the resultant purity of motion it imparts to the wheels, and for the suitability of the heights at which its roll centre may be arranged. Serviceability is of no moment to someone who is enthusiastically going to do his own: the owner of, for instance, a Super Seven will no doubt examine his car thoroughly at intervals and will think changing the A-frame pivot bush every 6000 miles small recompense for the positive and space-saving location it provides for the rear axle.

The compliance of bushes may be calculated but it is far too mathematical to do here. Gilbert McIntosh's appendix in the Costin and Phipps bible, pp. 124–5, offers worked examples comparing two possible bushes. Rubber bushes are cheap enough to experiment with and to replace often. In any event, my

short-cut has never failed (except on the rubber doughnuts holding up the rear silencer on my Volvo, which I have been replacing every six months for years now). If you are choosing bushes for, say, a rear radius arm, look for a car in the Ford range with similar power output and weight, look at a selection of the bushes at your local Ford dealer. There's bound to be something pretty near what you have in mind.

Coil and four link

This consists of four non-parallel links. Two are attached above the axle and two below. All four are trailing links, i.e. they run forward from the axle. The top two are splayed inwards from the extremities of the axle towards the centre of the car. The roll centre is at the level of the top-link mountings to the axle. It is possible to splay the bottom links instead but normally seating considerations prevent this. This design suffers from high noise transmission to the car and, with the top links splayed, as is normally the case, a roll centre that goes walkabye in roll and pitch and can therefore induce spurious handling effects.

Coil, two links and A-bracket

This has two parallel links plus, on the other side of the axle, an A-frame or A-bracket, forming a triangle that trails from the body to the final drive. This is a logical development of the four link system above and offers

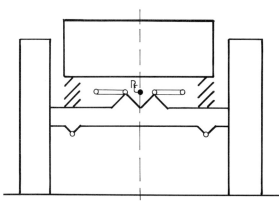

Figure 6.7. Beam axle and four links, two fore-and-aft and two splayed diagonally. The roll centre falls where the splayed links are located to the axle.

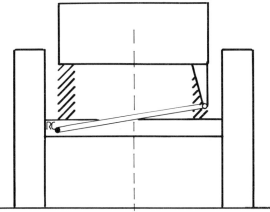

Figure 6.8. Coil springs and a Panhard rod for lateral location can be used with either a torque tube or radius rods for longitudinal location. The roll centre falls where the Panhard rod is attached to the axle.

better geometry but, as pointed out above, when the A-bracket is made very narrow to fit underneath a family car or a low-slung sports car, the loadings on the bushes can become very high. If there is space for a wide A-bracket the loadings will be much lower – but there might then also be space for a superior, more advanced suspension altogether. The roll centre falls at the point where the A-bracket is attached to the axle, which can be either above or below it but is normally above.

Coil, four links and a Panhard rod

The four longitudinal links are normally parallel in side view and most often in plan as well. The Panhard rod is pivoted at one end (normally the right, looking forward) to the car and at the other end to the axle as near to the opposite wheel as practicable. The roll centre falls at the point where the Panhard rod is mounted to the axle, either above or below the axle. The motion of the Panhard-stayed suspension is not as pure as the Watt linkage (below) because the Panhard rod is of course asymmetrically mounted; to avoid spurious asymmetrical effects, the Panhard rod should be mounted perfectly horizontally and be as long as possible. The radius rods are mounted above and below the axle and the Panhard rod normally behind the axle though it is sometimes found in front of the axle. (When the Panhard rod has to be cranked to clear the prop or the final drive, it is normally made much thicker than a straight bar for a similar application so that it doesn't bend.)

This one, though not ideal, is a favourite with many

special car builders for its simplicity and the ease with which the roll centre may be raised or lowered by simply building a tower out from the axle towards the pre-determined pivot point. It is also a "clean" system and I am surprised that it is not more often used for beam front axles with coil-overs and four-bars: the Panhard rod and the steering track rod can both run at the same level behind the axle and so be hidden or add pleasingly to the geometric pattern.

Coil, four links and Watt linkage

This consists of four trailing links, two above the axle and two below it, all parallel, with a Watt linkage for transverse location. The roll centre is at the point

Figure 6.9. Watt linkages can be used both for lateral location and for longitudinal location. The roll centre is at the pivot of the centre upright to the differential case.

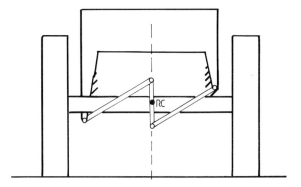

where the vertical link of the Watt linkage is attached to the final drive and is therefore predetermined to the depth of the final drive unit plus half the depth of the Watt central upright. Drawing several versions of the Watt linkage with the arms at different angles to the chassis will soon convince you that this makes a difference. Perfectly horizontal arms have a strong roll-reducing element when the body tilts. Where the chassis or mounting width is less than 32″, a Watt linkage, always far superior to a Panhard rod, is so far superior that the additional complication and weight and cost becomes a bagatelle.

An interesting variation is where the four longitudinal bars are made into a Watt linkage to each side: two parallel bars leading and two parallel bars trailing, the leading ones normally pivoted above the axle, the trailing ones below it, giving a Watt linkage running fore-and-aft on each side of the axle. Lateral location can be by Panhard rod or another Watt linkage positioned transversely or an A-bracket. The roll centre will be at the mounting point of the transverse stay to the axle. This system, with three Watt linkages gives a particularly pure geometry in that the axle can – if the designer commits no geometrical solecisms – move *only* vertically with no aberrations when seen either from the front or the side. It is, however, complicated, expensive and space-consuming, especially in that the leading radius arms (in a rear suspension, and the trailing arms in a front suspension) will need reasonably stiff mountings well outside the wheelbase.

Coil, torque tube, links

The torque tube is rigidly attached to the differential nosepiece and pivots on the body; it takes, as the name implies, the torque reaction, controlling axle wind-up. There are normally two links, one from each side of the axle, running forward either parallel to the torque tube or angled towards it. Lateral location is provided by a Panhard rod or Watt linkage. This gives excellent axle location but the reason for the popularity of this suspension system in luxury cars with pretensions to or real performance is that the torque tube offers very positive axle location together with very high insulation from road noise. Luxurious Opels, SDI Rovers and pre-independent V12 Ferraris all have torque tubes.

DE DION SUSPENSION

Designed before the turn of the century by Trepardoux (the steam model-maker who didn't stay in the De Dion–Bouton–Trepardoux partnership), this system was forgotten until applied by Harry Miller to some racers. It was then used at the front of the Cord L-29 (which had front wheel drive but was more noted for setting the classic half-the-length-is-bonnet styling trend), but sank into obscurity until high performance manufacturers in the 1950s wanted some of the advantages of independent suspension without the terrifying camber changes associated with swing axles, the only independent rear suspension designs then in use.

A De Dion is a dead axle, merely a piece of pipe cranked to clear *the final drive unit which is attached to the chassis or body* and does not form part of the unsprung weight; the wheels are attached to the ends of the De Dion tube and drive to them is by universally jointed half shafts. Since it does not have to carry the substantial weight of the final drive unit, the De Dion design shares the great advantage of independent suspension of low unsprung weight; this advantage may be increased by moving the brakes inboard, something it is not possible to do with a live axle. On the other hand, the De Dion also shares the great advantage of the beam axle, that in roll the wheels remain upright or at their preset degree of camber. However, it is not an independent suspension and in one-wheel bump the De Dion will change its angle just like any other rigid axle with the same undesirable camber change to the wheel on the other side. But there is no toe-in on bump, a problem that plagues many independent suspensions and of increasing importance with every advance that adds to the sidewall stiffness of tires.

De Dion suspensions are famed for their high-speed straight-running capabilities and in this context it is notable that the grandest of the Grand transcontinental Tourers, the 170mph Aston Martin, employs a De Dion rear end and that the designers have already decided to use a De Dion under the scheduled replacement. The definitive test is to drive at a speed in excess of 120mph off the smooth onto a section of that *pavé* the French specialize in and feel what happens to the rear end of the car. It is the De Dion's supremacy here that keeps an expensive (as expensive as independent suspension and sometimes more so) suspension in business going-on a hundred years after it was first invented.

The De Dion, being a beam axle, may be suspended by any of the linkages described above combined with leaf, coil or torsion bar springing; it is subject to the same design solecisms as any other application of the same linkages but an additional problem is that of setting up the geometry so that the De Dion tube becomes an impossibly stiff roll bar, for which the (expensive) cure is to put an articulated joint into the tube. A lateral location device particular to De Dion suspensions consists of a steel ball fixed to the centre of the tube that slides up and down in a vertical groove on the back of the final drive unit.

The last steered, front axle application of the De Dion axle was on a 1950s racer revival of the Bugatti name which by all accounts did not handle well. While there is every reason for the special car builder to consider a De Dion rear suspension, especially if a proprietary make of suitable track is readily available (look underneath pre-SDI Rovers), only the foolhardy will attempt its application at the front, where its advantages enjoyed at the rear over beam axles and independent suspensions are negated by the absence of drive gear (in a rear drive car) and the requirement that the wheels turn to steer the car.

INDEPENDENT SUSPENSIONS

Our criteria for choosing between the various independent suspension linkage designs are still the same: we want the wheels, and especially the outer wheels in a corner, kept upright or at some predetermined degree of negative camber and we don't want any spurious steering inputs from wheelbase or toe alignment changes.

The reasons for choosing independent suspension over beam axles are essentially threefold. At the front, heavy wheels, tires and brakes cause gyroscopic effects that could not be countenanced even in the 1930s; these provided spurious steering inputs that could make powerful cars with heavy brake–wheel–tire combinations on beam front axles quite dangerous to corner fast even on smooth roads. Independent suspension offers freedom to lower the roll centre and gain a larger measure of control over weight transfer and so roadholding; independent suspension at the front doubles the effective spring track at a stroke, increasing the roll stiffness as much as five times. Best of all, this increase in roadholding ability with independent suspension can be accompanied by an *increase* in passenger comfort because it is possible to use softer springs. Among the secondary reasons are reduced unsprung weight, already taken into account into some of the above consequences, and, at the rear, the absence of torque effect in the propeller shaft and torque reactions in the rear suspension leads to better traction under extreme conditions. Finally, and important especially in mass market designs, independent suspension allows a space saving for moving an engine forward or providing a bigger boot (trunk).

That is not to say that you *must* choose independent suspension at any cost. The reasons for having *advanced* independent suspension at the front are compelling: on high powered cars to be used on rough roads, it is probable that even a swing axle will be

Figure 6.10. Semi-trailing arms on the Ford Sierra. Many special car builders who find the Salisbury 4HU diff too expensive will be looking at this one.

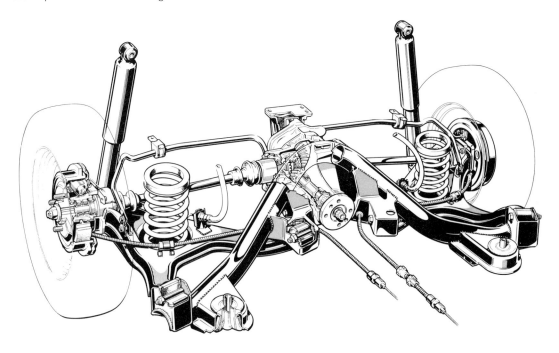

preferable to a beam axle at the front. At the rear, however, only the most advanced independent suspensions offer persuasive advantages over a well-located live axle, with the less advanced (often older) independent suspensions having no allure whatsoever.

This is because some independent suspension systems suffer camber changes directly related to roll and all independent suspensions are subject to a greater or lesser degree of jack-up (often called "swing-axle jacking"; don't confuse this with the much more esoteric "corner jacking") or tuck-under. It can easily be seen from Figure 6.11 that a substantial degree of jack-up will create a large overturning moment and the car will roll; a beam axle will most likely slide before the degree of tilt is achieved that would cause the same overturning moment. In addition it should be noted that independent suspension at the front combined with a live rear axle almost automatically gives that degree of understeer considered safe for everyday effortless driving on the public roads, in itself a compelling counsel in mass manufacturers' boardrooms.

top and bottom connection, or four quarter-elliptics with the "hole" between them filled by the engine.

Coil springs cannot be used as links, though in the McPherson strut suspension the coil is wound around a telescoping link.

Unless there are compelling reasons to the contrary, the special builder will normally choose the simplicity of coil-overs for his independent suspension, limiting his choice to those with built-in bumpstops, seeking location in positive links.

Swing axles

A swing axle is a beam axle split in half and centrally pivoted; on the driving axle the final drive causes a separation of 10–20 in between the pivots with obvious degradation of the geometry. The swing axle is the simplest and cheapest independent suspension: even Colin Chapman made his first independent suspension by sawing a Ford beam axle in half and hingeing it in the middle. The roll centre is always above the final drive or axle at the intersection of lines from the

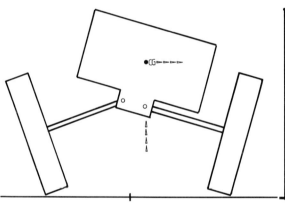

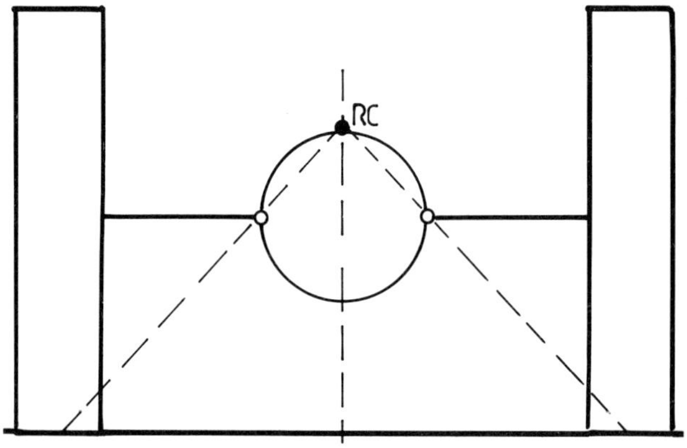

Figure 6.11. All independent suspensions suffer from jacking but none more so than swing axles because jacking effect is directly related to roll centre height.

Figure 6.12. The roll centre of a swing axle suspension is found by producing lines from the tyre contact centres through the driveshaft universal joints until they intersect.

Springs as independent links

Leaf springs may be used as links in independent suspensions but it must be remembered that they vary their length under load and are thus not positive links. The most common application is of a leaf spring lying transversely to form either the top or the bottom link, with a positive link above or below it. Some small Vauxhalls had this arrangement neatly mounted in a subframe which a number of special car builders transferred bodily. Other arrangements include two transverse springs one above the other to provide both

contact patch of each tire produced through the inboard universal joints or hinge-pivots. A swing axle can be stayed by one or more radius rods per side.

The swing axle is Dracula's Revenge, suitable only for the unimaginable abominations of Central European roads before the Second World War and for very cheap rear-drive cars; it is still found under some little cars. Swing axles suffer excessive camber change in roll, bump and rebound, jack-up dangerously during cornering, and on bumpy roads can tuck under in two-wheel bump so that the car lands virtually on the side of the tires.

Low pivot swing axles

Mercedes-Benz, characteristically, did not suffer swing-axle handling passively but did something to improve it by moving the pivot on which the arms swing underneath the final drive, thus taking the roll centre with it at the same time as lengthening the effective swing arm. They then went further and introduced a transverse spring linked to the halves of the swing axle by levers and lying above the final drive. This allowed them to make the springs at the sides

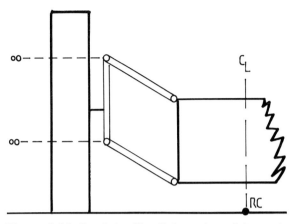

Figure 6.14. Parallel trailing links and parallel, equal length, double wishbones have their roll centres at ground level on the centreline of the car.

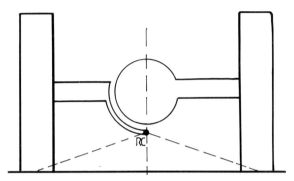

Figure 6.13. The roll centre of a low pivot swing axle lies on the pivot, normally under the differential.

much softer while at the same time increasing the roll stiffness of the complete rear suspension unit.

The roll centre is at the pivot point underneath the final drive. The roll centre vertical movement in roll will depend on the spring rates chosen but in the M-B version is obviously less than in the original swing axle design. Camber change is less because the arm is longer.

With the S-class, M-B turned their backs on swing axles.

Trailing links

In this suspension the stub axle is carried on two parallel links trailing from the body or chassis. The links themselves must be heavy to withstand bending loads and a stiff structure outside the wheelbase is required for the inboard mountings. The wheels move up and down absolutely vertically; roll centre is at ground level and camber change is directly related to body roll.

This serves to outweigh altogether the advantages of this system, viz: simplicity of very few links – no radius rods are required, suitability for torsion bar springing, low vertical space requirement and consequent utility for low sports cars.

Beetles and early Porsches used this system; it is

essential to use best quality bearings because a very small amount of lateral play can induce quite large spurious inputs to upset the roadholding.

It is possible to use a single trailing link; this is often done at the rear of front wheel drive cars.

Sliding pillars

This design is still seen holding up the front of the Morgan nostalgicar* and Lancia was loyal to it until well after the Second World War. Each wheel slides up and down on a fixed vertical member around which is wound a spring on which it acts; the damper is mounted separately. The roll centre is at ground level and the wheels move up and down vertically; camber change is directly related to the roll angle. The advantage over parallel trailing links is that bending and torsional loads are not only smaller but may be taken out into the chassis rather than in the suspension members.

Semi-trailing links

This system, normally used only at the rear, consists in most cases of a triangular wishbone with the wheel attached to its apex and the base attached to the chassis or body at an angle of around 20° to the axis of the wheel. The roll centre lies between ground level and hub centre height; camber is negative on bump and

---

*The Morgan is not a replica but a pastiche of itself in the days of its greatness – one scored a class win in the 24-Hours of Le Mans as late as 1962; the waiting list for a Morgan stretches four years.

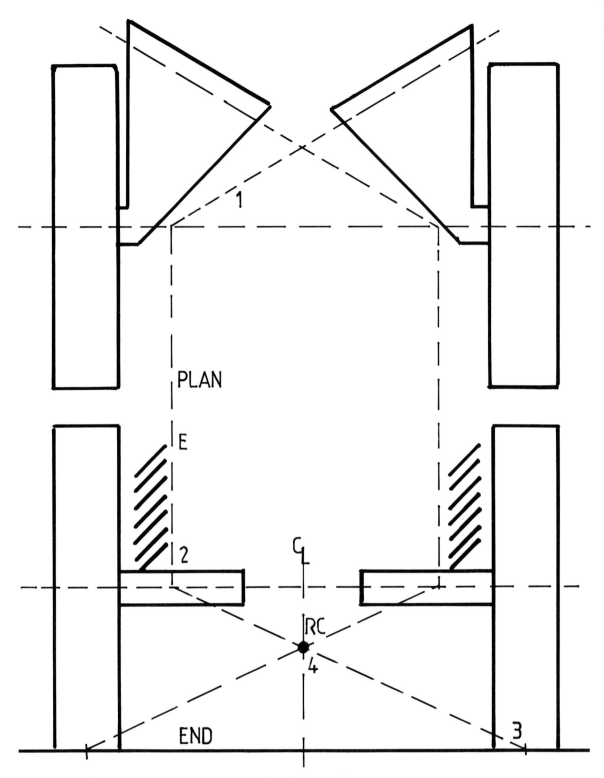

Figure 6.15. Finding the roll centre of semi-trailing links require drawings of both the plan and the end views and is done in four steps.

positive on rebound or, in roll, the outside, important, wheel can be arranged to be favourably cambered while the camber of the inner wheel is unfavourable but doesn't really matter. There is a modest arcuate movement of the wheel on bump or rebound but not so much as to negate the substantial advantages of this suspension design: low vertical space requirement and minimum noise transference; this is a favourite under big luxury cars. It is cheaper to produce than double wishbone systems, having fewer components providing location in all directions: the single wishbone provides both lateral and longitudinal location; its apex can be made wide enough to resist toe-in on bump; the driveshaft provides further lateral location.

Though an excellent compromise for the mass producer, for the special builder semi-trailing links hold less attraction unless he intends to use a proprietary system complete in its subframe cage – not desirable if much of the cage will be visible as most are very ugly. The reason is that, if he uses a separate chassis rather than a unit construction, the mounting for semi-trailing links can occupy space also required for the propeller shaft and the final drive unit. (I have been shown a solution where the chassis crossmember mounting the "semi-trailing" link lies at 90° to the siderails; this is not a *semi*-trailing link but a triangulated single *trailing* link with far less desirable geometry.)

Something to watch out for is that, when the angle

of the inboard pivots is about 45° and a line through them also runs through the inboard universal joints, the geometry of what appears to be a semi-trailing link system becomes that of a swing axle, and the remarks already made about swing axles apply in full.

Struts

Earl MacPherson's patents were used when British Ford introduced a brand-new front suspension of beguiling simplicity in 1951; the Australian engineer's name has stuck to a design today widely used, especially in Europe, at the front of cars of all kinds, sizes and performance, and sometimes at the rear as well, when it is often called a Chapman strut because the Lotus designer was the first to apply it to the rear wheels.

The pure, and only authentic, MacPherson strut consists of a telescoping column usually encircled by a helical spring and enclosing a damper insert; at the bottom the column incorporates a stub axle; there is a single arm for lateral location; and a roll bar. These are all the links, there is no separate upper control arm or wishbone, no separate longitudinal control arm; and there is no separate upright or stub axle. MacPherson showed not the genius of invention, but the often more merchantable brilliance of rearranging existing parts to the same or better effect for less cost. Specifically, the roll bar, running transversely across the chassis parallel to the axis of the front wheels, was obliquely angled at

Figure 6.16. The roll centre of a MacPherson strut suspension can be changed by altering the strut angle or the lower link angle or by widening the track of the car.

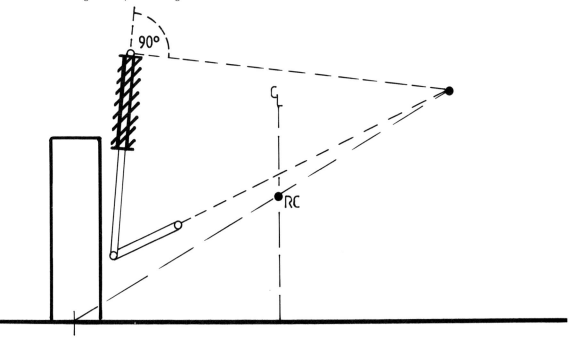

each end with the ends attached to the lower control arm via rubber bushes – and so the roll bar was made to do duty as a longitudinal control arm.

The top of the strut is flexibly mounted in a bearing or rubber bushing that allows some degree of rotation and a small amount of articulation. The disadvantages of the system stem from the fact that the strut must telescope, and from its length: because it telescopes on an axis at an angle to the desired movement of the wheel, it can sometimes bind; to give good geometry, the strut needs considerable vertical space which rules it out for low cars.

At the rear it is possible but difficult to use the MacPherson in its pure form by using the driveshaft as the sole lateral link and attaching the roll bar to the bottom of the strut; toe variations would be large, good geometry difficult to arrange.

Much more useful is the addition of a lower lateral link separate from the driveshaft, with the roll bar staying it longitudinally.

If the lower link is triangulated by another link without a roll bar or with a separately mounted roll bar, the strut is no longer, strictly speaking, a MacPherson strut (the essential patented feature of which is the use of the roll bar for positive location), but the distinction is hardly ever made today. Particularly at the rear, many so-called MacPherson designs have a trailing or diagonal arm to prevent toe-in on bump; the outboard mounting is usually offset a few inches from the outboard mounting of the radius rod or the lateral link to hold the wheel absolutely straight when seen from above.

The roll centre of the MacPherson strut lies between ground level and the axis between the wheel centres. It is found by extending a line at 90° to the top of the strut until it intersects a line through the pivots of the lower link, then drawing a line from the intersection to the centre of the tire contact patch: the instantaneous roll centre lies where this last line intersects the centreline of the car. It can be seen that, by angling either the strut or the lower link differently, the roll centre height may be varied as desired. The point where the two link extension lines intersect is called the instantaneous link centre and gives the virtual swing arm length; the virtual swing arm length is the length of a linkage that would give the desired arc of travel if a swing axle were used: the longer this length, the flatter the arc of wheel travel (so that, if there were no limit to track width, swing axles might be seen as the ideal suspension links).

MacPherson struts, having a very long virtual swing arm arc, have very little camber change – but they do not move the wheel up and down vertically either. They give positive camber on rebound – when it

matters little – and a very modest amount of negative camber on bump; in roll they hold the outer wheel upright or at a small degree of negative camber.

In practice, a MacPherson strut is only marginally inferior to the most advanced double wishbone suspension (it is indeed, strictly, a double wishbone suspension with the strut taking the part of the upper wishbone). Its problems for the special builder as opposed to the mass marketeer lie less in its handling abilities than in the design subtleties of overcoming desired camber, castor and steering inclinations all being in conflict, and – a practical problem – the requirement high up near the front corner of the car for a stiff upper strut mounting (most special cars either do not extend to this or, if they do, it consists of only the most exiguous aluminium or fibreglass skin).

Wishbones

The novice designer, who has read a few magazines and perhaps listened to the racers talk in the paddock, may be forgiven for thinking *any* wishbone design the ne plus ultra. This is a misconception: the earliest wishbone designs offered the advantages of reduced unsprung weight and interference from wheel to wheel but their camber in roll was directly related to the roll angle. I will discuss them in historical order.

Equal length, parallel wishbones have their roll centre at ground level and camber change in roll directly related to the roll angle. With the links horizontal at normal ride level, this design has the same geometry as parallel trailing links or sliding pillar suspension but better load distribution to the chassis.

Unequal length, parallel wishbones, also (usually) horizontal at normal ride level, still have their instantaneous link at infinity and therefore a roll centre at ground level but this design reduces camber change with roll, so that the wheels no longer lean in direct response to the angle of the body. Note that the short arm must be the top one or the effect will be reversed!

Unequal length, un-parallel wishbones are now the only ones in use and so common that Detroit engineers know them by the acronym SLA for short-and-long-arms. The top arm or link is shorter than the bottom link. The wishbones may converge towards the centre of the car, in which case the outboard pivots on the upright will be further apart than the inboard pivots on the chassis and the roll centre will be above ground level. This is the most common case and the links are usually so arranged and the virtual swing arm length so chosen, that a roll centre somewhere between 3–6 inches above ground level is achieved. It is possible to eliminate roll altogether by raising the roll centre to the level of the centre of gravity but, at roll

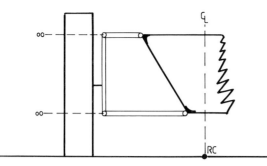

Figure 6.17. Parallel, unequal length wishbones also have their roll centre at ground level on the car's centreline but at least camber change is not directly related to roll.

centres much above 6 inches, the geometry becomes the same as that of the low pivot swing axle and, higher still, of a swing axle. The higher the roll centre, the greater the negative camber change on bump and the better the opportunity of setting the wheel vertical or with some desired degree of negative camber in roll. It is possible to have the wishbones converging outwards so that the outboard pivots are closer together than the inboard pivots; the roll centre will be below ground level and *inverse* jacking will result but this is mainly of interest to Grand Prix designers with their almost solid suspensions who use it to counteract noselift caused by acceleration-induced squat.

Various designs of SLA suspensions will, by differences in the angle and length of the links and the position of inboard and outboard pivots, achieve different roll centre migrations in bump; the design with the smallest spurious vertical roll centre movement is, all other things considered, normally superior.

Wishbones are, seen from the top, not necessarily symmetrical around the axis through the wheel

centres; they are often asymmetrical the better to lead braking and acceleration loads into the chassis or to provide a longer link with a larger arc as in the "widebased" wishbones which have the appearance of a single transverse link stayed by a long radius rod.

Nor are all wishbones arranged with their apex towards the wheel: at the rear toe-in may be prevented by turning one wishbone around so that its base pivots on the hub-carrier. Also at the rear, as in other designs, a universally jointed but unsplined driveshaft may be used as a positive link, usually the upper, with a wishbone below it. Many of these lower wishbones look rather strange, the one on the exemplary Jaguar design consisting of a tube forked at both ends which is longitudinally stayed by a trailing link. It is, however, the lower link of a double-wishbone suspension with the driveshaft forming the top wishbone. Jaguar front suspension is by the more usual "chicken"-shaped wishbones of equally exemplary geometry.

Readers whose curiosity has been whetted by these two chapters may look in the chapter on Roadholding in the book by Colin Campbell already mentioned for an excellent brief introduction to tires and cornering and may take the study further in L. J. K. Setright's *Automobile Tyres*. If you are not put off by mathematics, you could gain much from working through Appendices I and III to the Costin and Phipps book already mentioned. If you further can handle a spot of algebra, another book by Colin Campbell, *Automobile Suspensions*, will arm you with the technical, relational background not only to the conventional (metallic spring) suspensions we discussed above but to those that I ignored as simply too expensive to be relevant to the special car builder: pneumatic, hydropneumatic and interconnected systems.

Figure 6.18. Unequal length, inclined, double wishbones (short and long arms) are the most sophisticated suspension, giving the designer full control of camber change.

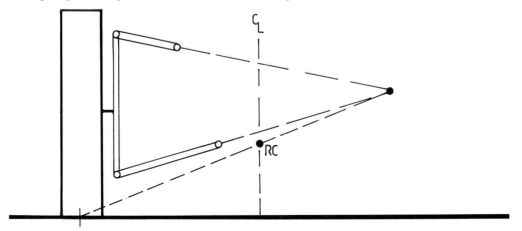

7 Suspension: Design

In all the hundred years of automobile history, the great suspension designers can be counted on the fingers of one hand; even if one admits those who made a significant contribution without achieving greatness, two handsful of fingers will suffice handsomely, with a finger or two left over for those, like Ettore Bugatti,

Figure 7.1. The unique characteristic of MacPherson strut suspension is the use of the roll bar as a locating link, so, strictly speaking, this Fiesta front suspension doesn't qualify – but the usage is pretty loose these days.

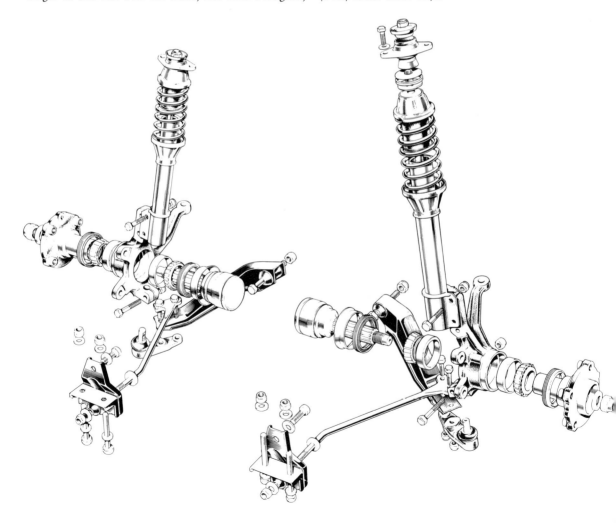

who made no specific lasting innovation but pointed up the essential *balance* required for a sweet-handling car. To me the greats are Lanchester, Ledwinka (in his time and his place), Olley, Citroen and Chapman. On the second hand I would count Fiedler, Channing, Moulton, Jim Hall – and then I run out of steam. Contrariwise, pull the name of almost any automobile designer out of the air and, however perfect his engines, smooth his brakes, or sweet his gearboxes, I can virtually guarantee to point to some serious solecisms in his suspensions. Ferdinand Porsche – whose name graces three particularly well-handling modern front-engined cars as well as the 911 which is a devastating illustration of the triumph of development over design – was particularly prone to suspension designs that were (even if one is being charitable) dangerous: for his better suspension designs we probably have to thank his assistant Rabe.

In this meagre sparseness of great suspension designers, in tales of otherwise great designers who were blind to the subtleties of suspension design, lies a dire warning for the special builder: a seized engine will not kill you but incompetent suspension *will*. Stick to well proven, established designs. There are, as we saw in the last chapter, enough designs to choose from and every basic design has so many variations that one *must* suit your application: further, each of these designs and variations is capable of infinite subtle modification. There is no call for a brand-new suspension design in a field where development beats innovation any day and at a fraction of the cost.

That is not to say you should be conservative in choosing your suspension. Beam front axles are only suitable for those who insist on proper replication in nostalgicars, under hot rods where the appearance is important, and under drag racers that never leave the straight and narrow. Unless cost is a consideration, you should choose the most advanced suspension that you can find or make space for. This will normally be by double wishbones all round, with coil-overs and anti-roll bars. Solutions to other design parameters, like high-speed straight-running, by De Dion, are likely to be more expensive than independent rear suspension. Live axles, when taken as a part of the total cost of the car, are in fact only marginally cheaper than proprietary independent rear suspensions (I include here the final drive, shafts, links, springs, dampers, cage if required, all in the definition of "suspension").

Even if you have long ago decided that your car will use proprietary suspension parts, say Triumph Herald/Spitfire/GT6 at the front and Jaguar at the back, it is a good idea to draw up an ideal suspension on paper and compare this with what you're fitting; in addition, even though the outboard pivots are fixed a certain distance apart by the proprietary upright, it may be possible to angle the links differently and mount them inboard at heights or a distance apart differing from the proprietary installation, so giving you control over the position of the roll centre.

Some special builders will, for the sake of appearance, modify or exchange the links even though they are retaining the link-length and mounting position exactly, for instance when replacing pressed Triumph wishbones with more easily chromed tubular wishbones, or when replacing the single lower wishbone on the Jag rear with two straight tubes. I'm not going to say you can beat those Triumph and Jag designers – but unless you draw up a picture on paper of what their suspension does, you won't even know the reason you're following them slavishly, and you're missing a golden opportunity to tailor their sterling work *exactly* to your application.

WHERE TO START

The purpose to which you're going to put the car, the number of passengers, their comfort, their luggage requirement, and the desired performance parameters, will all influence the wheelbase and track of the car. You will be able to make a good guess at its all-up weight, even if only by analogy with similar cars. Colin Chapman's first Lotus Elite came in about 12 cwt – mine, complete with inaudible radio, weighed 1388 lb fully fuelled. If you can get a two seater down to this, you're doing very well indeed, and probably in GRP with very spartan trim. Two seaters up to 2000 lb are still lightweights. 2 + 2s should not go over 2600 lb – 2400 lb is a better top weight. A deuce with a small block Chevy should weigh around 2200 lb. A Camaro comes in at about 3800 lb but can quite easily be slimmed to 3400 lb, even 3000 lb. A fast European four-door four seater runs to about 2800–3200 lb. Big luxury cars like Jags and Mercedes run from 3400 lb to 4200 lb. The big Panther de Ville scaled 4300 lb. A big American car runs to 5000 lb and a Rolls the same.

The weight in turn determines the size of the tires and wheels and the hub height follows.

If we're going to be designing an independent suspension – as I'll be assuming from now on (others follow the same basic routines) – the next step is to decide which upright you will use. At the front, Ford and Chevrolet or Vauxhall uprights are widely available. For cars up to 2000 lb, I normally recommend the Standard-Triumph upright found under Heralds and Spitfires and many earlier cars of the marque, and on

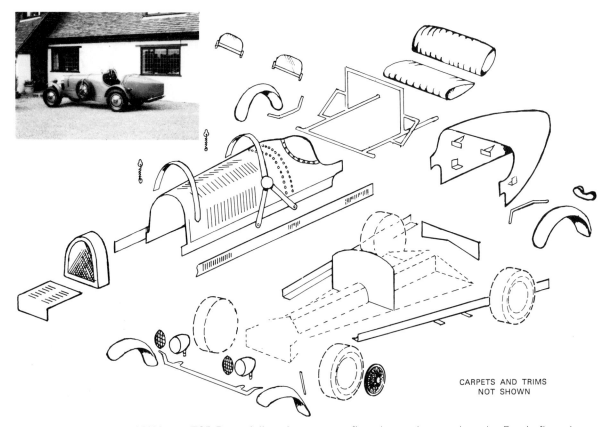

Figure 7.2. To turn a VW into a T35 Bugatti (inset), you must first alter and strengthen the Beetle floorplan. (This illustration is from the Replicar Imports instruction manual).

virtually every racing special ever built in England – still available new as a replacement part or as part of the complete front suspension assembly. For cars over 2000lb, the Jaguar upright from the Mk I/II forwards is hard to beat for availability and for the efficacy of the discs that will fit. In the States, Mustang uprights (and complete Mustang front ends) have found great favour. Whatever upright you choose, ask first which brakes can be fitted to it: the Herald upright became so popular not only because it was light but because a full range of drum and disc brakes were standard or optional fittings and therefore easily available.

At the rear, you can choose proprietary hub carriers (Jag, Ford Sierra, Corvette, a selection of European cars), or you can have them cast in magnesium (expensive) or fabricated in steel by welding (bothersome because of distortion) with, in either case, the bearing (TR5 is good) pressed in. Various racing uprights in magnesium are sometimes available off the shelf or by mail order but, though usually cheaper than casting your own, are still very expensive—but you do get the assurance of proper design and testing. Theoretically at least, you can also machine your uprights from a bar

of suitably hardened steel or alloy but this is prohibitively expensive and unnecessary when so much cheap choice is available: a whole Jag rear suspension in its cage and complete with diff, all in working order, costs £50 (or $75) – worth it just for the uprights and the Salisbury 4HU final drive even if you don't want the links. Any welding to alter uprights must be professionally done; take the uprights to your local precision engineers and tell them what you want done – they're sure to know a capable welder from a precision viewpoint, or a specialist welder if it's an alloy. Note that magnesium burns if you weld it yourself.

Both front and rear uprights are usually somewhere between half the wheel height and a little over, rarely more than three-quarters wheel and tire diameter. Better control and load distribution could be obtained with an upright of the wheel's diameter with one pick-up at the top and one at the bottom just where the tire joins the wheel but such an upright would be heavier than is necessary (unsprung weight!) and, because of the angle of the links to find the required roll centre, it might be difficult to find space for the inboard mountings simultaneously with the engine and the luggage at the front and the rear respectively. Costin and Phipps (and others) mention the problem of designing a suspension when the loads become so low as they would with a wheel-height upright but they are talking about racing cars whose purpose is the ultimate weight reduction both outboard and inboard; the problem of loads being *too low* does not normally arise for the non-racing special builder because he traditionally builds with a substantial safety margin: if the load on a member is lower, then it will also be stressed less, which is more often than not a good thing.

The best design of upright is simply an upright tube with attachment points, braced to the tube as required; the tube is normally solid for manufacturing reasons. The best design for a rear upright is a tube flattened at one end, the round end at hub level, the flattened end leading all torque loads down to the bottom wishbone. Again, the tube is often solid.

DRAWING YOUR OWN SUSPENSION

First, you will have to make a few arbitrary decisions. You must choose roll centre heights at the front and the rear: 3 inches at the front and 4 at the rear is a good place to begin; don't go over 6 inches at either end with independent suspension by advanced wishbones (other suspensions have roll centre heights determined by your choice of linkages) or your fine suspension will have all the disadvantages of a swing axle layout. The front roll centre should always be lower than at the rear. You must decide how much wheel travel you will allow: this has an effect not only on the wheelarches but also on ground clearance. A good compromise is $5\frac{1}{2}$ inches on bump and $3\frac{1}{2}$ inches on rebound. You must decide what roll angle will be permissible, i.e. how much the car will lean in a corner. You want enough roll to give you "feeling" for when the car is at the limit, yet you may not want it to wallow like a small Citroen or a Renault: it's a matter of taste. Again, a compromise of 3–4° is not a bad start and you can change it later. You must also decide how much camber change between normal ride and full bump you will allow – on rebound or droop the camber change is less important, but even so should not exceed the ETRTO (that's the trade body of the European tire manufacturers) recommended standard of 5°. Finally, you must decide what virtual swing arm length will give you the desired handling (i.e. camber change) characteristics but this you find out on the drawing by trial and error. The virtual swing arm length is usually between $1\frac{1}{2} \times$ and $3 \times$ the track and is limited by the fact that the length of the links determine how far apart the inboard mountings are (the further apart, the smaller the loadings you have to

cater for) and, very important this, the length of the links also determine, with other factors, how much the roll centre will move around. With most cars 9–10 feet is a good virtual swing arm length to start with. Prepare yourself for further compromise and redrawing with different values for these decisions.

Six drawings are required. For each of the front and the rear suspension you will have front view, plan view and side view. Work in pencil on graph paper to scale or full size on a blackboard, or make an adjustable model with strips of plywood and a few lengths of string plus some thumbtacks.

Do the front view first. Draw the wheel either upright or with about $\frac{1}{2}°$ of positive camber for disturbance-free steering and a bit of understeer. Now draw the upright in its correct position beside it. Draw the centreline of the car and on it mark the roll centre height you have chosen. Draw a line from the centre of the tire's contact patch with the ground to the roll centre and produce it to the swing arm length. From this point draw two lines to the upper and lower balljoints on the upright; your inboard pivots will lie somewhere along these lines and may be decided by your parameter for permissible camber change or may

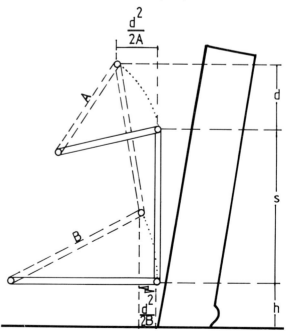

Figure 7.3. It is possible to determine link lengths and lateral displacements mathematically. The lateral movement of the upper pivot will be $d^2/2A$ and of the lower pivot $d^2/2B$. Steering head movement (i.e. a line through the top and bottom outboard pivots) when projected to ground level will be *nil* when either $hB=A(h+s)$ or $A/B=h/(h+s)$.

have to be compromised with the other functions the chassis must perform in this area. The upper arm will be shorter than the lower arm. The purpose is to keep the tire square to the ground or nearly so at all positions of bump and through the normal ride position into rebound; towards the limits of rebound, positive camber becomes permissible as a lightly loaded wheel (the weight is mostly on the other wheel) can do no harm. The arm lengths are chosen to achieve this desirable state with the *minimum of camber change* – this assumes that you're looking for performance on modern wide tires; on narrow, older tyres, a slightly larger degree of negative camber could be beneficial though you would pay for it in tire wear.

For the moment, put the upper mounting on the return line from the virtual swing arm arc and $18\frac{1}{2}$ inches from the centreline of the car; the lower pivot you can place similarly 11 inches from the centreline.

Now draw the wheel and upright at full bump and rebound and determine where the roll centre has wandered to at each movement. Measure the camber change. What you want is the least movement of the roll centre *and* enough camber change in bump to compensate for camber change in roll. It is likely that your maximum permissible roll angle and your minimum camber change will correspond exactly if you started with zero or small negative camber; if you start with a small degree of positive camber at normal ride height, your minimum camber change might be slightly larger than maximum permissible roll angle in order to have the wheel vertical or leaning inwards at the limit of cornering. In practice, it is normally necessary to compromise some roll centre height to achieve the desired camber change.

A good trick is to draw one wheel at full bump and the other at full rebound and then tilt your drawing so that the wheel at full bump sits on your t-square or some other horizontal reference at the desired negative camber angle or vertically. Now measure the angle at which the body leans. Draw in the lowest part of the drivetrain – normally the sump – and see that it has at least *two* inches of clearance. (Some authorities offer 1 inch as a minimum but they're normally into circuit racers, i.e. smooth roads policed by marshals; you will of course also check that this two-inch minimum clearance applies in the two-wheel bump event as well.)

If the amount of roll centre movement does not please you, or the camber change is too large, you can do one or more of several things; lower the roll centre, decide upon a greater virtual swing arm length (which will move the inboard pivots of the links further apart), change the relative lengths of the arms themselves, move the inboard pivots closer to the centreline of the car, i.e. make both arms absolutely longer (space permitting). Now, having gained an insight into how all the knowledge of the previous chapters work together practically, take a shortcut: don't go through the whole rigmarole but simply change the arm lengths or the distance between the inboard mountings until pleasing geometry coincides with acceptable roll centre movement.

At the rear, you must watch that your gear runs at the smallest possible angles as friction in universal joints and sliding splines on the half-shafts can lose quite a bit of power. In particular, though the purists prefer separate upper and lower wishbones with a splined driveshaft, the frictional problems and losses involved have always inclined me towards the design, such as the Jaguar, where a solid shaft, universally jointed at each end, serves both to drive and locate the wheel. On this front view of your rear suspension, you should also draw in the final drive and inboard brakes and check for clearance in two-wheel maximum bump and cornering at the limit.

Later, when you design the chassis, you may have to alter the layout you now finalize in order to take suspension loads into the chassis with the minimum of offset but such changes should be very small: it is better to redesign the chassis than to compromise the suspension geometry.

THE SIDE VIEW

Until now we have assumed that wishbone triangles are stacked one above the other and parallel to each other and the horizon. This is not so; nor are radius rods (except on hot rods) necessarily parallel. The reason for this is that under acceleration weight transfer will cause the car's nose to lift and tail to sink towards the ground; braking, conversely, causes the nose to be lowered while the tail rises. This is called squat and dive respectively and causes spurious vertical movement of the roll centres. The solution is quite simple: you angle the upper arm's base (the line through the inboard pivots seen from the side) downwards to the rear of the car. The lines through these front inboard pivots should meet behind the centre of gravity on the centre of instantaneous rotation, which is that length of radius arm that would give the axle the required arcuate motion. It should be obvious that you cannot choose a point below the road surface, nor below the roll centre, nor beyond the other axle. There are two such centres of instantaneous rotation, the one for the rear wheels being between the centre of gravity and the front axle. And that is all there is to anti-squat and anti-dive geometry.

Except that things are never that easy. The first

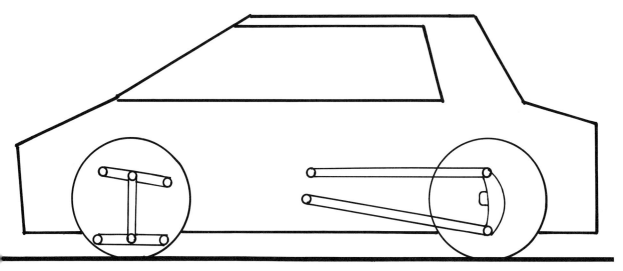

Figure 7.4. Anti-squat and anti-dive link angles to combat the effects of unwanted weight transfers in braking and acceleration.

problem you're going to run into is one of space to put those control arms; this was discussed on page 71. Secondly, besides geometry, there may be mechanical engineering requirements to take into account, e.g. with the Jag (Salisbury) final drive, it is desirable that the centre of instantaneous rotation lies on the extension of the pinion centreline. The hot rodder's rule of thumb is to make the radius rod as long as possible and mount its forward pivot near this pinion centreline extension, which is nearly as good.

It is essential that, for each wishbone, the two inner pivots are in a straight line otherwise special bushes will be required, which might cost a lot of money.

PLAN VIEW

First check that your inboard pivots for each wishbone lie in a straight line.

Again, we have to demolish an assumption: we have until now talked about these wishbone inboard pivots as if, seen from above, they were parallel for the top and bottom wishbones and both were parallel to the centreline of the car. It is sometimes possible to arrange this but there is no advantage to be had from the effort. Though it is not often necessary to make the baselines of the upper and lower wishbones non-parallel, a modest asymmetry will do no harm, especially if rubber bushed; larger asymmetries will probably upset the castor in bump. More normally the baselines of the two wishbones on each side are parallel to each other but are angled to the centreline of the car because the chassis curves in or out.

At the rear, the driveshaft, whether splined or used as a positive location link, should run perpendicularly to the car's centreline.

SPRINGS, STEERING, ETC.

It is probably as well at this stage to draw in your springs. The outboard mounting on the bottom wishbone should be as near the lower outboard pivot as possible without interference with the wheel; the upper mounting to the chassis is less critical but looks neat if it can be combined with one of the upper wishbone inner pivots – it is for this reason that many racing car designers like a single top link running perpendicularly to the car's centreline and stayed by a fairly long radius rod.

For predictable springing, the spring should be as nearly upright as possible, so that the spring and damper are compressed as nearly as possible an amount equal to wheel movement. This is not always possible but you may use the resulting deficiency to your own purposes: an hour with a piece of paper and a compass and pencil and ruler will soon demonstrate that the same spring works differently at different angles.

The relation between wheel travel and shock absorber travel is called the link ratio and the required resistance in the damper rises as the *square* of the link ratio; remember this if you take a standard unit but mount it at a different angle to the proprietary installation.

You should also draw the steering in the front and

plan views (and on open-bumpered cars and all those with other than rack-and-pinion steering, the side view as well); it is neat to mount the steering behind or in front of the upper wishbone and at the same level as a small wind-cheating detail.

These drawings are also the ones to determine the length of brake pipe you require; it must allow the wheel to move to full lock but not have enough length to get tangled in anything.

Besides toe-changes between the extremes of bump and rebound, camber and castor also change: camber because you've designed it like that; castor change can cause spurious steering inputs (feedback) or camber changes but at least these are fairly predictable as castor change is linear.

ADJUSTABLE SUSPENSION

Once upon a time professional designers laughed at those of us who built adjustable suspensions. Nowadays grand prix cars are just one large adjustable suspension hung on a monstrous engine and with incidental space for a *pilote*.

Adjustability is achieved by having several mountings on the chassis for the same link and by making the length of links adjustable through screw-in-and-out or shimmed bushed or balljointed ends. Sometimes eccentric nuts are used for the same purpose (one side lower than the other).

I wish I could tell you that is all there is to designing your own suspension but, in all honesty, you will have to return to these drawings to compromise their ideals for the other functions of your car.

8 Steering and Brakes

STEERING

The factors that make for good or bad steering are so closely entertwined with the suspension geometry that both must always be designed at the same time. The steering geometry is fixed by the relation of the upright (kingpin or spindle support arm) to the wheel and will influence or determine kingpin inclination, castor angle, camber angle, and steering offset or scrub radius. Suspension movement will through these dispositions affect the directional alignment and stability at speed of the front wheels through toe-in and toe-out. Whether your car will be heavy to steer at parking speeds, whether it will need constant small corrections to the steering when driven at speed, whether you will get adequate road "feel" will depend on the decisions you make here, which will also have a great influence on the roadholding and handling of your car and consequently on its drivability and safety.

ACKERMANN

A publisher called Ackermann gave his name to a principle first formalized by Lankensperger and before that handed down from master coachbuilder to apprentice; this was modified in 1878 by Jeantend. The basis of the Ackermann steering layout is that the inner wheel turns about a smaller radius than the outer wheel, and to achieve this

$$\text{cotangent } a - \text{cotangent } b \text{ must equal } \frac{T}{W}$$

Figure 8.1. Suspension, steering and brakes should all be considered a single design job, as shown on this Fiesta layout. Note the anti-roll bar at the rear.

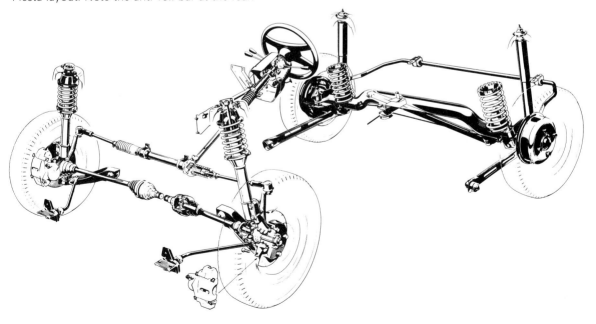

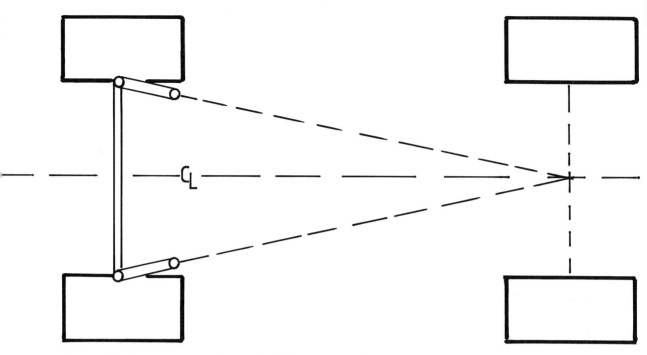

Figure 8.2. Steering arm inclination for Ackermann steering.

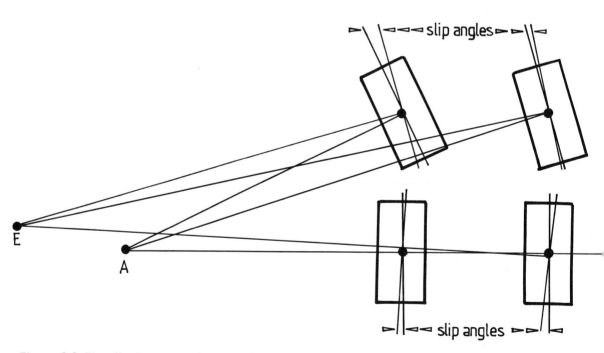

Figure 8.3. The effective centre of a corner lies at right angles to the slip angles of the tyre whereas the Ackermann centre lies perpendicular to the tyre centrelines.

where a   is the angle between a line perpendicular to the centreline of the front outside wheel and the axis through the rear hubs

b   is the angle between a line perpendicular to the centreline of the front inside wheel and the axis through the rear hubs

T   is the track

W   is the wheelbase

but a moment's thought – or manipulation of a drawing, much more certain! – will show that there will be different angles a and b for different angles of front wheel movement, i.e. for travelling around different radii. Coachbuilders had a rule of thumb that, if the links connecting the track rod ends to the wheel steering pivots were angled inwards (with the wheels in the straight ahead position) so that lines produced through their pivot points met in the centre of the rear axle, approximately the correct geometry would be produced, i.e. the wheels would at most times be nearly parallel. The Jeantend modification was to move the intersection forwards, so that it lay on the car centreline about two-thirds from the front axle to the rear; this allowed – and on vintage cars still allows – for the fact that our kind of tires, as opposed to the iron tires of Ackermann's time, need slip angles to generate cornering force.

Unfortunately, this solution, so pleasing for its simplicity, and offering such easy parking, is positively dangerous for high-speed motoring: it gives the heavily loaded outer wheel a smaller slip angle than the lightly loaded inner wheel!

Designers of modern high-speed cars use *negative* Ackermann to allow both the inner and the outer wheels to run closer to their natural slip angles in a corner. In this reverse Ackermann layout, the lock of the outer wheel is greater than that of the inner wheel. This makes for heavy steering at low speed. Most modern mass-produced cars have the steering arms either parallel at all times or a modest amount of Ackermann effect, achieved by angling the steering arms to intersect about a wheelbase length behind the rear axle.

The easiest way for the special designer to choose between negative, zero and positive (modified) Ackermann effect, is to ask himself two questions. How fast will the car go? Will it be used a lot on winding roads? If the car is going to be small-engined and struggle to reach 100mph, use parallel arms or moderate Ackermann geometry, unless you regularly intend beating up the country lanes, in which case you just have to grin and bear the heavy parking or fit power steering. If you're regularly going to drive the car over 120mph, and even if most of your use will be on motorways,

negative Ackermann geometry is highly desirable; at 150mph it is quite incredible how tight a sweeping motorway curve can become.

TOE-IN AND TOE-OUT

The force of wind, road friction, braking and forces induced by wear in the linkages, combine to make the rotating tire toe-out at its forward end. The result is not only fast tire wear, but directional instability and quicker wear in linkages that are supposed to have no play, as well as greater stress in the chassis. Rear drive cars therefore have the wheels aligned with toe-*in* in the static position, normally specified as a fraction of an inch (rarely more than one-eighth) or so many millimetres (up to, normally, three) difference between the fore- and rearmost parts of the rims of the two wheels with the wheels in the straight ahead position.

On front drive cars the torque has the opposite effect, forcing toe-in when the wheel rotates, so that it is preset with toe-*out* in the static position. Special builders who take the drivetrain of FWD hatches complete with their suspensions to make into mid-engined baby rockets must remember this when deciding on the length and robustness and the distance between the outboard mountings of the links that will resist toe-loads.

In an ideal world, the suspension and steering will be designed and crafted so that the wheel is held straight ahead when the steering points it straight ahead. In the real world, these toe changes are the result of minute (and sometimes substantial) wear in all the linkages that make up a modern steering/suspension unit.

Because the toe-alignment is so crucial – if it is not right it will upset all your other careful work – it is usually the last to be adjusted, *after* castor and camber (and after the kingpin inclination and the turning radius if these are adjustable; note that the offset or scrub radius is the result of the kingpin inclination and the camber angle and changes with the camber angle).

KINGPIN INCLINATION

There are no kingpins any more; we still use the leftover term from the days of beam front axles, though early independent front designs did use a kingpin with a bearing about which the spindle swivelled about half-way from the top to the bottom; present designs have a ball bearing top and bottom and the whole upright turns. A more descriptive term is *steering axis inclination* or, equally, *steering swivel angle*. Whichever term you prefer, it measures in degrees the divergence between the true vertical and the centreline of the upright; the

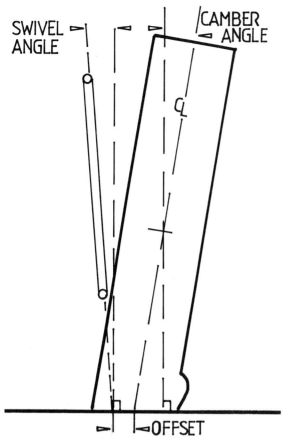

Figure 8.4. Offset, and camber and swivel angles. Camber and swivel angles change with suspension movement. The offset influences steering ease and stability.

upright is always angled towards the centre of the car at the *top*.

The first purpose, since the weight of the car must be reacted through the wheel and tire at the point where the wheel is joined to the suspension (or beam axle) is to "aim" the weight at the contact patch of the tire. We shall come in a moment to where exactly we want to aim in the contact patch. The swivel angle also reduces the need for excessive camber angles at normal ride height and works with castor angle to provide steering stability through self-centring.

Steering axis inclination directly controls scrub radius, a very important determinant of steering response and feel.

SCRUB RADIUS

This is the distance that a line through the upright pivots (i.e. its centreline) when produced to ground level will be *offset* (the other name for this distance)

from the longitudinal centre of the tire's contact patch. (Loosely, from the centreline of the wheel, but there are some tires with asymmetrical contact patches.) Scrub radius is positive if the swivel axis reaches ground inside the centre of the footprint, negative if the swivel axis reaches ground outside the centre of the tire's footprint. Normally, cars have positive offset; some Audis and their VW derivatives have negative offset to aid stability in unequal-traction situations, i.e. if one-half of their diagonally split braking system should fail! Positive offset is not normally greater than about $1\frac{1}{4}$ inches and negative offset should be between $\frac{3}{8}$ inch and 1 inch. Negative offset almost inevitably gives less steering feel than normal positive offset. Zero offet, with the kingpin axis meeting the tire equator at ground level, results in feel-less steering and directional instability. The correct amount of positive offset will result in directional stability, help easy steering at low speed, cut tire wear, and make choosing a camber angle to suit all seasons so much easier.

While the special builder, in practice, must take his upright as it comes, complete with swivel angle, he can still retain some control over the offset. Merely fitting a wider tire will increase the offset (if it started positive). Keeping the same width of tire but fitting a spacer will have the same effect; machining the spindle face will have the opposite effect. Wheels are normally available with "inset" and "outset" centres, allowing you to move the wheel in and out in relation to the hub and therefore the upright; if you're keeping to steel wheels, you can have them cut and rewelded, though that might well cost the same as a set of smart alloy wheels. We have already dismissed the alternative of designing and making your own upright for reasons of cost.

Do not confuse scrub radius with turning radius, discussed under Ackermann above, or with the inset and outset of wheels in relation to the hub mounting face.

If possible, choose your upright so that, with the tires you intend fitting, you will have a scrub radius of between $\frac{3}{8}$ inch and 1 inch. If the car, once built, then doesn't suit your driving style or expectations, a relatively small (in the context of building a car at least) operation will probably put matters right and you may get away with merely a camber adjustment so small that it doesn't upset anything else, or even a castor adjustment.

CASTOR ANGLE

The castor angle is the steering axle inclination as seen from the side and is measured as the angle between a vertical line through the hub centre and the upright's centreline (seen from the side). Positive castor is when

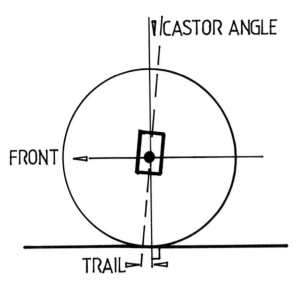

Figure 8.5. Castor generates self-aligning torque in the front wheels; without it, you would have to turn the steering wheel to return the wheels to straight ahead after corners.

the *top* of the upright leans towards the rear of the car, negative castor when the top of the upright leans towards the front of the car. The purpose of castor is to provide the wheels with some measure of self-centring, such as is found on castors under furniture or at the front wheel of a bicycle or motorcycle, which leads to stability in motion, resists road irregularities, and aids easy parking. Too much castor can lead to excessive effort being required to make the wheels turn.

Some big American 55mph highway cruisers have negative castor … perhaps their designers feel that the loss of directional stability is compensated for by the easier steering – irrelevant since over-assisted steering is standard, easier parking and greater insulation from road irregularities – and therefore any feel that escapes the power-assistance, and from road shocks.

Three to five degrees of castor is a good compromise to start with.

The distance at ground level between the kingpin axis seen from the side and the centre of the tire contact patch is called trail. The actual effective trail distance will be somewhat larger, as it is known that the effective centre of the tire lies behind the geometric centre, so that even a wheel set at minimal or zero castor will have some self-righting action.

CAMBER CHANGE AND STEERING FEEL AND EFFORT

It should be obvious that the kingpin inclination has an effect on camber change in that, should the same inboard mountings be used, a greater kingpin inclination will cause the upper wishbone to be shorter, will change the relationship between the upper and lower link lengths, and therefore the arc through which the wheel moves.

There is, not so incidentally, a very good reason for choosing the upright which has the smallest kingpin inclination: consider the car standing still and level, with the wheel being turned. The kingpin inclination will make the wheel fall slightly – but the wheel stands on the ground which is solid, so in fact the driver is lifting the front of the car by turning the steering wheel. With weight transfer in cornering the effort becomes bigger. Or you might say that excessive kingpin inclination adds its own weight transfer in cornering. Notice that this "fall" is related to the scrub radius and with negative scrub radius is reversed.

The effect of castor is the opposite: it forces the outside wheel up towards the car and, since the weight is on the outside wheel which should be firmly on the earth, the nose of the car sinks down over the outside wheel. It is thus possible to specify a combination of kingpin inclination and castor angle that will offer very light steering at parking speeds. To this purpose, the larger the castor angle the better.

However, note that if you incline the axis through the inboard pivots of the upper wishbone downwards to the centre of the car, the castor angle increases in bump and decreases in rebound; you must therefore compromise between easy steering and decelerative pitch control.

There are further complications. If there is too much trail from too large a castor angle, the weight of the steering can build up substantially and very quickly as lock is applied in a corner, and the result is that understeer increases or is generated to such an extent as to overcome the oversteering or neutral steering tendencies of your car. To alleviate this, BMW set the strut at its chosen castor angle behind the hub: the castor angle is then maximized for easy steering yet the trail dimension is reduced to decrease understeer by increasing the negative camber of the outer wheel towards full lock.

If you're by now tempted to throw up your hands in horror and go out and buy your front and rear suspensions off a Jag, complete in their subcages with steering and diff, nobody will blame you. If you have designed a good suspension, it will probably be a near-clone anyway, with only the spring and damper rates differing to take account of the different weight of your car. You could use the cages for measuring and make your own mountings on the chassis or buy better looking subframes from the likes of Geoff Jago or Jerry Kugel.

If you're still designing your own, you've now reached the end of steering and suspension complications of a theoretical nature. All you have to do is plot the wheel at the limits of its movement and several points in between in all three dimensions, taking due account of the influence of the changes in angles of the linkages and upright. This is tedious but, assuming that you've made an effort to understand thoroughly what we've been at for a good while now, not really difficult. Some grand prix designers, before the advent of computer graphics, didn't bother with a whole bunch of drawings but built a model from scraps of angle iron and wood: this could save you a lot of time. Once you've done this, all that remains is to decide which proprietary parts come nearest your specification or in which materials to have your own made up.

SUSPENSION AND STEERING HARDWARE

For the enthusiast – which includes all special builders – there are only two kinds of steering mechanisms: rack-and-pinion and the kind that comes in a box and has a drop arm. There is only one kind of special for which the box type of steering is recommended and that is one with a beam axle. There is no space here to go into the technical pros and cons and history of steering boxes but any box off a modern car will work well (the recirculating ball type better than the others in my opinion) and the only question you have to ask is what its reduction ratio is; you want about three turns of the steering wheel to turn the road wheels from lock to lock for a good but not sneeze-directed steering. The steering shaft is connected to the box, the drop arm moves fore and aft and is connected by a drag link to the steering arm on the hub; from each hub a track arm runs either backwards or forwards and these are connected across the car by the track rod. This is all there is to it; the geometry of these components we've already discussed.

Rack-and-pinion steering is *not* suitable for beam axles. Whether the rack is mounted directly on the axle (unsprung weight!) or on the chassis, there is always the most terrible bump steer.

On the other hand, a box steering is ill advised for

Figure 8.6. Rack-and-pinion steering is the special builder's prime choice because it helps him beat linkage problems. But it is *too* responsive for beam axles under hotrods.

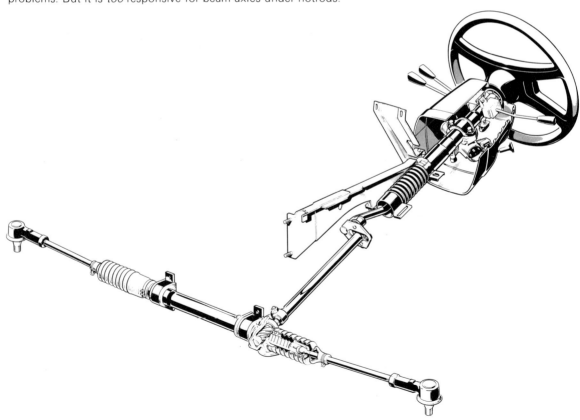

the special car with independent suspension unless the complete proprietary system is used without alteration and with all its linkages intact. This is because, in order to eradicate bump steer, the linkages are pretty complex to give them the same arc as the wishbones, and include all kinds of idler arms. Designing and building your own own will cost a fortune, altering a proprietary system to fit your application ditto.

For the special with independent suspension, the answer is rack-and-pinion. The steering wheel is connected via its shaft and the pinion to the rack which lies transversely across the car either in front of or behind the front wheel axis. This is a fully reversible steering system in its cruder forms, i.e. it operates in both directions so that you can feel every pimple on the road; modern racks are helically cut to reduce the amount of feedback. There is no steering system that gives the enthusiastic driver the same satisfaction as a good rack-and-pinion.

To obtain the correct geometry, mount the rack so that its inboard pivots, with the steering wheels in the straight ahead position, are on an axis through the inboard pivots of the upper and lower wishbones (aerodynamically, the best position for the rack is in line with either the upper or the lower wishbone); this avoid spurious arcs binding the links awkwardly. It is no great trouble lengthening or shortening the track rods on the ends of the rack to suit your track (though you should first try to find one from the manufacturers' extensive catalogues) and for certain "standard" applications – a Saab rack to a '32 Ford using Jag E front suspension, say – people like Total Performance sell adjustment kits. Welding should of course be done to the highest standard, and sleeving, preferably pinned, is an excellent idea.

A steering wheel arranged with perfect verticality will need a high degree of power assistance or you will have to sit very close to it to bring adequate force to bear to turn the front wheels. If the steering wheel is angled – between 10° and 30° according to your personal preference and the amount of force required and feel desired – you can sit further away from it and still apply adequate force because, as your hands turn with the wheel, the rim comes closer to you, turning a rotary motion into push–pull at which humans are better. An adjustable steering wheel – reach *and* height preferably – is a good idea even in a made-to-measure special because you never know when circumstances will change; I hurt my back hoisting a Bentley engine and now not only sit more upright and have the lumbar support turned harder into my back in the family Volvo, but had to sell a hardly-used car in which I could no longer find a comfortable driving position.

The problem that a steering wheel angled to your taste brings in its wake is that the shaft may then no longer be pointed straight at the steering box or rack take-off without erupting through the headers or something even more vital to your car's wellbeing and progress. This is no bad thing in itself, because it forces you to split the shaft and, in case of accident, can aim it past your head rather than at your heart. The shaft, split into as few pieces as required to lead it to the box or take-off past the mechanical parts it should avoid, is then universally jointed where it is split. Universal joints should be professionally welded, sleeved and pinned. The smallest and neatest knuckles that I know of are used on Jaguars but Ford will also supply UVs in virtually any size you can name.

Power steering is a misnomer because it implies that there is no mechanical connection between the steering wheel and the road wheels. Power-assistance is what it should correctly be termed. The assistance is by a hydraulic pump driven off the engine and the special builder will normally fit steering, pump and shaft complete. If you replace the steering shaft with one of your own, don't forget to include a slim torsion bar between the steering wheel and the power box or rack (see the one you got your power steering out of) so that, in the event of hydraulic failure, you still have manual steering. The torsion bar twists so far and no further before it "takes up" the steering; changes in the bar can also give you better steering feel, but it will be a bit artificial; best power steering is either variable (lots at parking speeds, nothing at high speeds) and expensive or the barest minimum to make the car drivable in town.

There is no reason steering and suspension hardware should not be made up in suitably dimensioned mild steel: the reason that many special car builders use superior materials is mainly because they polish and chrome better. Geoff Jago's dropped beam axle, for instance, is made up as standard from $1\frac{3}{4}$-inch outside diameter, $\frac{5}{16}$-inch wall CDS2 (cold drawn seamless) steel, which offers a useful safety margin for cars up to, say, 2500 or even 3000 lb, but the main reason for the choice is that this steel chromes well and no one fits a beam axle without chroming it; for really heavy cars, Jago, as most axle manufacturers, offers a 2-inch OD, $\frac{3}{8}$-inch wall axle. Beware of the cheap $\frac{1}{8}$-inch OD muffler tubing axle which is only good under ultralight dragsters and on real roads will surely kill or injure you.

Drag links, track rods, steering arms and radius rods are usually made in mild steel or materials all the way up to expensive 4130 chrome molybdenum. The same applies to independent suspension links. Do not under any circumstances use anything with less than $\frac{1}{8}$-inch wall thickness even in chrome-moly, nor more slender

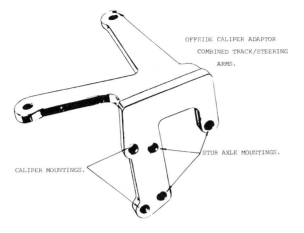

OFFSIDE CALIPER ADAPTOR
COMBINED TRACK/STEERING
ARMS.

CALIPER MOUNTINGS.

STUB AXLE MOUNTINGS.

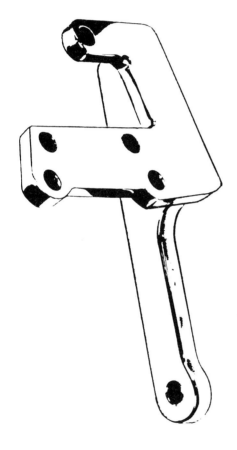

NEARSIDE CALIPER ADAPTOR

TRACK ARM.

Figure 8.7. Amateur welders stay away! These adaptors fit Cortina hubs, calipers and discs to Ford Transit stub axles.

in OD than $\frac{1}{2}$-inch and then only for very light cars. For most applications $\frac{3}{4}$-inch OD, $\frac{1}{8}$-inch wall chrome-moly will do as will 1-inch OD,, $\frac{1}{4}$-inch wall mild steel. For the heaviest applications you should go to 1- or $1\frac{1}{4}$- by $\frac{1}{4}$-inch chrome-moly and forget about mild steel because at about $1\frac{1}{2}$-inch OD it starts looking clumsily like plumbing. I'm well aware that these recommendations are for heavier links than you can see at any race track or any hotrod meeting but better safe than sorry ; when you have more experience, come down a size in your links.

Holes should be drilled in links after they are welded. Thickwall pipes in short sections welded in where there will be holes drilled makes precision easier. There is absolutely no reason not to chrome your axles or links; unless they are stupidly underweight, or incompetently welded, they will not crack and it is an awful bore keeping nicks on painted suspension parts rust-free and repainted or, if bare, polished. Chrome wipes clean.

Threads – in track rods for toe-adjustment, in wishbone links for camber and castor adjustments – must be tapped with the same care as holes for pins are drilled.

Finally, to repeat, unless you're building a racer, if there's any possibility of rubber bushing a pivot, do it – in everyday use you'll be glad you did.

BRAKES

The purpose of the brakes is to slow or stop the car, preferably without disturbance to the direction it is travelling in. Braking is not a subject normally discussed under the heading of suspension but the qualification – that brakes when applied should not disturb the car's direction, only retard its velocity – plus the fact that outboard brakes are always unsprung weight, persuades me this is the logical place for a discussion of the brakes.

The maximum braking force that can be applied to a vehicle through its wheels – the mass of air having its own retarding force – is limited by the friction between the tire and the road, and is equal to the weight of the vehicle multiplied by the coefficient of friction. On a dry pavement, this coefficient could be as high as 1; with a coefficient of unity, retardation would be 1.0g or $32.2\,\text{ft/s}^2$ and the stopping distance in feet would be

$$\frac{V^2}{29.9}$$

where V is the speed in mph.

I must stress though that this is on an ideal surface such as does not exist outside of a test facility; other everyday factors bedevil the situation almost beyond

Figure 8.8. *Determining the Centre of Gravity of a car.* First weigh the car accurately, then weight the front and the rear accurately and then calculate what percentage of weight is on the front wheels and what on the rear wheels: if 55% of the weight of a car on a 100 inch wheelbase is on the front wheels, the CoG is 55 inches behind the front axle and 45 inches in front of the rear axle. The height of the CoG is a bit more difficult. First pump up all the tyres as hard as they will go, then block out suspension travel by replacing the dampers with solid links. Fill the fuel tank completely. Raise the car at the rear: below 10 inches isn't worth doing, 15 inches is better (measure at hub centre for accuracy). Now record the weight on the front wheels. The height of the CoG is then available by the trigonometric principles of right angles:

$$CoG_h = \frac{\text{Change in weight on front wheels} \times \text{Wheelbase} \times \cos\theta}{\text{Total weight of car} \times \sin\theta}$$

where θ is the tilt angle, which can of course be calculated and then used with trig tables to look up the numbers we want. But it is far easier just to calculate the numbers, which are:

$$\text{Cosine of tilt angle} = \frac{\text{adjacent side}}{\text{hypotenuse}} = \frac{b}{c} \text{ and}$$

$$\text{Sine of tilt angle} = \frac{\text{opposite side}}{\text{hypotenuse}} = \frac{a}{c}$$

where c is the wheelbase, which is known, a is the raised height, which is also known, and

$$b = \sqrt{c^2 - a^2}$$

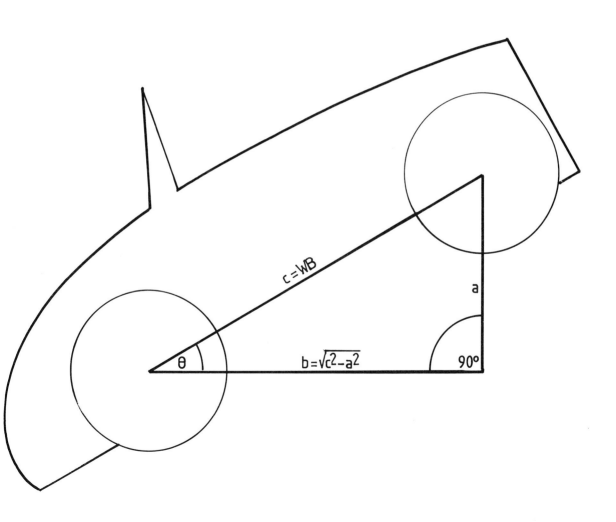

comprehension, the most obvious being the suitability of the tires for the reigning conditions and their state of wear. Regardless of the grip you can apply to the brakes, *it is under any and all circumstances the friction between tire and road that sets the upper limit of braking ability.*

Disc brakes do not *brake* intrinsically better than drums. Their great advantage is that they disperse heat more efficiently and therefore are not subject to the fade experienced by a hot drum brake. Nor are ABS brakes – anti-skid brakes, the Germans call them Anti-Blocker – intrinsically better than expertly applied non-ABS brakes; their appeal lies in the fact that most people have neither the experience nor the skill to operate the brake on–off–on so that the wheels are permanently within 0.001% of locking up (while the brake is being operated). ABS exploits the principle that maximum retardation occurs just before the wheels lock up, something that has long been a part of the armoury of top rally drivers. All the ABS systems use electronics to work with the hydraulics to relax the pad pressure against the disc just as the wheel locks up or a nano-second before. There is no reason, except cost and the complexity of the electronics and hydraulics, why you shouldn't relieve a Mercedes, BMW, Audi, Porsche 928 or a Honda of its ABS brakes for your own special; it will not make you a better driver nor will it prevent you having an accident (experts say 85% of accidents would *not* have been prevented by ABS brakes) but it will give you a certain olympian certainty that, whatever the road surface on which you brake, your car will go where you point it within the limits of your suspension design.

Various government bodies publish codes regulating the minimum stopping distance vehicles should achieve from various distances. If you get a copy, don't forget to add the $\frac{3}{4}$ second it will take before you react and your foot actually depresses the brake – at 80mph that's 88 feet. I'm not going to list these various regulations here because, if your car does not exceed the regulated stopping abilities so far as to make them irrelevant, you shouldn't be building special cars. For this reason, I cannot recommend drums to be fitted to new specials; on specials of elderly mien already fitted with drums, you may be able to uprate them (talk to club members about the possibilities) or you will have to limit yourself to driving within the capability of the brakes rather than the engine. Modern proprietary parts that come from the scrapyard with drum brakes attached almost always, in the case of front suspensions, have an upmarket or "GT" sibling in the range from which the discs will bolt on Meccano-style; at the rear, with live axles, sometimes only drums are available but this is bearable for all bar out-and-out

performance cars because the rear end has to provide only 40% of the braking or less.

The special builder is not confined to the discs that come with his proprietary upright: it is often possible to bolt bigger or better disc/caliper combinations straight to the hub – or the solution to better braking may lie higher up the line in a greater pressure, to which we'll return – or the spindle may be machined to take a different hub or the hub itself may be machined to take different discs. Purveyors to the hotrod community do these esoteric things daily and at surprisingly modest cost; before you lay out cash for the parts you want matched, ask the man who'll do the machining if it is indeed possible. For instance, only the pre-1968 Transit spindles work with Jago beam axles, the post-1968 Transit spindles being of a different design. And, before you splash out for machining, look up-market: even the exemplary XJ6 Jag has a fat cat brother with ventilated discs (cheap off an XJ12 at the breaker's) and, if you're pushing really hard, even further upmarket there are AP's ventilated racing discs for stopping 500bhp circuit-racing V12s. Even if no public-sale model has better brakes, ask if a "police special" was built.

To calculate the force required to stop your car, plug into the following formula:

$$T = W + R \times D$$

where T is the torque required in inch/pounds, total for all 4 wheels

W is the fully loaded weight of the car, lb

R is the rolling radius of the tires (on the fully loaded car the distance from the hub centre to the ground), inches

D is the required deceleration, fraction of g, normally taken as unity (1) to allow a margin of safety (g = 32.2 ft/s^2)

Figure 8.9. The effective disc radius is the distance from the centre of the disc to the centre of the caliper pad. You need it to calculate what it takes to stop your car.

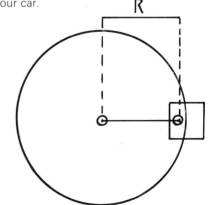

– if there was no weight transfer, T/4 would then give the braking requirement for each wheel. Things are never so simple, though for the ground-up special designer, who *knows* where the centre of gravity of his car lies, life is a little easier. Those modifying existing cars or uprating the brakes of kit cars must do some hard work with a jack, a weighbridge, a measuring tape and a calculator first to find the CoG – see Figure 8.8. The formula is:

$$\text{Weight transfer} = \frac{C_f \times W \times H}{L}$$

where C_f is the coefficient of traction, fraction of g (for safety, calculate this to be 1)

W is the car's all-up weight, lb

H is the distance the CoG is above the ground, inches

L is the wheelbase dimension, inches

and we can then see that the weight actually determining the braking requirement on the front wheels is:

$$W_f + W_t$$

and on the rear wheels:

$$W_r - W_t$$

where W_f is the static weight on the front wheels

W_r is the static weight on the rear wheels

W_t is the weight transferred

Again, the importance of a low centre of gravity becomes clear.

Once you know the torque required at the front and the rear, it is a relatively simple matter to compare the requirement with the capability of various disc/caliper/master cylinder/pad material combinations. The formula to use is:

$$T = \frac{R_d \times A \times F \times N \times P}{n}$$

where T is the clamping ability required per wheel

R is the effective disc radius, which is the distance from the centre of the disc to the centre of the caliper's piston, inches

A is the effective area of piston top (i.e. not including the area occupied by the seal), square inches

the area of a circle is half the diameter squared and multiplied by pi: $\frac{1}{2}D^2 \times 3.14$ – and you count all the pistons on one side (or half the pistons in opposed-piston designs)

F is the coefficient of friction produced between the pad and the disc (the manufacturers tell you this one, sometimes on the box) – say 0.2 for a hard pad and 0.4 for a soft pad

N is the number of surfaces the pads grip (some now obsolete designs had a pad only on one side of the disc), normally 2

P is the line pressure in pounds per square inch

Figure 8.10. If you don't trust or can't find space for the Jaguar handbrake, Total Performance has a neat kit to fit a snowmobile disc to the propeller shaft.

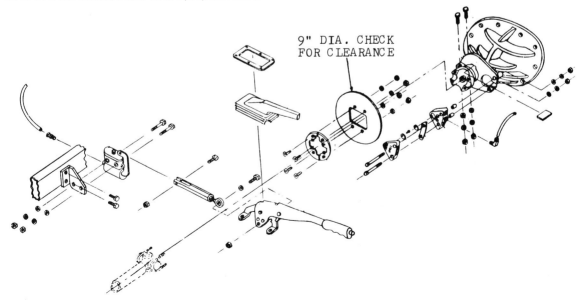

9" DIA. CHECK
FOR CLEARANCE

n   is the number of wheels at that end of the car fitted with discs, normally two (or four wheels all separately braked on the same or double axles at the rear or the front)

You solve it separately for the front and the rear wheels. As a rule of thumb, or first approximation, you can solve it for the total all-up weight of the car as a whole and divide the result so that the front wheels carry 60% of the braking force and the rear 40% for front engine, rear drive cars; sports cars often have the braking distributed 35/65 rear to front. The ideal to aim for is that the front brakes should lock up – if any wheels have to lock up – before the rear ones; all four wheels locking up simultaneously is also less desirable than just the front wheels locking up.

The line pressure, P in the equation above, must not exceed the caliper manufacturer's recommendation or failure will result. I tell you this for the sake of completeness as it is not usually a problem special builders encounter.

All of these thousands of pounds – several tons – of force does not come directly from your leg: it is multiplied both mechanically and hydraulically in the braking system. To find out how much pressure you must apply to the brake for a 1 g stop, you multiply all the enhancement factors together back from the wheel cylinders to the master cylinder to the brake pedal (if pivoted for mechanical advantage) and divide the result into the required force. The answer will be the force in lb your foot must apply to the brake pedal and, if it is too large, you can go back along the line and change the pads, the size of the wheel cylinders, the number of calipers, the size of the master cylinder, or the lever-length of the brake pedal. That is the theory.

In practice the special builder selects a set of discs and installs the master cylinder and often the pedal box from the donor car and makes, if any alteration at all, only a change in the front/rear braking effort by changing the limiter valve in the line to the rear brakes. I prefer light pedal effort of up to, say, 130 lb for an unassisted 1 g stop; if the brakes are assisted, a 1 g stop should *not* require less than 60 lb of pressure and 90 lb is better; these are personal preferences and readers, especially Americans, may prefer a "softer" pedal. For the record, a man who has a firm seatback and can get his legs straight can brake with 300 lb of force, a woman with about 200 lb, and even a lady on her way to Charles Atlas can manage the 130 lb I have specified above as a maximum. (Citroen brakes, in which you merely rest your foot either on a sort of rubber orange or a pedal rather than actively pressing on it, are exempted from my strictures against over-light brake pedals.)

All mechanical and hydraulic connections must be absolutely tight with minimum lost motion and absolutely no leaks for efficient braking. In enclosed bodywork, very careful attention must be paid to ducting sufficient cooling air to disc brakes – and ducting it away again! Inboard disc brakes – normally used only at the rear – are particularly prone to overheating but I still think, despite the fact that the saloon racing fraternity now tends to move inboard discs outwards whenever the rules allow, that it is far easier arranging proper air delivery than coping with the additional unsprung weight.

A mechanical handbrake is a legal requirement most places in the world. Aftermarket units applying go-cart discs to the prop shaft are expensive and space consuming; if you can, use the handbrake that came with your proprietary rear suspension/brake set-up for the fewest hassles. The Jaguar handbrake barely works and is probably illegal but testers most places will usually let it go if you tell them it came off a Jag. In nearly twenty years I have never used the handbrake to hold the car stationary, to restart on hills, or for an emergency stop; for the first two purposes intelligent use of the gearbox and pedals suffices; for the last, the handbrake in all but the most experienced hands is a sure prescription for disaster and it is as an *emergency* brake that our legislators insist on it! They would do a lot better to insist on dual braking systems operated from the footbrake.

However, while the handbrake is a useless appurtenance, especially with split circuit braking, the brakes must not be overdone. As we have seen, maximum retardation is achieved with the wheels just on the verge of locking. If your car is over-braked, the wheels will come onto the lock suddenly and at quite low pedal pressure and it will be difficult to modulate the pressure. The result is an instant skid.

Moderation in braking, as in all other things automobile, is the golden mean.

Neither suspension, steering, nor brakes will work as intended if the chassis bends, flexes, gives, twists or does anything other than provide the utmost rigidity. It is this rigidity, together with the careful planning of all the arcs through which each part of the suspension and steering will move, that results in that perfect predictability that makes a great-handling car. We will now, into the space between our inboard suspension pivots, design a chassis to provide the desired rigidity.

9 Chassis: Principles

The original definition of the chassis held it as the base on which the motorcar was assembled. The current and more acceptable definition is that it is that part of the motorcar which holds all the other parts together in a spatially correct structure. The operative word is *structure*. The chassis must have beam stiffness: it must not bend under load. The chassis must have torsional stiffness: it must not twist under load. Beyond the requirement for rigidity, it must mount all the other units and appurtenances that make up a motorcar in the most advantageous manner, which we normally take to mean without excess weight and without undue restriction to the ingress and egress of passengers or the servicing or removal and replacement of drivetrain parts.

As you have by now come to expect in everything

Figure 9.1. Note the use of rubber bushes in this rear suspension of a Ford frontdrive Fiesta. Keep the rubbers if you redesign the links for aesthetic appeal.

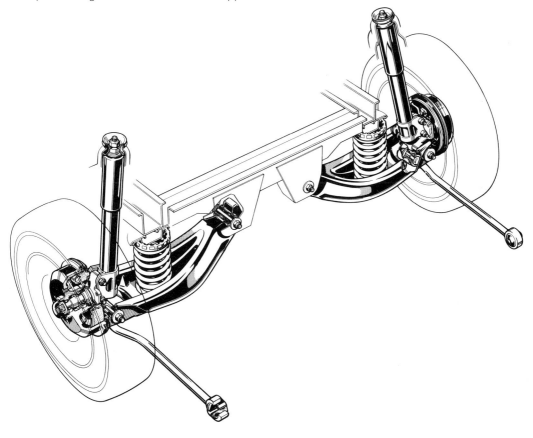

automobile, the choice of chassis type and construction method and materials are all subject to compromise with the functions you wish the car to perform: the "best" design for your particular application is the one that compromises rigidity and accessibility least, while staying within your particular lexicon of skills or – if you're putting the work out – your budget. The next chapter will compare various chassis types and in the one after will discuss material choices and construction methods, but none of this will make sense unless you first know which general engineering principles lead to the greatest rigidity for the least weight in whatever material you are using.

FLATS, CHANNELS, TUBES

Take a piece of material (steel, alloy, wood, plastic) about $2'' \times 6'' \times \frac{1}{8}''$ thick and fasten it in a vice. If you press against the flat side, it bends. If you press against the thin edge, it resists. This is known as lozenge stiffness. If a piece of flat material is then bent into a U-shaped channel, it gains a little lozenge stiffness but not all that much. However, it you close up the fourth side, so that a square or rectangular section is formed, the lozenge stiffness is increased out of all proportion to the additional weight of material. Whereas the channel section has negligible torsional stiffness, that of the square section tube is increased by 500% for an increase of only one-third in weight. If the flat plate is instead formed into a round section tube, the torsional stiffness will be increased even further but, for the builder of road-specials, the difference is irrelevant and his choice normally governed by the greater ease of attaching the chassis members to each other, and the brackets to the chassis, with square or rectangular section tube than with round. Racers looking for the very last ounce of weight will find it by switching from square to round tubes but they should note that even on a car of such exemplary parsimonious weight as the Lotus-licensed Caterham Seven, square section tubes are used to facilitate rivetting-on the stressed body panels, round tube being used only where it will not cause complications.

Square section tube is more rigid in bending than round section tube but this is, again, normally irrelevant to special car builders because it is difficult to conceive of a chassis which is sufficiently torsion-resistant which is not at the same time inevitably also more than sufficiently resistant to bending.

All this assumes that the special builder will want to buy as few different sizes and shapes of a given material as possible because one normally has to buy a complete length; if there is a choice, and mounting complications do not arise, then by all means choose the more efficient shape for the application.

Rectangular sections are arranged, where possible, with the longest side in line with the bending load because that arrangement is more resistant than with the short side in line with the bending load; in most applications that means the long side will be vertical.

A flat sheet of material may be bent in any direction. If it is shaped with a crown, it will take more force to bend it. If it has a channel bent into it (or welded on) it will be difficult to bend in one direction only, across the channel. If all four the edges are bent into returns, so that the erstwhile flat plate forms a shallow tray, it will be more difficult to bend. The deeper the shaping – crown, channel, returns – the greater the force necessary to overcome the bending resistance.

The compressive strength of a material is related to the third power of its thickness. This puts a premium on low density materials. Low density materials have other advantages to which we shall return but for the moment note that you gain more by thickening than

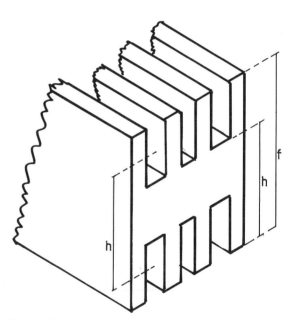

Figure 9.2. How to get something for nothing – very expensively. If you mill a sheet of material in ridges, it will have the compressive capability of f but only the weight of h.

you lose by thinning, so that a sheet with stiffeners will have greater capacity than a sheet of the same total volume that is flat but without stiffeners (and therefore thicker but uniform).

For a discussion of bending loads, those of you of mathematical bent can refer to Timoshenko's *Strength of Materials* (Van Nostrand Reinhold, various editions since 1930) or the more practically inclined book by Urry, *Solution of Problems in Strength of Materials* (Pitman, various editions since 1953) or any civil or construction engineers' reference books. The Costin and Phipps book, already mentioned, shows in its Appendix some members in the spaceframe example designed by local bending, but, if you cannot handle the maths, note that they're designing a road racer and their pipe recommendations are *minima*: for everyday peace of mind and long-term rust-free use (if you build in steel), you want somewhat heftier wall thicknesses.

TUBE MATH

A tube is a hollowed-out rod. Since the greatest part of the load is borne by the outermost parts of the rod, around the circumference, hollowing it out to leave a thin tube does not detract greatly from its torsional strength – in fact lightens it disproportionately to the amount of strength lost. If the same amount of material that was in the rod is used to make a much larger thin-wall tube, it will be many times stronger than the rod in resisting torsion. A rule of thumb which does, however, need to be treated with caution states that torsional capacity of a tube increases as the fourth power of its diameter.

The manufacturer of your chosen material tells you its shearing stress. You can calculate the load a member (or complete chassis) must bear. For instance, to resist the load transmitted to the chassis via the spring, requires a torsional stiffness of

$$C = \frac{cd}{D}$$

where C   is the torsional stiffness of the member required, lb/inches
c   is the spring rate, lb/inches
d   is the spring deflection, inches
D   is the permissible chassis deflection diagonally across the chassis, fraction of an inch (or zero)

The shear stress in a tube is calculated by the following formula:

$$\text{shear stress} = \frac{M_t}{2Ah}$$

where M_t is the torque, lb/inches
A   is $3.14(r - \frac{h}{2})^2$ with r as the outside radius of the tube
h   is the wall thickness

If the tube is then not capable of handling the torsion, you can change it for one with a thicker wall or a bigger cross-section or both until it will take the load plus a safety margin of 500% (that is, *five times* the actual load) in cases where there is a load reversal or fatigue factor. (In GRP, the safety factor for load reversal is 1000%, that is, the part must be designed locally to withstand 10 times the expected load and lead it away into less stressed areas of the chassis.)

The shear stress tells you only how much the tube will take, not how much it will deflect in the process. To calculate the angle of twist per unit length, plug into this formula:

$$\text{angle of twist per unit length} = \frac{\text{sheer stress} \times s}{2AG}$$

where   the shear stress is as calculated above
s   is the length shown in Figure 9.3
A   is $3.14(r - \frac{h}{2})^2$ with r as the outside radius of the tube and h as the wall thickness of the tube
G   is the modulus of elasticity in shear (or just "shear modulus") supplied by the material manufacturer (relevant only if you're comparing different materials – if you're comparing different sizes in the same material, it is constant and can therefore be taken as 1 or whatever number will make your figures easier to handle)

Figure 9.3. s, r and h in torsional calculations.

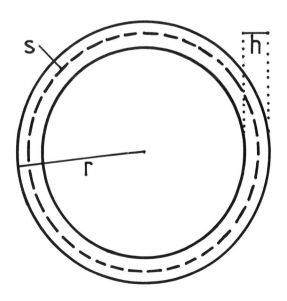

It is easy to see that the lower the shear stress of the material and the shorter the member, the less twist, or, the bigger the section and the higher the shear modulus, the less twist. You can therefore contrive to load the member less heavily – difficult in most instances; to make it shorter, or even effectively shorter by bracing that will lead some of the load away; change to a more suitable material; or – most common solution – choose a bigger section or a thicker wall.

So you have a lot of choices. In most cases the special builder will not involve himself in this kind of calculation but will choose his members by example and analogy, by looking at what works for others and copying the dimensions or going up or down perhaps one size; when changing materials, say from steel to ali or GRP, weights are chosen by reference to the known quantities of steel and the special advantages of the new material are exploited by stages as experience teaches that a little paring here or there may be safe as well as beneficial. It is true this is an ultra-conservative kind of design but it's also ultra-safe for the amateur designer who, in any event, doesn't have the money to put him in the forefront of the latest hi-tech developments. Normally I do my design and then do a few spot calculations to prove how clever my intuitive choices were: with practice you will get amazingly good at it.

Below are a few of the terms used above that will appear again, a little more closely though briefly defined. Those of you who want to make a real study of the principles of hi-tech construction should go directly to the fountainhead: aircraft construction; the best, most accessible and simplest explanations are to be found in *Understanding Aircraft Structures* by John Cutler (Granada, 1981).

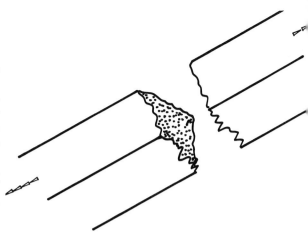

Figure 9.4. Tension load and failure mode.

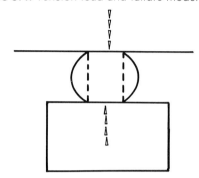

Figure 9.5. Compression load and failure mode.

NEWTON'S LAW

There is no load without equal and opposite reaction.

TENSION

If you were to pull at the opposite ends of a tube in opposite directions along the longitudinal axis of the tube, the tube would be in tension and the failure mode would be for the metal to part somewhere between the opposing forces, literally pulled apart. This is a very important load function in unit constructions.

COMPRESSION

This is inward pressure from two sides, diametrically opposed (force and reaction diametrically opposed, if you want to be a purist) and the failure mode is for the material to reach such a compression of its atoms that it bulges outwards or buckles. It is an essential part of the aeroplane designer's armoury (or it was until recently they started looking a little shame-faced about it mainly on the grounds that it doesn't *look* like elegant engineering) that a sheet which has buckled can still carry a load and may be designed to operate in a buckled condition. The Porsche 911 has a flat plate, free to bend, serving as a link in the rear suspension and some FWDs have an open U-channel at the rear designed to twist; otherwise I cannot think of an example of any part of a modern car (some veteran chassis were designed to flex because the springs didn't!) that lacks rigidity except by incompetent design but you might think whether the principle will not allow you to design an ali monocoque even lighter than Kevlar . . .

SHEAR

This is outward pull to two sides. If you were to pull at the end of two rods joined by a bolt, eventually the bolt would be torn – or sheared – in half roughly at the mating faces of the two rods.

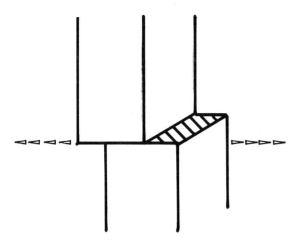

Figure 9.6. Shear load and failure mode.

TORSION

Take the tube and twist the ends in opposite directions and eventually the tube will buckle and shear, probably not straight across as in pure shear (and often in tension) but at an angle.

BENDING

Support a tube or rod at both ends on bricks and load the middle: if you load it enough, it will bend visibly; if you load it too much, it will not recover its original shape and may be torn in two.

STRAIN

Strictly speaking, *unit strain*. This is the ratio of length extension caused by a load divided by the original length:

$$\text{Strain} = \frac{\text{Length extension caused by load}}{\text{Original length before loading}}$$

STRESS

The stress in a member is a measure of the load compared to the amount of material carrying the load:

$$\text{Stress} = \frac{\text{Load}}{\text{Width} \times \text{thickness}} \text{lbf/in}^2$$

Note that strain is a dimensionless ratio and stress is the same for any material, so that, not to overstress less capable materials carrying the same load, you must choose larger dimensions.

MODULUS OF ELASTICITY

Stress divided by strain is a constant:

$$E = \frac{\text{Stress}}{\text{Strain}}$$

called the Modulus of Elasticity, E, or Young's Modulus with the result given in pounds force per square inch (lbf/in^2). This is an important measurement of a material characteristic for the special builder interested in Life Beyond Mild Steel.

POISSON

Another dimensionless ratio.

$$\text{Poisson's ratio} = \frac{\text{lateral strain}}{\text{longitudinal strain}}$$

(whereas above we were interested only in longitudinal strain).

Figure 9.7. Shear centres and optimum load axes for various sections. The optimum load axis of a channel falls *outside* the channel and requires an outrigger built out to it.

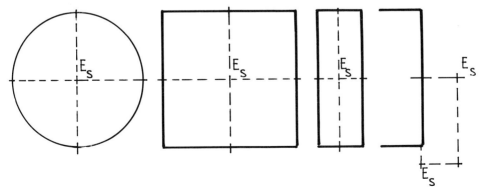

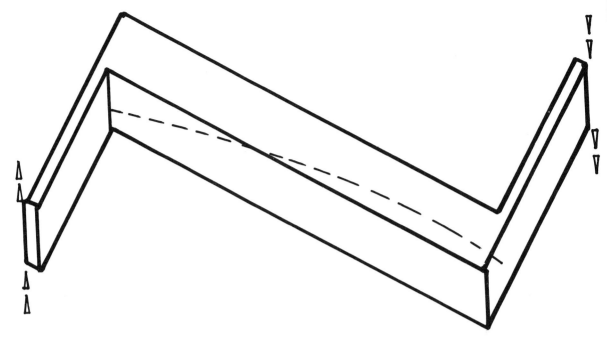

Figure 9.8. Torsional load and failure mode.

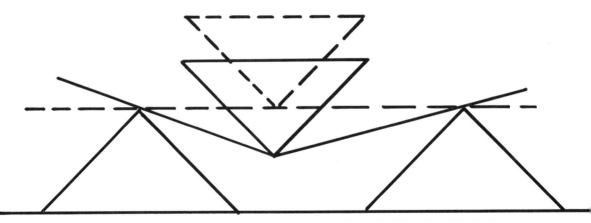

Figure 9.9. Bending load and distortion. Failure would occur when the member remains bent after removal of the load.

ALL TOGETHER NOW

The importance of Poisson is that his ratio is often found in tables together with E, the modulus of elasticity, while G, the shear modulus, is absent but can be generated from E and Poisson (usually abbreviated with the Greek μ):

$$G = \frac{E}{2(1 + \text{Poisson's Ratio})}$$

COMPLICATIONS

The modulus of Elasticity, E, does not hold true all the way to the ultimate tensile stress: beyond a certain stress (the uniaxial yield stress in mild steel, the limit of proportionality in ali), the strain increases dramatically with little or no increase in load until it reaches the ultimate tensile stress. This point is nowhere near as sharp for aluminium as for steel.

The decision the special builder must make is how

near the yield stress or the limit of proportionality he wants to go for his strength requirement including his safety margin. Racers may well calculate the total requirement including their safety margin right up to the ultimate tensile stress; for road cars there is little to be gained from going on to those tricky slopes beyond the yield stress, the limit of proportionality or the 0.2% proof stress. Once more, the question does not arise until the special builder wants to do something radically different, either in material or dimension; until then he is safe in the bosom of time-hallowed practice as followed by other special builders or even mass manufacturers.

EGGS AND TRIANGLES

The strongest shape known to man that is vaguely automobile-like is the spheroid: try squashing an egg end to end between your fingers and you will almost certainly fail. But even a small hole in the thin shell degrades the structure to the extent that it is much easier to squash.

Next best automobile-like shape is a tube with the ends capped. If the tube is tapered towards the ends or pierced for any reason, stress concentrations around the changes in diameter and the edges of the holes will ensure that it fails at the application of less force than the whole straight capped tube.

The problem with eggs and straight tubes is that they hardly resemble functional motorcars, which are much more like two or three boxes stuck together.

A box, either square or rectangular, may be made by sticking together two three-dimensional triangles made up of tubes. And the triangle is by far the strongest structure known to man in compression or tension – all that remains is to apply ingenuity to the conversion (what engineers call resolution) of all loads into compression or tension.

Even in a flat plane, a triangle is stiffer than a rectangle or a square. A square or rectangle with a

triangulating diagonal is also a structure rather than a mechanism.

The test is to make up a model of your chassis and pin rather than glue the joints. If pressure against any joint causes it to fold up, it is a *mechanism*, if not, it is a structure.

Figure 9.11. A structure. Force against any corner must either compress or stretch the diagonal; no bending forces are involved. This is the basic space frame structure.

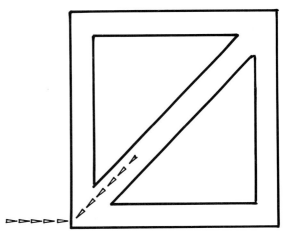

Figure 9.10. A mechanism.

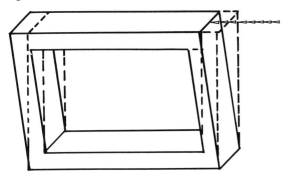

10 Chassis: Choice

Once upon a time, the word "chassis" had a much wider meaning than it has now: it included the chassis frame, the suspension, all the running gear, lamps and electrics with the spare wheel(s) ready mounted plus, often, the wings as well. On this combination the body was then mounted. Today, in the most common application, in Europe anyway, the "chassis" is the complete body, glassed, often with bonnet and bootlid and doors hung, to which the drivetrain is attached. Even in the American sense, where the body and chassis may be separately produced, they are often welded together to form a unit, the purpose being to gain additional stiffness. The fascinating history of chassis development is a chronology of increases in the stiffness between the axes of the wheels of all cars of every type and price.

WOODEN RAILS

Earliest chassis were built from wood, either straight or bent. Wood is not a high-strength material but it is very durable if properly seasoned and treated, and it does not suffer from fatigue. The use of flitch plates (metal strengthening plates screwed or bolted onto the wood at strategic points) led naturally to sandwiching the wood between two pieces of metal plate. Ettore Bugatti did this, but it was a more expensive process than making up pressed steel channels.

   With modern glues, there is much to be said for building cars with wooden chassis. The aerodynamicist Frank Costin (brother of the Mike of Lotus and the bible) was an early prophet of the application of marine ply to motorcars: his name has gone down as one-half of Marcos; the early Marcos cars had chassis of plywood arranged in a series of torsion boxes with the GRP skin merely filling in the gaps. The Midas, which is a descendant of the Mini-Marcos, still uses a plywood insert into its GRP monocoque to give it beam strength. William Towns, who designed all the current Aston Martins, sells a kit and plans from which

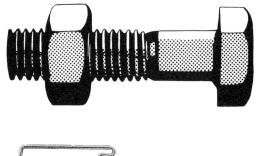

Figure 10.1 and 10.2. Fasteners will be a bigger cost than you thought– the minimum protection for bolts and nuts is cadmium plating and painting. The easiest sprayers to use are the hot-air low-pressure models, like this Apollo.

to build an all-wood Hustler alongside his metal-framed Hustlers; the wooden car preceded the metal-chassised ones but, like Marcos, he found customer resistance to the idea of riding around on nothing more than ash and plywood. Such fears are entirely misplaced and the special builder could do well to consider the claims of wood – easily worked and glued without expensive tools or moulds – against metal or GRP.

PRESSED CHANNEL RAILS

Depending on your viewpoint, this is another of Wilhelm Maybach's signal contributions to the automobile, or Maybach's revenge for having lived so long in the shadow of Gottlieb Daimler: the pressed steel channel side rails that were to be with us so long were first seen on the Mercédès (the accents were not to be lost until 1924) he launched in 1901, a year after Daimler's death.

For over a generation these rails, changed in shape but not in function or performance, would be spaced rather than braced by crossmembers of channel or tubular construction. In time, instead of being a straight, constant depth channel, they would become deeper in the middle where the weight was most concentrated (and on some Rolls and Bentleys gain bracing girders that distinctly betrayed a railway-shed education, hanging obscenely like a dignified lady's underclothes sagging below her skirt), and be swept up over the axles to lower the car; the more aesthetically inclined designers turned their exposed chassis side rails into eloquent sculptures, none better than Bugatti on his Type 35, perhaps the most beautiful car ever built.

Beautiful or ugly, pressed channels, braced by the ladder-steps of more channels or tubes, were subject to lozenging and twisting between the planes of the axles. Designers were aware of this but, it should be said in their defence, were more interested in keeping control of the two wheels on the same beam axle than in controlling movements diagonally between one front wheel and the opposite side rear wheel. In any event, many of them saw the chassis as a *springing medium* assisting the springs: they could not use long-travel soft springs because of the early onset of dreadful tramp and dreaded shimmy, and so looked to the chassis to compensate for painfully hard springs; many vintage cars seem sprung only in their seats, which accounts for the popularity of air cushions (inflated by bicycle pumps) even in luxury cars. In addition, many cars had no dampers, relying on inter-spring friction instead, a practice which would of course have had deleterious consequences if the springs were softer.

Pressed channels find modern applications on goods vehicles where their flexure is a designed-in and desirable purpose and protected by a multitude of regulations about where and how you may weld or drill the chassis for attachments in order not to interfere with the channel's free movement.

For the special builder, open-U-channel is only justifiable if he's a demon for replication. The hot rod fraternity will sell one a set of replica Ford A or B rails (and some other popular cars are catered for too) and various fabricators, like Rubery Owen (now called Chassisbuild) in England, will handbeat to order a chassis for the more esoteric makes.

Most rodders use softer springs and better dampers, and have better control of their axles, than the constructors of old; many rodders also fit modern independent suspension all round to twin U-rail chassis. In either case, to gain the superior control over camber change that comes only with greater stiffness of the chassis, they box the rails by welding a plate over the open end; the box should extend from the rear suspension mount or crossbar to the front suspension mount or crossbar – there is no need to box the frame horns at the front and the rear. These rodders then fit various K- and X-members for further stiffness and by then a basic Model B chassis has become a very different animal.

TWIN TUBES

The better manufacturers soon started boxing their side rails for additional stiffness and the crossbraces of the ladder grew in size so that they offered additional stiffness, if only by the weight of their metal. At first, the chassis rails were pressed and the open side closed by welding on a flat plate, just as today's rodders do: the result was a rectangular box section. Soon this came to the attention of the cost accountants and construction was switched to a frame welded up from round or square or rectangular ready-manufactured tubes. Auto-Union racing cars, big and fast Mercedes, even the post-War Lister which was successful well into the 1960s – all used twin tube ladder frames, with uprights to hang the suspension welded on, plus perhaps a hoop to hang the steering and instruments. We shall return to the evolutionary importance of these additions in a moment, after looking at what happened in the centre of the chassis in the search for greater stiffness.

K- AND X-BRACES

With the advent of independent suspension at the front of even heavy and fast cars in the middle 1930s, even greater stiffness was demanded from the chassis by the suspension designers. This was gained in two ways. By making the tubes bigger in diameter, a certain amount of stiffness was gained; this was of course at the expense of weight: though it is true that for a given weight of tubing, the greater diameter will offer the greater stiffness – but the wall cannot be made infinitely thinner for reasons of weldability, attachment by bolts, and durability (rust!). The next step was to triangulate the chassis by running two diagonals through it from the front wheels to the rear wheels on

QUALITY CONTROL:
Design and Structure of Parts

The heart of the Marlin kit is its chassis. This is constructed from 50mm x 100mm and 70mm x 70mm box section steel 3mm thick. It is built in such a way that no open ends remain: all through fastenings are sealed with tubes and body parts are attached to a steel strip welded to the chassis. This is the only way to guarantee an air tight and thus corrosion free frame. The three dimensional structure of the chassis affords good side impact resistance and the strong steel screen frame provides proven roll-over protection.

Bonnet, bulkheads, transmission tunnel and engine compartment sides are made in 16 gauge aluminium. Doors are welded 12 gauge aluminium and the remainder of the panels and the wings are moulded with a generous thickness of GRP. Welded to the front and rear of the chassis are strong tubular bumpers to shrug off the knocks and hazards of every day driving.

Although the body is intended to be painted by the customer we can supply coloured mouldings at small extra cost.

To make repairs and maintenance as simple as possible body fastenings are predominantly zinc plated M6 nuts and bolts.

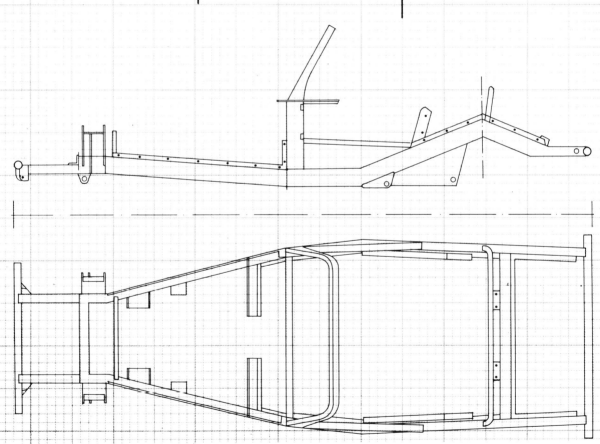

Figure 10.3. The Marlin not only looks like the right stuff, it is an immensely competent and thoughtful design in three dimensions – though I would weld in a floor for even more stiffness.

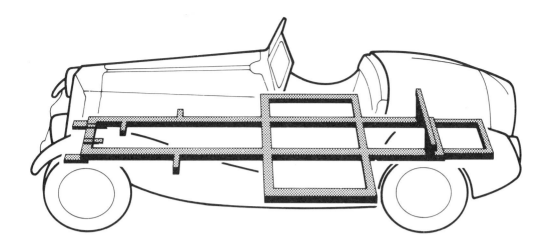

Figure 10.4. You can get any type of chassis built by specialists. This ladder frame, by ST Cars, is for Triumph-based specials.

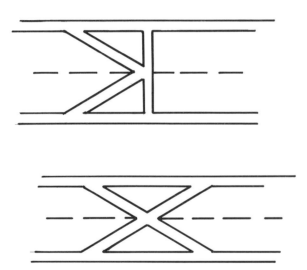

Figure 10.5. Twin rail chassis should, if at all possible, be braced by, preferably, a cruciform and, failing that ideal, a substantial K-frame or K-frames for stiffness.

the opposite side; the diagonals met in the middle and the intersection was pierced to pass the propeller shaft; people still sat on top of the chassis rather than in it. The modern special builder sometimes cannot find space for his feet and the X-brace and then uses only half of the X plus a transverse member to form a K-brace – it is not as good as an X but better than a ladder-braced frame – or two opposing K's, with the laterals no further apart than is necessary to find footspace is almost as good as an X. The K- or X-frames should be made of the same weight of material as the side tubes but there are often overriding reasons to compromise on the size of the X or Ks: lower seating, space for master cylinders, piping, wiring, etc. But even a long and heavy and fast car braced by quite a modest X-member will be at least 200% as stiff as a (probably heavier) ladder frame.

BACKBONES AND CRUCIFORMS

If the X-brace provides most of the resistance to twisting, some wide-awake designers reasoned, why not do without the side rails altogether? A post-War Lagonda used a substantial X-frame as its sole chassis, with a wheel at each corner and the passengers sitting on top, but it was chronologically preceded by what should have been a logical development. Ledwinka's Tatra and a big Austro-Daimler of the same period had backbone chasses split at each end to allow fitting of the engine and the suspension, the passengers sitting low down beside the backbone; the body was fitted on outriggers from the backbone. The backbone fitted under Lotus road cars from the Elan forward is a direct descendant and so is the TVR spaceframe backbone, though the latter is the more advanced, with inputs from other schools of chassis design – or, such is the towering presence of the man, from a different period of the long and diverse contribution to suspension and chassis design by Colin Chapman.

The backbone is inferior in stiffness to the true cruciform but the exact degree of the latter's superiority depends not only on the size and wall thickness of the component parts but also very much on the detail design. In both it is desirable to lead suspension loads to the centre of the X or the backbone as directly as possible. The Elan design lacks purity, especially at the rear where two towers accept the spring struts at a considerable offset from the body of the backbone; torsion bars leading the suspension loads forward into the backbone would have been far superior. The centre box is about 24L × 6W × 10D inches, the whole is made of welded mild steel, and the GRP body bolts to flanges on the members but adds only marginally to the stiffness of the whole, though it carries fuel tank, spare wheel and passenger without aid of outriggers. Despite my quibble about the detail of the rear suspension offset, torsional stiffness between the wheel planes approaches the very impressive figure of 5000lb/ft per degree of twist. Despite its level of performance in the stiffness-for-weight stakes, many designers fear that public acceptance of the design is not enhanced by the greater difficulty of providing protection against side impact intrusions; many special car builders also dislike backbones for exactly this reason.

For the special builder who is not worried about side impacts, the backbone seems an attractive design for its ease of construction or – if the size is right – for the time saving which may be had by buying a Lotus or replica backbone either in sheet metal or as a spaceframe, ready to take all those proven and desirable Lotus parts. But do try for one of the later galvanized chassis – or rustproof it yourself – because local repairs to corrosion damage is difficult and sometimes impossible to do effectively. Unfortunately, backbones give special builders a lot of mounting headaches.

MULTITUBES

The uprights on twin tube chassis to which suspension links are attached have to be substantially braced for adequate stiffness. In time the bracing across the front wheels and across the rear wheels were joined, then a longitudinal was run from the rear suspension tower to the front on single seaters or doorless two seaters. From there it was only a small step to making the frames on top of the twin tubes bigger and making the twin tubes smaller. The four tube or multitube chassis was born.

The student of these things can hear in the pubs in the South of England how the Coopers père et fils, with nothing but their native English wit, a pile of pipes against the wall, and a few chalk marks on the floor, carpetbagged their way to two grand prix championships and founded almost single-handedly the preponderant importance of Britain to present grand

prix racing. All of this is true, though partisans are likely to give the native English wit and the chalk marks on the floor equal billing. There may have been chalk marks on the floor but the Coopers had too much wit to do anything random.

Their multitube chassis brought home two grand prix championships. They were simple to manufacture and very sturdy, though – as Costin and Phipps point out at some length and more than once – heavier than contemporary and comparative spaceframes. The multitube chassis consists of four longitudinal pipes, braced by a number of bulkheads. The exact placement of the bulkheads depends on where the suspension inputs fall, on the placement of the engine, and the placement of the driver. At the front of a front-engined car there would be one bulkhead for the suspension, possibly a second (sometimes less substantial) bulkhead also for the suspension, then a bulkhead behind the engine bay for the pedals, another for the steering wheel and instruments, and another one or two for the rear suspension, the forward one of these also doing duty as seatback. The Coopers used fairly heavy weights of pipe, bent some to clear components, avoided welding more than two pipes at the same junction if at all possible, didn't triangulate bulkheads and frames, fed suspension loads into the middle of members that were therefore bound to bend – they horrified the fastidious crowd at Lotus … whose own much more elegant designs kept breaking while the Coopers kept going.

There is a lesson here for the special builder: simplicity and strength may win the day, while more sophisticated but difficult to manufacture designs fall by the wayside. All the same, it is unlikely that the special builder will choose a multitube design; it is almost as simple and easy with modern welding processes to build a spaceframe that will be much stiffer; the special builder must, however, resign himself to not building the ultimate lightweight spaceframe because that way lie all the problems that beset early spaceframes. It will still be lighter than a multitube design.

SPACEFRAMES

A spaceframe is a chassis built of small diameter, thinwall tubes in such a manner that, were all the joints pinned rather than welded, it would still form a rigid structure. We shall return to the implications of this in a moment; first we must describe the practice of spaceframes a little more comprehensibly.

A spaceframe, from a designer's viewpoint, consists of a series of bulkheads lying transversely across the car, accepting loads from the suspension and reacting

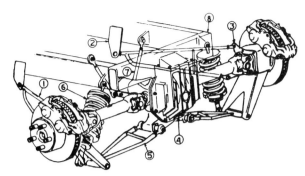

Figure 10.6. Very sophisticated suspensions can be hung on quite simple frames, like this Corvette rear, modified by Total Performance, on the back of a Model A frame.

loads from the drivetrain and payload (you and your luggage). The bulkheads define the forward and rear ends of various functional bays and are joined by longitudinal pipes. All bulkheads and each side of each bay is *stabilized* in one of four ways: by running a diagonal across it between two corners; by "plating" it through welding a sheet of metal across it (riveting or bonding are common alternatives); by building a pierced diaphragm as in Figure 10.7; by triangulating it externally. The portal frame and the Y-frame are variations of the diagonal.

It should be obvious that triangulating each bay on

Figure 10.7. If you can't fit a diagonal through the centre of a frame, a pierced diaphragm will allow access for people or machinery without detracting from stiffness.

each side with a diagonal will make it difficult to put in the engine and passengers and, once in, to service or remove them again: that is what pierced diaphragms, Y- and portal-frames, and external triangulation are good for in that they provide stiffness with access.

The definition of a spaceframe implies that no loads will be led into members in such a manner that they will bend; all loads must be resolved into tension and compression and must therefore be led to a joint where a minimum of three pipes meet – often more.

Short of an aluminium or GRP/Kevlar monocoque, a mild steel spaceframe clad with ali or GRP panels – stressed or unstressed, stressed being those attached to the chassis in such a manner that they add to the overall stiffness such as riveted-on diaphragms – is the lightest chassis you can build. Racers will build the chassis from $\frac{3}{4}$-inch, 18-g steel up to $1\frac{1}{4}$-inch 14-gauge but the special builder tempted to tackle a space frame will be well advised to stick to $1\frac{1}{2} \times 1\frac{1}{2}$ inch 16-g – and even 12-g material if he's going to do the welding himself. It is sometimes difficult to avoid five or six tubes coming together at one joint and welding without pre-stressing or distorting the frame is so difficult that a twin tube is often the more practically advisable way to go. In any event, the spaceframe is no longer the ne plus ultra of chassis design – regardless of what certain kit car builders, whose "spaceframes" are nothing better than vastly inept multitubes, will tell you. It may be possible, by careful design and the application of newer materials and jointing methods, for the special builder to construct (or have constructed at not too ruinous cost) a unit-construction or monocoque of superior stiffness to a spaceframe.

One area where the spaceframe still has application in special cars is for subframes, sometimes major and very important ones. *The* major example that comes to mind is on the Jaguar E-type, where the central tub, a monocoque, has a neat subframe attached at the front and the suspension and steering and engine are in turn attached to the subframe (which also hangs the non-loadbearing flip-forward bonnet). Many sports racing cars with mid-engines have "tubs" to carry the front suspension and driver with a spaceframe rear to carry the drivetrain and suspension.

UNIT CONSTRUCTION

This is often called monocoque, meaning single shell, but it is no such thing: it is a series of monocoques – most commonly in steel, but sometimes in ali or reinforced plastics or even wood – joined together by whatever means is appropriate to the material: welding, riveting, bonding. The whole then forms a rigid structure, sometimes including the outside skin

Figure 10.8. The world's longest running spaceframe is that of the Lotus Seven, now made under license in Mk III form as the Caterham Super Seven.

Figure 10.9. While the Caterham Seven is undoubtedly king of the mountain, it is expensive. Some other contenders are cheap and catastrophic or cheap and cheerful but this one, the Sylva Star, is cheap and competent. It uses Viva mechanicals.

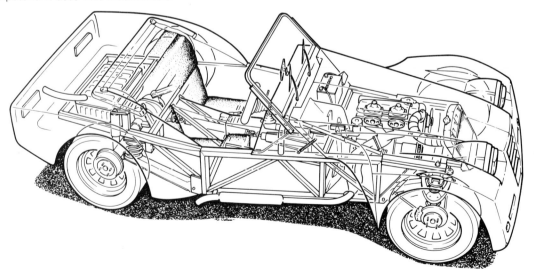

(stressed skin), sometimes requiring the external skin to be bolted on (endo-skeletal as on the old Rover 2000 shape and the Citroen DS), and always requiring doors, bonnet and bootlid. This is a convenient way for mass producers to make a frame to carry drivetrain and trim and your commonplace car is of mild steel, welded together – it is torsionally stiffer than racing cars of only a few years ago. Though Jim Hall had Troutman and Barnes construct for him a GRP unit construction consisting of a series of torsion boxes needing only minimal outer skinning and weighing but 150lb, this is not a method to be recommended to the special builder: it is too intricate and too easy to get distortion through temperature change. Paradoxically, the special builder is better advised to choose the real thing – a monocoque – and then to brace the inside, as we will discuss below.

You will sometimes hear the phrase "platform chassis". It can refer to any of the chassis we have discussed plus the perimeter chassis, in each case with the floor attached to whatever other members there are, normally with the floor shaped to take some of the stress. The ubiquitous VW Beetle floorpan is a platform chassis. The body can be bolted to the platform, or welded to it; in the latter case, the platform becomes part of the unit construction. A peripheral frame is an American twin tube that follows the outside periphery of the car to give more footroom. Its stiffness by itself is doubtful but the stiffness of the whole car can be vastly improved by welding the body to the perimeter frame and this is sometimes done in production, in which case the perimeter frame too becomes a part of the unit construction.

Except in the very cheapest cars, it is essential to isolate the suspension and the engine from a unit construction (as from a monocoque) by subframes and/or rubber bushes to avoid the transmission of vibration and road shocks.

Though unit construction in thin metal sheeting is almost impossible for the amateur, and unit construction in small GRP boxes fraught with dangers of disparate distortion, almost all special car builders will have enough woodworking skills to build up a series of torsion boxes in wood, which can then be skinned with several or a single large GRP moulding. The question must, however, arise, unless you are enamoured of wood or just like working with it: Why use two materials, why not do the whole job in GRP?

MONOCOQUES

There is no such thing as a true monocoque but modern materials, especially plastics, allow us to come closer to the ideal. A true monocoque would be a *single* shell. It is obvious that doors and lids for engine and luggage degrade such a single shell and that it then no longer *mono*-coque. But let us call any car chassis/body unit a monocoque that flows from nose to tail with only holes for the various doors and lids and that is made without any other apparent breaks on its surface. So far, no one has yet managed to press such a thing from a monster sheet of metal or to cast it (though Gregoire's 1937 Amilcar Compound could well in a decade or two of development have come very close indeed).

Certain chemical resins, when bonded to glass filaments, allow this ideal to be approached and, wit permitting, reached. These plastics are *plastic* – their name tells you they can be shaped or moulded. They harden in heat; the ones the special builder is interested in provide their own heat but some require external heat. Since these plastics, suitably reinforced with glass fibre, were light as well as strong...

Colin Chapman was a leader in the field. His first Elite was not a true monocoque in that it actually consisted of three separate shells fitting one into the other and bonded to each other so that the finished product formed a single loadbearing unit (a few pieces of metal were bonded between the shells and there were a few minor mouldings as well) into which all the suspension and other loads were fed. But it was so far in advance of the unit constructions in steel of that or any other day – and so light! This was in the early days of GRP manufacture and bonding problems were experienced. Lotus dropped the reinforced plastic monocoque for the backbone design and have stuck to it since, though they have long since gained so much experience in GRP (they still make all their bodies of GRP) that they are hired as consultants to other GRP users; Lotus claim that, per unit of usable internal volume, the backbone-chassised Lotus is as weight-efficient as an all-GRP one.

The Midas is by our definition the only monocoque car commercially available as I write this. It consists of a single GRP shell, suitably reinforced with some not very large pieces of plywood and zinc-sprayed metal at strategic points, with apertures for the hatchback, two doors and the engine; it takes Metro components and mountings for the front suspension/engine subframe and the rear suspension subframe (Midas modifies this) are provided on the main shell. There are four main closures – two doors, engine cover and opening rear glass – and a number of minor mouldings for trim. The outer gel colour is not over-sprayed and the finish is excellent. The shell is extremely resistant to torsion; Harold Dermott claims that his is the stiffest 2 + 2 chassis in the world. It is also the lightest, and truly impressive top speed, acceleration and fuel consumption figures are obtained without any sacrifice in

Figure 10.10. This rather smart car is a recycled Cortina/Pinto called the Merlin TF, or Witton Tiger in the States. The kit is notable for being complete even to weather equipment.

creature comforts; here good aerodynamics assist the low weight.

A monocoque in GRP (or more esoteric materials – all of them plastics) has many seductions for the special builder. It is a large effort, but then building a car is an altogether large endeavour and this particular exertion will result in both chassis and body with, if the finish of the original plug was good enough, a self-coloured gel-coat that does not need painting. Curves can be especially seductive and may be required for stiffness. Even an incompetently designed all-GRP car need not weigh more than 60% of a comparable unit construction of welded metal. GRP does not rust. If properly designed, a GRP car will offer exactly the same integrity in fatigue or an accident as a metal car: this is insured by the correct selection and placement of inserts, or by local thickening of the material; progressive crumple resistance is achieved by using various types and grades and weaves of glassfibre from the front and rear of the car towards the passenger compartment.

Surprisingly, the objection is one of cost. A full-size model must be built and finished to a high standard, a mould must be taken from this and braced so that it does not distort, and then the final moulding must be built inside this: it all takes a lot of materials that do not go into the final car. It is in fact cheaper to build a one-off body in aluminium and this is what the manufacturers of GRP bodies routinely do: build one in ali and take the master mould from that. However, the special builder must add the cost of a separate chassis, a separate body, paint and labour for such tasks as he will put out, and may then well find a GRP monocoque pays him better; he may in any event have thought first of making his body in GRP – which would involve the steps above – and then incorporating the chassis as well must be cost-effective.

However, there are those of us who feel that riding

cocooned in nothing but plastic is decidedly queasy-making; if this includes you, save up for the extra a metal chassis will cost.

BULKHEADS AND PILLARS

For the novice designer the temptation is to look at the outer skin and the longitudinal bracing – the sills and driveshaft tunnel – and believe that they are the most important parts of a unit construction or monocoque. This is a false impression, fostered by the amount of material in these longitudinal parts as opposed to the amount of material in transverse braces. As in space-frames, the bulkheads provide stiffness hugely out of proportion to their weight. It would in fact be well for the special car designer to design his unit construction or monocoque by first specifying his bulkheads, as on a spaceframe design, and then to join them longitudinally. Next to the bulkheads, the pillars holding the roof on are substantial contributors to the stiffness of the whole in that they complete the sides of the "box". The floor and roof of the car resolve much of the load, which is why you cannot simply cut the roof off a tin box to make a convertible without strengthening the whole but especially the scuttle first. The deeper and the more complex the returns on the pillars and the curve on the roof and the "patterning" of the floor, the stiffer they will be and the better they will perform their function. The sills provide bending strength and serve to strengthen the edges of the floor by giving it a deeper dimension than the swaging of the floor; see the sills as twin tubes with the floor welded in and the body welded on and their importance in the scheme of a motorcar will become clearer. The drive tunnel, usually of larger diameter than the sills – and retained even in rear drive cars – also resists bending but adds far more to the torsional stiffness than the side sills.

The importance of the bulkheads is nicely illustrated in cars where the designer, in every other department solicitous of the owner's comfort, yet retains a high loading sill to the luggage space: that transverse bulkhead right at the rear of the car cannot be removed without endangering the complete structure, because, in spaceframes, unit constructions and monocoques alike, the integrity of the whole is determined by the fitness of the least competent component.

THE SCUTTLE

One prominent designer built and sold over a good number of years at least one of his successful cars by first drawing the scuttle and, when he was satisfied with it, designing the rest of the car around it. The scuttle is so important to the torsional rigidity of the car that this apparently hare-brained procedure has much to recommend it for the special builder.

The scuttle is that three-dimensional part of the car directly in front of the driver and steering wheel. Its great virtue lies in its three-dimensionality on virtually every kind of design. It is, or can be made, a box closed on five sides by the engine bulkhead (firewall), the floor and bonnet top, and two body sides or footwell sides, and partially closed on the sixth side by the dash at the top and the depth of the door pillars at the sides; the sixth side can be further braced by a panel between the dash and the drive tunnel. Even at your first try you would probably succeed in designing such a simple, obvious structure immensely stiffly.

YOUR CHOICE

If you now weld such a box onto even a ladder frame, its stiffness will be immensely improved. Anything you can do to make your chassis more three-dimensional will make it stiffer. Disregarding the channel-frame, which under modern specials is useless for anything but show, round and square hollow section tubes can be made more stiff simply by choosing a bigger diameter and rectangular hollow sections by choosing a greater depth (making the bigger dimension larger still). Welding-in the metal plate that will serve as your firewall will help, as will stretching the frame from which you're going to hang your pedals right across the chassis – this also works with the steering and instrument hoop and the roll bar.

From consideration of the strength added to a ladder or other two-dimensional framework by the scuttle, it is but a short step to the "tub". This is a construction of sheet metal (or GRP or wood) together with, sometimes, hollow sections and angles, riveted, spot-welded or bonded together (especially in the case of ali, which until recently could not be easily welded, riveting and bonding was very important) to form a scuttle, passenger compartment – usually split by the drivetunnel, and rear bulkhead. Sometimes sheet metal "wheelbarrow" arms extend from the tub at the front and/or the back to attach the suspension and drivetrain, sometimes separate spaceframes are used at one or the other or both ends. There is no reason why the tub shouldn't have screen pillars and a roof but in most instances the special builder will find it stiff enough to be used as a convertible with perhaps a removable hardtop. The tub can be so made that it needs no outer skin – like the E-type Jaguar centre tub – or it can carry an unstressed skin. Great attention must be paid to the points where the spaceframes feed their loads into the sheet metal tub, and all attachments chosen so that loads are resolved into compres-

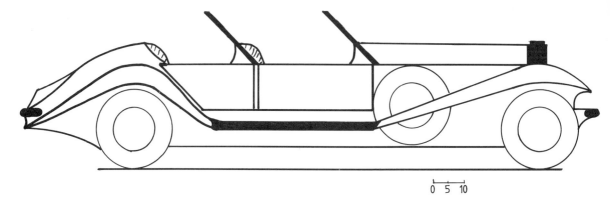

Figure 10.11. This unit construction nostalgicar needs only doors, bootlid and bonnet assembly to turn the chassis into a car. All dimensions are scaled to the largest suitable tyres.

sion and tension with none taken in bending, which normally means that attachments to flat sheet must be made so that the failure mode would be by shearing the attachment bolts or welds, unless the sheet metal is reinforced to spread the load.

As you will see, the somewhat rigid separation of chasses into classes for lucid discussion in practice becomes quite fluid: you choose from each type what best suits your purpose or skill and combine the various elements and advantages in search of your criteria of strength with lightness within the parameters of your ability or pocket. It may well be that your body design influences your freedom to choose a chassis type – or liberates it. The large vintage torpedo in Figure 10.11 has only three panels with compound curves (the two wings and the bootlid) which can all be made in GRP; the rest of it can be welded up from sheet and hollow section alloy (or steel, or made from GRP in a pretty cheap mould) and be used as the body shell without the addition of outer panels because it is acceptable in a vintage car that flat surfaces show. It is not, however, difficult to design even a modern car on which flat panels show and the curvature is produced by unstressed GRP panels of quite modest dimensions. Note that this car is completed by the addition of the doors and the bonnet assembly and that there is nothing more to it except the roof in inclement weather: the design of a not overly-complex chassis has eliminated the need for a separate body altogether. Unfortunately, honesty compels me to admit that this apparent simplicity took almost three years of my spare time and two expensive false starts in-the-metal to achieve.

Which type of chassis should *you* choose?

Figure 10.12. The author's Panther de Ville chassis as found. The scale of the 142 inch wheelbase can be judged by the car on the double carriageway in the background.

120

11 Chassis: Design

If you're building on a proprietary chassis, either to a design of your own or a kit car, you have no choice except in your alterations which should follow general engineering practice as described in the appropriate sections of this book.

If you're building a unique special from the ground up, your choice is limited by your skills, tools and resources. If you cannot weld, you must put welding out to professionals or use different materials or jointing methods. Almost any special can be built in a single garage but building in glassfibre becomes a bit crowded if you have to handle plug, mould and moulding all at the same time; and note that GRP will not cure below a certain temperature while you can weld or rivet until you freeze stiff. The depth of your pocket is also important, though initially expensive here the GRP may often save money elsewhere, such as a combined body-chassis unit. The desired style and

appearance of your car can also limit your choice of chassis type or material, or liberate it, as we have just seen.

Whatever your chassis, you must design and construct it to accepted engineering practice, aiming all the time for stiffness and strength. In this chapter we'll discuss a chassis designed and built in metal; construction in GRP is discussed in the next chapter together with the applications of wood, etc.

WHICH CHASSIS FOR YOU?

If you're designing a small, low-powered nostalgicar, I have no hesitation in recommending that you build it out of plywood, either in sheets bent to simple curves or in strips laminated to complex curves. You will find it a very cost-effective material and it has the great virtue that it is *different*. Also, from this end of the scale up to large and powerful cars, GRP has its own

Figure 11.1. The standardized special car is well known to rodders who can mailorder this complete 1928–31 Ford Model A chassis, plus body parts, from Total Performance.

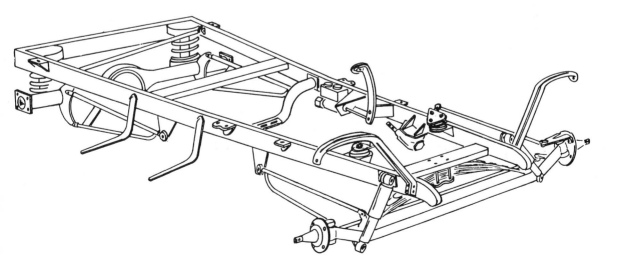

virtues – and disadvantages – for load-carrying body-chassis units; the most modern plastics laminates, such as carbon reinforcement and Kevlar, are not cost-effective for amateurs. If you must have a metal chassis and cannot weld, the cheapest way to obtain one – if you can make your car measurements fit what's available – is to buy a twin rail, twin tube, spaceframe, backbone or tub from one of hot rod, restoration, kit car and formula racing car suppliers. You'll find them advertising in the specialist magazines; they're mostly very friendly chaps who all know each other, so a phone call to those nearest to you can save you a lot in long-distance phone charges and time hunting around. Some kit car manufacturers will refuse to sell you only a chassis but they're usually GRP fabricators who buy their chassis in; find out who supplies the chassis to them and you can probably buy an improved model cheaper. At the same time, ask what else they do in the fabrication and moulding line: you may well need this later.

That leaves us with the hardcore special builder whose suspension design is so superior that it demands a chassis of extraordinary rigidity or whose car is so different it cannot comfortably fit any available chassis, the rare man who designs and builds a chassis himself, or the less rare one who has welding skills and wants to save the money. What should he choose, assuming he insists on a metal chassis?

The simplest, most time- and cost-efficient chassis is the twin tube, braced by a substantial cruciform or K-member(s) and with well-braced uprights for the suspension, given three-dimensionality by permanent attachment of as many vertical members as possible. Some of the kit car brigade (whose own professed spaceframes lack vital diagonals and credibility) will pour scorn on your design: let them. Three- to 4-inch diameter tubes of 10-g ($\frac{1}{8}$-inch) wall will be rolling around long after their not-much-lighter thin-walled confections have rusted away.

Forget multitubes; your properly planned and braced twin tube will in practice be as stiff and offer greater accessibility. Spaceframes also suffer from accessibility problems and are difficult to keep dimensionally stable without jigs. Unless you're an expert welder, forget really light spaceframes or buy yours from the recognized champs, Caterham Cars.

The bifurcate backbone chassis appears attractive to the special constructor and can be made mainly in two weights either of fairly heavy-wall channel ($\frac{1}{4}$-inch down to $\frac{1}{8}$-inch depending on the size of the car and the depth of the web) or thinwall rectangular or round hollow section. If you add brackets for everything else, it can get complicated; even at the least complicated, with the body attached to the backbone without the

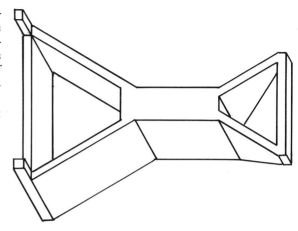

Figure 11.2. The bifurcate backbone chassis is not the solution to the special car builder's problems it first seems: it needs too many brackets and additions.

need for outriggers and with the body supporting literally *everything* other than the drivetrain and suspension, you will still need a complete and reasonably substantial body. A backbone is not a short-cut for the one-off special builder constructing his own chassis.

Far more practical than the backbone for the special builder is the tub built of sheet metal, perhaps with reinforcement by double plating, angle or tubular members where necessary. This is easier to build than at first appears and any jig, if required at all, can be made of scrap wood. Essentially, you can cut flat sheet metal to shape, bend flanges onto the ends, then rivet, glue or weld the whole lot together. Your choice of metal is normally mild steel, an aluminium alloy, up to the progressively lighter and/or stronger space-age metals, all increasingly expensive. In practice, the easy way to proceed is to attach square or rectangular section hollow section door uprights to square or rectangular side sills, then to attach these, together with the square or rectangular hollow section drive tunnel to the large flat sheet that is the floorpan (perhaps the floorpan is braced transversely with some small top hat sections). At the back and the front the side sills may be joined to the drive tunnel by four short pieces of rectangular hollow section but more often the bulkhead (stiffened with top hat sections if necessary) simply runs down to the floor and is also attached to the drive tunnel and side sill. The scuttle sheets, made up into a sub-assembly, are joined to the sills/drive tunnel/floor assembly, and attached also to the door hinge uprights. A similar subassembly, consisting of the rear passenger compartment bulkhead and two pieces coming around to meet the door closure face uprights is usually bent from a single sheet and is attached to the floor/sill/drive tunnel/door closure face uprights. That is the tub. Subframes attached to the front and the rear will hold the engine and suspension. Often the rear is built so that the suspension there can attach directly to the tub, requiring a subframe only at the front. Body panels, if required, are attached to the tub or the subframes. Tub panels may be shaped by panel-rolling and beating before assembly but this is costly; on production cars they are shaped by huge hydraulic presses. If you decide to build a mild steel tub, I suggest you pop rivet it together (or self-tapping screws or nuts and bolts will do) and then have it spot-welded by specialist welders; don't go any lighter than 16g for the sheet metal and 12g or even 10g is a better weight for the sills and drive tunnel – a little weight can be saved by bending these up out of sheet into top hat sections rather than using hollow sections. Alloys, depending on specification, will have to be two to four times as thick; whether the final construction is lighter depends not only on the alloy but on construction method and the choice you make between lightness and corrosion resistance on the one hand and cost on the other. Alloys are more difficult to weld, though specialist welders with TIG or MIG plant can weld even thin ali quite satisfactorily these days; I suggest you bond and rivet your alloy tub, the grand prix designers did until they switched to Kevlar. If you intend having an alloy tub welded, do not use glue, as that may interfere with a proper bond in the welding.

A tub with integral sheet metal structures front and rear to attach the suspension and drivetrain is a unit construction and quite a bit more difficult to make in that it is so much larger and more intricate, with therefore the greater opportunity for distortion. Designing and building the sort of unit construction that the mass manufacturers toss out is well-nigh impossible for the special builder, even if he should want such a thing. But, with a little ingenuity in design, and a little wit in contriving suitable jigs, a much superior compromise can be achieved.

It is not impossible to build a compound curved monocoque – in our definition from the previous chapter – in metal, but I cannot advise anyone to attempt it, except perhaps for the most miniature of city cars (for which there are more elegant solutions).

A MINIMUM MEGALOMANIAC MOTOR

Figure 10.11 (page 120) shows a twinscreen convertible torpedo in the style of the 1920s and early 1930s. Besides the appearance of the car, functional parameters included the ability to carry four large adults with the same legroom as a Mercedes SEL and with touring luggage in an overall length of not more than 15'6" (two inches shorter than my Volvo station wagon, between a foot and two feet shorter than normal large European cars and therefore by American standards very compact indeed) at a speed in excess of 100mph, and not to weigh more than 30cwt (3360lb) with all fuel, oil and water (DIN kerbweight); i.e. the weight of a big Mercedes and 800lb less than a Jaguar XJ6. A preliminary study indicated that 100mph would with a worst-case Cd of 0.8 require 156bph – which happens to be the output of one of my favourite engines, the Rover SDI 3.5 V8 – *if overall height could be held down to 54 inches*, the overall width being fixed by the intention of using unmodified XJ6 suspension. This meant, in turn, that cruciform-braced twin tubes were out, though substantial K-frames could be used; whatever construction materials or methods were used, the feet of passengers and drivers could not be separated from the ground clearance by more than the thickness of the floor and the carpet.

It should not be thought that these design parameters were instantly clear. They developed over a number of years from a variety of diverse designs around the central theme and from a number of cars built, owned or driven that approximated the ideal but were in various ways compromised. Note that even this design is compromised in that the engine bay at 43 inches from the bulkhead to the grille shell is bigger than need be; though the Jaguar straight-sixes will fit and even the exemplary V-12 can be massaged in, further horses will just run into an aerodynamic brick wall requiring aids that will spoil the lines. In any event, the SDI has an in-house 190bhp sibling and can easily and cheaply be made to give 200 or 220bhp, the maximum the design could probably use sensibly. The extra space is purely for the sake of appearances, though it has the added benefit that the engine will run cooler.

The final design parameter to consolidate the shape of the chassis was that it should need as few panels as possible to complete the car. The obvious corollary is of course that any panels that needn't open (doors, engine and luggage lids and roof) or be removable for repairs (the wings – here in a different material anyway), should be firmly and irrevocably fixed into the chassis.

The alert reader will note that I have just defined a unit construction or monocoque, which one will depend on the materials used and the apparent peripheral distinctions between the various units. Unit constructions in very thin sheet metal with multiple torsion boxes welded together as practised by the mass manufacturers are not for us.

But a little wit and ingenuity goes a long way. The

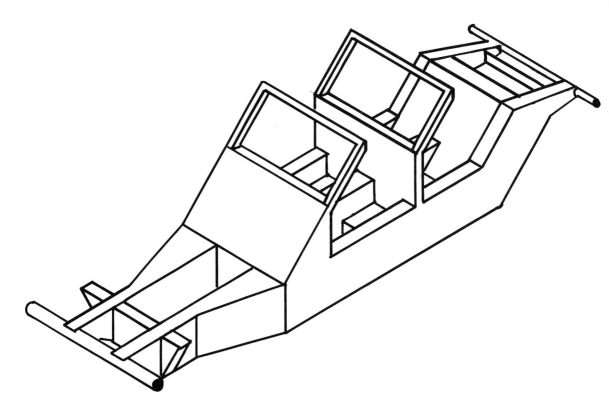

Figure 11.3. This is the body-frame unit-construction of the car in Fig. 10.11 (page 120). Note that the floor, not shown, is an integral part of the structure, which is completed merely by fitting the closure panels; doors, boot and bonnet.

chassis I finally designed answers fully to all the design parameters set for it and compromises with a possibly superior unit construction from a mass manufacturer in two or maybe three areas. The entry sills are higher, but not as much as at first appears, a matter of only 2–3 inches higher than on a Volvo for instance, but note that the boot loading sill is lower than on many exemplary hatchbacks. Because of the fat drive tunnel and the high sills and low seating position, seating is limited to four passengers including the driver, each cocooned in his own tub 17 inches wide (most people are narrower than that). There may be a weight penalty over a conventional robot-welded mass-market unit construction in that the special builder will have to build in extra material to prevent distortion in manufacture but this can be overcome to a large extent by detail design or in total – or even turned to advantage for a lighter *and* stiffer structure – by choosing different materials and processes that are cost-effective for the one-off constructor. In particular, aluminium (welded or bonded and riveted) and GRP

should be considered; detail design for each will differ but the main principle will not.

Though I wanted to end up with a full-length, three-dimensional unit-construction tub, I started by laying out a twin tube ladder frame around the spaces occupied by people's feet and the various mechanical bits. This, I felt strongly, was an extension of my knowledge and experience, rather than an attempt to break new ground; we shall return to the sense of this below when we attempt to calculate whether the complete chassis will actually do the job.* The two side tubes were made as deep as possible within the confines of the design and commercially available hollow sections. Note that, from the start, it was intended to use extrusions wherever possible rather than bending up odd shapes.

Next, a substantial drive tunnel was introduced, the

*I could of course have chosen to see it as a fully panelled spaceframe but the calculations would be more involved.

same depth as the side sill but twice the width and the "steps", one underneath each row of seats, of the ladder, then made as wide as possible (within the limits of standard sections and material buying economy) by making them of the same section as the drive tunnel, but turned over sideways because the seats must be mounted on them. Front and rear bulkheads close the ends of the passenger compartment, the front bulkhead being triangulated by the footplate; a central bulkhead between the front and rear seats divides the passenger compartment into two longitudinally. The rear bulkhead is joined to the rear suspension/fuel tank crossmember (this one is an odd shape to allow for the slope of the rear seat backrests). The front suspension will be hung on the front crossmember, of the same section as the side sills. Though the side tubes sweep inwards from the front door to the front suspension mountings, so offering a measure of triangulation, the side rails are further braced back to the firewall by substantial triangular constructions which would lead some of the suspension loads directly to the drive tunnel and through that back to where it is attached to the rear suspension crossmember. Front and rear bumpers are an integral, permanent part of the chassis, being mounted (welded in metal constructions) across the side tubes front and rear; progressive distortion is given by using channel section instead of closed rectangular hollow section in front of the front suspension crossmember and behind the rear suspension crossmember. The centre and rear of the box was then closed by the floor running from the firewall to the rear bulkhead and by the luggage space bottom running from the rear suspension crossmember to a return 2 inches short of the rear bumper; in both cases across the full width of the car's body.

Thus far the tub, which is of course already very satisfactorily three-dimensional. To make it more so and to extend those vital bulkheads as far up as possible, the door pillars complete with windscreen frames are then added as an integral feature; there are two of these pillars to a side, the third, rear door shutface, being served by the upsweep of the chassis/body side. They are joined across the car by the bulkheads and for additional rigidity the two windscreen glasses are bonded to the frames; the front one certainly, and the rear one unless it must be made to open or be removable. It is intended that the grille should be rigidly attached to the front suspension crossmember and braced to the bulkhead with removable tubes. The scuttle structure is completed by fixing in the dash permanently.

In my design the roof is removable but that too could of course be rigidly fixed to the rear suspension crossmember, the centre door pillar and the front screen, to make a sedan; this would probably double the torsional rigidity of the design.

Though it is possible that a removable roof, if its fittings are correctly designed and made with tolerable precision, would contribute to the stiffness, I prefer to ignore it altogether for the simple reason that in multi-panel constructions the play in catches can become quite considerable. It is in any event not conservative to pluck a figure from the air and hope for the best. The side frames to support the running boards (not shown) may or may not add to torsional or bending resistance; conservatively, they must be treated as so much dead weight. The doors, if properly braced internally between hinges and latches, are quite likely to carry some load but, again, how much will be tedious if not impossible to calculate; ignore them; the bootlid and bonnet assembly are dead weight and I do not wish to stress the wings (though, if the whole were designed in GRP, I would certainly bond the wings onto the main structure because they can be made to work hard for their living).

So, made in mild steel or an alloy, this would be a unit construction; made in GRP, with the necessary detail changes to the design, it would be as near to a monocoque as mortal man will get. Alloy would certainly be choice for ease of manufacture and cost-effective corrosion resistance without arousing the anxieties of the anti-plastic brigade; other designers will have their own reasons for choosing mild steel or GRP. But will an alloy do the job? The stresses in structures of this kind are notoriously difficult to ascertain or calculate; the professionals do it by rules of thumb gained empirically (by experiment) and by making up samples of proposed constructions to be tested, the results fed into computers for spot checks on various points of the skin of a unit construction. The special designer cannot and does not want to proceed so tediously. The solution is to calculate by analogy.

In this particular example, I reckoned that the 4300 lb, 142-inch wheelbase Panther de Ville was just the thing with which to compare my 3400 lb postulated maximum kerb weight, 133-inch wheelbase car. My Panther chassis was made from $6 \times 3 \times \frac{1}{4}$-inch mild steel side rails with substantial "union jack" (a cruciform with an additional transverse crossmember through the centre) bracing plus substantial further transverse bracing all in $3 \times 1\frac{1}{2} \times \frac{1}{4}$ inches, plus additional frames in lesser material to attach the propshaft middle bracket, the exhaust, the air-conditioning piping, etc., but even the etceteras added to the stiffness. The frame was cranked front and rear to clear the suspensions (by XJ6 Jaguar links complete in their subframes) but the only other three-dimensional effect was the pedal mounting frame. My Panther frame weighed very nearly 600 pounds. Panther built their body on top by welding on pressed mild steel production car side frames (from an Austin Maxi!) plus a pipework frame of 1 inch round and square tube, to which the ali panels were then attached. Heavy Jaguar engines and luxurious trim and appointments made up the rest of the weight – no more than a standard Jaguar saloon's weight though. Since the body was effectively loadbearing, the whole made a very stiff structure, as required by suspension of Jaguar's sophistication. However, even the bare chassis was more than stiff enough, as one would expect from its depth, design and weight of material. Though I have no proof one way or the other, the Panther chassis fully fitted with mechanicals and drivable felt to be stiffer than a similarly driving Mk VI Bentley chassis which weighed 500 lb more in this condition – and nobody's ever complained about the stiffness of this particular Bentley chassis!

To make the calculation of the comparison easier, I try always to work in unitless figures and convert the results to ratios, with the known quantity as unity. In applying the formulae from page 105 for shear stress and angle of twist per unit of length, I have simply ignored the differences in weight and wheelbase length of the two cars, so that the comparison has an inbuilt safety margin. Thus, setting the torque M_t at 20,000 (this is merely a convenient number to facilitate calculation – we could choose unity because the purpose is *comparison*) for both cars, the only variables are the cross-sectional size and wall thickness of the sections (A, h, and S in the formula) and the modulus in shear which will differ between materials (if you're merely comparing sizes in the same material, G can be unity). However, to lessen the possibility of calculation error, I reduce G to a ratio: in this case we will be comparing mild steel to a typical light alloy and the ratio is steel 1 to alloy 0.33.

A section through the Panther de Ville chassis at mid-car would show the two rails $6 \times 3 \times \frac{1}{4}$ inches plus the bracing. Taking somewhat of a liberty, we could equate it with a rectangular section $46 \times 6 \times \frac{1}{4}$ inches – the outside edges of the two side rails are just on 46 inches apart. A section through the Megamotor chassis at midpoint, taking not quite so large a liberty and forgetting for the moment about the substantial scuttle and bulkhead structures above the 12-inch depth of the main side rails, would show two 12×3-inch side rails, a 12×6-inch drive tunnel, plus the bracing plus the floor; the wall thickness of these members would depend on the material and is what we want to calculate, in this instance for an overall section $46 \times 12 \times ?$ inches.

Tables 11.1 (top) and **11.2** (bottom): **Engineering by analogy with no more than simple math.** These two tables enable us to *compare* an aluminium alloy with mild steel as described in the text. Forget actual figures and the units of measurement: all you're interested in is the *comparison* of aluminium with mild steel and all you have to know, beyond that something works in mild steel, are the formulae on page 105 and the fact that ali can take only 33% the stress that mild steel can handle.

Table 11.1

Material and dimension	Maximum stress	Angle of twist
Mild steel		
$46 \times 6 \times \frac{1}{8}$ in	290	54.6
$46 \times 6 \times \frac{1}{4}$ in	145	27.3
$46 \times 12 \times 0.064$ (16 g)	283	29.2
Aluminium alloy		
$46 \times 12 \times 0.192$ (6 g)	94.4	29.7
$46 \times 12 \times 0.375$	48.3	15.2

Table 11.2

Material and dimension	Maximum stress	Angle of twist
Mild steel		
$6 \times 3 \times \frac{1}{8}$ in	4444	2222
$6 \times 3 \times \frac{1}{4}$ in	2222	1111
Aluminium alloy		
$12 \times 3 \times 0.192$	1447	1808
$12 \times 3 \times 0.375$	740	926
$12 \times 6 \times 0.192$	723	543

Tables 11.1 and 11.2 show my results. (For reference in technical information you may get from materials suppliers, 10^{-4} at the top of a table means you must move all the decimal four places to the left before the answer makes sense in amateur's English.) It can easily be seen that if the stress in a chassis with a section $46 \times 6 \times \frac{1}{4}$ in mild steel is set at 1, the stress in a chassis with a section 46×12-inch alloy should be no more than $\frac{1}{3}$ and that this can be achieved with a wall thickness of $\frac{3}{8}$ inch. As Table 11.3 now shows, building the body chassis unit mainly in $\frac{3}{8}$-inch alloy with a few unstressed parts in $\frac{1}{8}$-in alloy will – with the chosen mechanicals but only very light trim – result in a car weighing 3400 lb. It will, however, be far stiffer than the less three-dimensional Panther design, twisting just about half as much for the same torsional input. At nearly 1700 lb for the body-in-white, it is no

Table 11.3: Material thickness and kerb weight. By halving the thickness of the light alloy used in the chassis, 822 lb – nearly one-quarter – has been cut from the projected all-up weight of the car. Some of it is likely to be put back on as deeper padding or better weather equipment or lusher entertainment or convenience fittings but some weight will stay shed, leading to better fuel economy and acceleration.

	lb	*lb*	*lb*
Body/chassis unit, $\frac{3}{8}$ and $\frac{1}{8}$ ali		1645	
Body/chassis unit, $\frac{3}{16}$ ali			823
	lb		
Welding deposit	17		
Fasteners, etc.	25		
Paint	10		
Glass	52		
GRP wings and supports	100		
Seats and light trim including weather gear	234	438	438
FULLY TRIMMED BODY READY FOR MECHANICALS		2083	1261
MECHANICALS, ELECTRICS, OIL, PETROL AND WATER		1317	1317
TOTAL KERB WEIGHT		3400	2578

lightweight, but it does seem, intuitively, considering the additional stiffness that the scuttle, rear suspension crossmembers and (to a lesser extent) the rigidly attached and braced grill shell will lend the whole, that some – perhaps considerable – relaxation may be called for. The Jago Model B chassis is made from rectangular side rails roughly $5 \times 2\frac{1}{2} \times \frac{1}{8}$ inches – very approximately the dimensions of channel rails from the "gennie" article and seems decently stiff on a 106-inch wheelbase at a normal all-up weight of about a ton and a quarter. I also happen to know that the de Ville wall thickness was chosen not so much for stiffness as for corrosion resistance: their last chasses were not even zinc-sprayed. Thus, if a $46 \times 6 \times \frac{1}{8}$-inch section in steel will suffice, in ali the wall thickness can also be halved to 0.1875 (though we would choose the next commercially available dimension which is 6-gauge or 0.192-inch or nominally $\frac{3}{16}$-inch) without endangering life and limb. This chassis will have moderately less torsional resistance than the steel one with $\frac{1}{4}$-inch thick walls, but that disadvantage will be offset by the greater capacity of the various structures rising above the minimum 12-inch depth of the alloy chassis and also by its shorter wheelbase.

One other check on the overall section can be done. The lightest gauge mild steel in which the most experienced special car builder might attempt – with expensive jigs – to build a design such as this is probably 16 g (nominally $\frac{1}{16}$-inch, in fact 0.064-inch); 16 g is also probably the *heaviest* gauge a mass marketer would use should he ever be tempted to build so

unsophisticated (in cost-accountant's terms) a design, with perhaps a few 10- or 12-g brackets where the rest of us would also have to use small areas of double plating or heavier material. Such a mild steel construction would of course have to be extensively rust-proofed but, by analogy with a section through a mass market car that you can see at any scrapyard, would be a competent and sturdily stiff car. It is exactly comparable to the 6-g alloy structure.

If you go any thinner/smaller, your calculations will have to proceed to greater levels of precision and I suggest you get the end result checked by a professional engineer. Note in particular that we've been misapplying Timoshenko's formulation for thin wall tubular members which presupposes an absence of re-entrant corners, of which any chassis has plenty. Above it doesn't matter largely because we have been using the formulae mainly as a handle on an analogy with a car that's known to work, and the safety margins have been generous. The deeper you cut into the margins, so your precision and skill with the math, and your knowledge of quite abstruse engineering (or your pocket for fees if you lack friends with the required academic background) will need to increase quite disproportionately. My advice is always not to attempt to beat Colin Chapman at his own game: you can't win and there are heavy penalties if you lose.

In any event, the car we have just described can be built to weigh, as a body-in-white, a very modest 850 lb, which translates into an all-up wet kerb weight of about a ton and a quarter – almost down in the hatchback weight class, not bad for a large four seater convertible capable of nearly 120mph. Searching for the minimum weight of a structure in aluminium is also complicated by – this is very important – aluminium's low fatigue strength especially in full load reversal; the fact that some of the more attractive aluminium specifications are severely weakened by welding (H30-TF for instance) while there were doubts about stress corrosion in one of the more attractive specifications (H17-TF) which is very little affected by welding; and by the greater deflection of aluminium in comparison with steel. The ideal will be sections of greater thickness milled in pleasing or functional patterns so that the final mass is the same but the effective thickness greater; this is done for aircraft and the principle illustrated in Figure 9.2 (page 104) but the cost is offputting.

EQUAL LOAD PATHS

A mistake the novice often makes that then causes a failure baffling the best minds – and that, alarmingly, professional designers are also prone to – is to provide load paths along two routes, neither of which can bear the full load but which are so unequally loaded that one, normally the shorter, is bound to fail before the other. The result, especially where the structure has been refined to pare the last ounce from it, can be disastrous or even fatal. Fortunately, most special builders watch their safety margins carefully.

In considering the load paths in the chassis above, it is convenient to split it into two component parts: a twin tube ladder and a backbone chassis. Both of these will lead suspension loads from the front wheels to the rear suspension; we are assuming that if they will not twist they will also not bend and we're neglecting entirely the effects of the bulkheads in spreading and, we hope, equalizing the load, nor are we considering the equally beneficial effect of the rigidly and permanently fixed floors or, in case the roof is fixed, the roof. All of this can be calculated but it is tedious and probably unnecessary. If the main paths are multiple and adeqate, the details become less critical; on a sheet metal backbone, have your calculations checked by someone else.

The easiest way is to proceed by analogy, though here the values inserted in the formulae will provide precise answers and must be so used when you're approaching the limit of a particular material's capability, or if you can find no suitable analogy (which would surprise me immensely). Setting the torque, M_t, equal to a convenient 20,000 (or unity, since the purpose is comparison) for all calculations, and the modulus of rigidity, G, at unity for mild steel and 0.33 for my representative alloy, we can see from Table 11.2

that the $12 \times 3 \times 0.192$-inch alloy side tube is stressed only a third as highly as the $6 \times 3 \times \frac{1}{8}$-inch mild steel member we have previously declared quite adequate, and will twist less per unit of length under similar torque.

There will of course be two of these side rails, so we must choose our drive tunnel wall thickness so that it is stressed only half as much as each side tube and therefore able to bear the load of both side tubes. Fortunately for materials-buying economy, this turns out to be 0.192 as well on the 12×6 section we are committed to.

IMPORTANT DETAILS

Whether these sometimes rough and ready shortcuts serve the special builder well depends on the attention he pays to the detail design of each little corner of the chassis – on the construction integrity as much as the aptness and wit of the design of the structure. This construction integrity is not something that can be left to the fabricators to work out, or even for you to work out in the metal: it must be done at the drafting stage. Even if you're putting welding out to people who routinely work on special cars who will correct any solecisms between your drawings and the metal, doing the job right earns respect and avoids misunderstandings.

The main considerations here are that construction details: should not by their design raise avoidable stresses; should be designed to reduce and spread stress wherever possible, to lessen the possibilities of corrosion and not to add unnecessarily to the weight of the whole; must take consideration of material and labour costs. Since construction details by even the most fanatically functional designers of special cars will often be inspected by other special car designers – and must in the majority of cases add to the aesthetic appeal of the car – neat and tidy design is the very minimum requirement. Remember, if it looks right, it very probably is right.

Jigs cost money and, if you're building a strictly one-off car and intend destroying the jigs to protect your exclusivity, money that cannot be recovered elsewhere. The ideal is to use no jigs at all. Next best is to rig up your vice, G-clamps, rented sash-clamps, etc. as a temporary jig. Jigs for spaceframes can be made by welding pieces of angle iron to a flat sheet; the sheet may be usable later: this is a consumable jig. Another unit or subassembly of the car may be used as a jig: Lil' John built his own '32 rails by using the upside down body tub as a combined jig and worktable. A number of small, simple jigs to make subassemblies may be cheaper than one very large one.

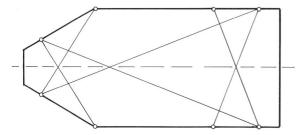

Figure 11.4. Checking suspension and chassis squareness is best done by raising the car above a level floor and using a leadline to drop points to the floor.

Whichever route you choose, any saving made on jigs will be meaningless if the car is not square. This is best determined by raising it off a level floor with the aid of a spirit level to make sure it is not twisted or canted in any direction and then dropping plumb lines from four fixed points at the front of the car, four fixed points at the rear of the car, plus the centre of the car front and rear. The best points are the suspension mountings. If lines between complimentary mountings, connected diagonally across the frame (Figure 11.4), do not meet on the centreline, the frame is out of square. A twisted frame is one on which you cannot get both the front and rear suspension mountings perfectly horizontal at the same time. On the vintage channel rails and the most sophisticated modern racing suspensions, working with scales at the four corners also gives good results that are put to the same purpose, but, if your chassis is square, not twisted, and properly designed to be reasonably stiff, it won't wave around like vintage rails. For normal road use corner jacking is rather irrelevant unless you want to carry ballast in the passenger seat of your car every time you don't have a passenger (this is different from swing axle effect jacking and refers to having different weights on the two wheels at the same end of the car – important for all-out racer handling).

Intelligent detail design adds to the chances of building an untwisted, square chassis without the use of too many jigs. Figure 11.5 shows the correct way to join two rectangular or square sections frame members at a corner: this joint is stronger than merely mitring the two tubes together at 45° and offers the same advantage of capping both tubes.

All tubes should be capped wherever possible so that the chassis forms an airtight structure and cannot corrode from within. Attachments can be made by brackets or mounting strips welded to the main members, or by welding-in tubes for through-bolting – this last is in any event essential to prevent pinching the chassis hollow section and so providing a high-stress point to start fractures.

All edges should be chamfered before welding to give a greater area of weld for greater strength. Beads hammered flat while the weld is hot are stronger than those merely ground down. At critical joints, files should be used for dressing the weld rather than the ubiquitous angle grinder or, better still, the joint should be redesigned so that the weld can be left undressed and out of sight. Construction should proceed by mirror-fashion – welding first one side, then the other – tack welds later filled in; electrodes lighter than the material being welded allows a proper build-up of the weld. Butt welds in thin metal should be avoided as an invitation to distortion.

Wherever possible, attachment brackets should be made in the same weight and shape of material as the main frame: this looks tidy and uses up offcuts, and normally automatically provides a three-dimensional bracket without further welding. Wherever possible, each bracket should be made to do more than one job. Brackets should be closed on as many sides as possible without restricting access. Brackets should preferably not be mounted where their load is taken into the

Figure 11.5. The right way and the wrong way of joining chassis members with an automatic cap. There's even more weld area for a stronger bond with bevelled edges.

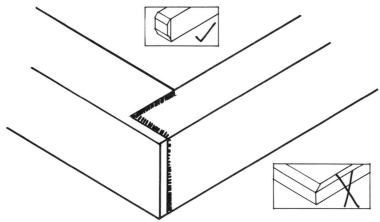

member in bending: a member taking the load in compression or tension can be made much lighter. Brackets should always be mounted so that the load is taken into the reacting member with the least possible offset: the ideal is to feed loads at 180° to the reaction, i.e. in a straight line. Two-dimensional attachment brackets made by welding on a flat plate are not very efficient and usually need to be made with material far heavier than the rest of the chassis because their stiffness is provided only by their thickness; avoid flat-plate brackets. An exception to the rule that what looks good is normally good is the practice of some hotrodders to build damper mounts up from the frame and then curl them round to meet the damper top – this is a monstrous offset and should lose points for incompetent engineering.

Attachment points and joints can be strengthened by flitches (or double plating) but this must be done with care if the reinforcements are not themselves to become stress raisers and stress points. Suitable flitch plate designs are shown in Figures 11.6 and 11.7. If the reinforcing plate is thicker than $\frac{1}{16}$ inch, I bevel the edges at 45° as an additional precaution.

Many small fastenings are preferable to a few large ones. The shear resistance of a bolt is directly proportional to its cross-sectional diameter. Bolts are made in a variety of materials and qualities: steel in its various forms is very cost effective but corrodes; cadmium plating or galvanizing offers good protection, as does chromium plating; stainless steel fastenings cost more but last better. Because of electrolysis, certain materials must not be put in contact with other materials in the presence of moisture and this sometimes makes stainless steel perfectly cost effective. A good example is in bolting together aluminium parts, where the steel would have to be cadmium plated and further separated from the ali by zinc chromate jointing compound or tape. Aluminium nuts and bolts are not suitable for critical loadbearing applications in automobile work. It is far better in suspension and other critical parts to replace any fastenings with replacement original parts, chromed if you want them bright; otherwise you must seek out aircraft-spec fastenings of a reliable quality, though this is time-consuming and expensive and you must know the exact specification.

Normal riveting practice prescribes the use of rivets one to three times the diameter of the thinner of the two materials being joined, pitched at three to six times their diameter, with the centre of the rivet hole no nearer than twice its diameter from the edge of the sheet. Parts to be riveted must be carefully clamped and precisely drilled because misaligned parts will reduce the effective area of the rivet by twice the area

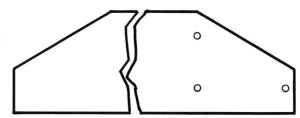

Figure 11.6. Flitch plates, on channel chassis, should be attached only to the web of the chassis, the sides should be mitred at 30° and all corners radiused and edges bevelled.

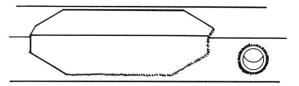

Figure 11.7. Double plating a tube chassis helps to spread the load: mitre and radius and bevel doubler plates just like flitch plates. Welding in pipes for through connections protects against rust and adds strength.

of misalignment. Aluminium rivets must not be used to join mild steel sheets because the electrolytic corrosion will be accelerated when the amount of ali is small in relation to the other metal. Nor must copper-bearing aluminium alloy rivets be used even on ali sheets due to the lower resistance to corrosion.

Of course not only fastenings are subject to galvanic corrosion, whole units and assemblies are too. The cure is to keep ali away completely from copper. Small parts can be cadmium plated. Zinc chromate paint or tape, bituminous paint, bitumastic compound, non-absorbent washers and gaskets of neoprene or bushes of Tufnol will all help. Large steel parts like a chassis can be sprayed with pure aluminium (which is anyway an excellent alternative to the more usual hot-zinc spray which you have to leave for several weeks to "age" before some paints will take on it).

All parts, in whichever material, must be designed to conduct water off and out of the car. There must be no crevices to retain corrosion promoting moisture. To this end, all adjoining parts should be close-fitting and securely bonded as well as riveted or jointed with one or the other of the compounds available.

If you've just bought a welder, I can recommend *Teach Yourself Welding* by C. G. Bainbridge (Hodder, 4th edn, 1980). *Fundamentals of Vehicle Bodywork* by Jim Fairbrother (Hutchinson, 1981) offers a lot of information about building commercial vehicles useful to the special car builder.

12 The Body

The bodies described in this chapter can be either loadbearing body-chassis constructions or separate bodies for attachment to separately constructed chassis either permanently or temporarily. The principles of construction would be the same, though the material weights used and the bracing might well be lighter if a separate chassis is to carry the load. Suitable materials for bodies are metals, wood, and plastics. We have seen in the previous chapter that building a unit construction of metal is not too difficult if no compound curves are required and if we are willing to pay extra for a low density material like aluminium.

METAL BODIES

It may be possible for the special builder to make metal bodies with compound curves, though the process will be either tedious or expensive. If you can make a simple wooden buck such as in Figure 12.1, there are coach builders who will roll a sheet of alloy or mild steel between large rollers to the compound shape you require. This is likely to be expensive: the larger the panel and the more complex the curves, the more expensive, as you will be paying two highly skilled artisans for very fine handwork. Then all your panels will have to be fitted up and attached to a framework or to each other, which is also a specialized and expensive task, though not as specialized as rolling the panels.

The other way is time-consuming but very rewarding for those willing to take the trouble. This is to design a car with compound curves to your taste – and then to divide the car up into a multitude of small panels each with only single curvature or very modest compound curvature. (Think of a soccer ball: a perfect sphere made up of many almost flat squares.) Build a wooden framework to which all these pieces are screwed, weld the pieces together, remove the wood, and you have a compound-curved shell which you may now brace internally. If you intend keeping the internal framework, bent small diameter tubing of the same material as the skin will do admirably, with the skin welded directly to it.

A worthwhile trick to remember here if you want an absolutely smooth skin is that you *can* rivet even thin sheets of mild steel or aluminium without the heads showing. You cannot countersink the thin sheet but, if you countersink the heavier material underneath, the thin sheet will pull into the depression, the rivet head will nestle in the depression, and the result can then be filled and smoothed off.

If you don't mind that your construction method shows – as on Jaguar's Pop Rivet Special – or that all those rivet heads and slight discontinuities of the skin will cause aerodynamic turbulence, you can just overlap your small sheets and rivet them together along the edges, or butt them up to each other and rivet them into a strip about $1\frac{1}{2}$ inches wide on the inside. In either case you will still have to build some kind of a buck or model to fit all your pieces on to see that the whole forms a proper shape.

The general principles of making full-size models is discussed below.

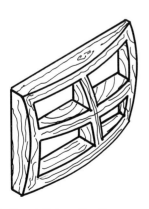

Figure 12.1. Specialists will roll you complex-curved metal panels if you supply a buck that gives the shape. Make the buck in hardwood or laminate and it can be the panel frame.

Figure 12.2. The problem with building modern-shaped cars in any material but GRP is that even apparently flat panels are subtly curved – and in both directions.

The "patchwork" method requires not only unusual patience but great skill and precision as well, especially if you want to use a body constructed in this manner to accept some or all of the suspension loads, in which case it is essential to ensure that all the little panels fit accurately, are not bent into shape with the welder or riveter, and are not pre-stressed because otherwise the loadpaths may not be quite what you had in mind and unpredictable failures could occur. Unless you're very experienced, I cannot recommend this method.

There is one other method of achieving a curved shape in metal that is suitable for a specific type of special car: this is for leathercloth covered Weymann-replica nostalgicars (or for owners of the real thing wanting deeper curves or no more hassle with the woodwork), or for those who want their special to have the same rough appearance as some of the pre-war mud-pluggers. Mild steel may be used or alloy in the soft condition or up to half-hard (H2 or H4). Dig a hole in the ground after some thought of the required shape; place the sheet of metal over the hole and jump on it until it is approximately the right shape but be

careful not to go too far. Further shaping can be done over a sandbag or a wooden block and, when a reasonably smooth shape has been achieved, the panel is filled with lead or body-plastic, sanded and fitted, and covered with outdoors-type expanded vinyl or leathercloth. This is rougher work than most special builders will want to know about, I think. The trials special is usually left unfilled and unpainted to save weight, all the final hammer dents showing: produced in the authentic manner!

WOOD

Except for the early Marcos, the Costin Amigo, and the Hustler, no wooden cars come to mind and, to be objective, the Marcos acquired a metal "spaceframe" in 1969, the Amigo never went into serious production, and the Hustler soon acquired a number of metal-framed clones because of consumer resistance. It is the same prejudice that applies to all-plastic cars. The Hustler is currently offered as a set of plans and aluminium window frames by William Towns and has

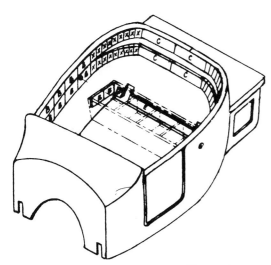

Figure 12.3. Wooden motor cars suffer customer-resistance, so the main use of wood in cars is as GRP reinforcement and decorative trims to the dash and door caprails.

a small but dedicated following; I do not know of a single other wooden car, kit or one-off special, available or under construction, a baffling circumstance because wood is an excellent material for the special car builder not merely as trim but to bear loads. Wood does not rust. Wood, properly treated, will not rot in any way. Wood does not fatigue like metals. Designs made especially for the application of wood can be functionally as strong as those in metal or reinforced plastics. Wood is a low-density, lightweight material. Wood can be a cheap material – cheap grades of wood can be laminated together to make very cost effective loadbearing members. Wood is very easy to work with for even the totally unskilled with no more than hand tools. Wood is pleasing to the touch and the eye not only in the variety of aesthetic satisfactions it offers in its natural state but for the additional variety of finishes that may be applied to it. Virtually any shape that can be made in metal or GRP can be made in wood. Above all, for the special car builder, wood guarantees his car's uniqueness among the plethora of GRP specials; the wooden Hustler is a *very* exclusive kit car if you decide not to design your own from the ground up.

Wood does have disadvantages. It is dimensionally sensitive to moisture and, to a lesser extent, to temperature. It is stronger with the grain than across it (but metals in the forms special car builders use are arranged to be stronger in a desired direction). Not all woods weather well: these must be protected by paint or varnish. Corrosion of metal parts in contact with wood can be a problem, e.g. steel screws should not be used in oak. Wood is not of uniform strength in that knots and other discontinuities weaken it but this is not important if the special builder uses mainly laminations. The main restraint to building in wood is that there is a lack of general experience and information. Compare the novice seeking advice from someone with experience of working ali: he can ask at the local hot rod club, probably the 750 club, the club dedicated to his own mechanicals (the BDC put me in touch with no fewer than three members who had built aluminium-bodied Bentley specials and an equal number of GRP special builders – *they* could have put me in touch with a man who had built a wooden body for a 3-litre but we're here talking about stressed skin or loadbearing wooden construction), local truck body builders, trailer makers, panel beaters.

Douglas fir has approximately one-tenth the elasticity (Young's Modulus, E) of medium strength aluminium alloy, the limit of proportionality is approximately one-fifth that of the alloy (compression *with* grain), while the wood's ultimate tensile stress capacity approaches one-fifth that of the alloy – but the wood is only one-fifth the density of the alloy: what you lose on the roundabouts you may gain on the swings.

Strength properties of timber and joint fasteners vary according to the direction of the stress: parallel or perpendicular to the grain, in the Hankinson relationship which is expressed as

$$N = \frac{PQ}{P\sin^2 A + Q\cos^2 A}$$

where N is the stress at angle A to the grain

A is the angle between the direction of the load and the grain

P is the stress parallel to the grain

Q is the stress perpendicular to the grain

and which holds good for the permanent loading of solid beams.

In practice, the special builder will for the most part use laminations, either as plywood or of his own manufacture, in loadbearing units; and the characteristics of laminations are superior to those of solid timber. A lamination is made by glueing together a number of thin plies of wood either straight or to shape to make a thicker member. In automobile work the laminations should be vertical for all beams to ensure that the zones of equal stress are shared between the laminations – the corollary of this is that the strength of the beam is the sum of the individual laminations. Intra-laminal joints should be scarfed together – butt joints do not transmit stress – and common sense tells us that the scarf joints should be spread along the length of the lamination: that a weak spot will be created by adjoining scarfs, or scarfs in line abreast. Laminations offer not only increased and less-interrupted strength, but also greater dimensional stability.

Plywood is made by glueing rotary-cut veneers at right angles; there is always an odd number of plies so that the grain of the two surfaces run parallel. For automobile applications, only marine ply to BS 1088 is suitable; the most common woods in this ply are mahogany, utile, sapele, gaboon and makore, plus others that may have to be specially ordered by your timber merchant if you really must have a greater grain-pattern choice. Plywood, even marine grades, can deteriorate if not protected, particularly along the edges, with paint or lacquer. Plywood provides excellent shear resistance for a very modest cross-section. Remember, when using the information that comes from the manufacturers or other sources, that American design standards consider only the "parallel plies" which are those plies that lie in the direction of the load, an approach that is based on the basic stresses and moduli for solid timber. The Brits and the Finns use the "full cross-section" approach in which grade stresses and moduli for the full cross-section have been determined by empirical testing.

Wood can be bent. The radius depends on the type of wood and the straightness of the grain. If supported by a strap, wood can be bent to a very small inside radius: 1-inch white oak stock can for instance be bent around a radius of $\frac{3}{8}$ inch; more common woods through larger radii: beech $1\frac{1}{2}$ inches, birch 3 inches, ash $4\frac{1}{2}$ inches and so on. To steam wood for bending all that is required is a long pipe capped at one end, rags to stuff in the top, water to boil in it, and a fire; do not let the steam pressure build up explosively.

Plywood bends easily around reasonable radii, the thinner the section, the smaller the radius it will take. If you need a thick ply bent to a small radius, you can make it by bending several pieces of thinner plywood and laminating them together; make sure alternate plies lie at 90 degrees to each other.

A large construction in plywood, say a complete flat-sided boat-tail speedster in the 1920s voiturette style, can be built canoe-fashion without any frame whatsoever. The ply is cut to size with the aid of cardboard templates and drilled along the edges. It is then wired together with the wire knots on the outside. The seams on the inside are then joined by GRP strips and when this is cured, the wires are clipped and pulled out (they are covered with parting agent before insertion). The inside of this structure can be totally glassed if you like; it is in any event braced with plywood bulkheads and longitudinal beams of plywood or foam and GRP. If you work neatly, small holes can be filled to be

virtually invisible by the application of varnish or lacquer.

If you do have a wooden internal frame, the ply should be screwed or nailed to it after bonding. Copperhead panel pins become virtually invisible against the darker woods after varnishing. If the frame is to be loadbearing, it should be laminated rather than made from solid wood.

A complex-curved monocoque can be made from wood. Again this is a process "borrowed" from boatbuilding practice. A master mould is built up from a series of bulkheads (which you may want to use in the finished article) on a backbone and the shape is given by longitudinal wooden laths fixed to the bulkheads. Long, narrow strips of thin wood (or ply, if you like) are laid diagonally across these laths (covered by polythene or newspaper so that you don't glue the shell to them), the first layer merely stapled on, the next layers glued and stapled. Each layer is diagonal (i.e. at 90°) to the previous layer. It is best to remove the staples as you build up the layers; if you do not, you must use copper staples. You can glue in the longitudinal laths complete with bulkheads if you wish, but the compound curves of the monocoque should provide ample stiffness if you build up enough layers. When you have enough layers, you remove the staples from the outside layer and sand it down. Remove the framework from the inside and bend any staples you didn't remove or nip them off flush. Now your bulkheads can be bonded in together with such beams or torsion boxes as may be necessary. Attachment of the mechanicals is subject to the normal considerations when using stressed skin constructions: spread the load as widely as possible, use backing plates and local thickening where possible.

Car design in wood can take up a whole book. Much of what I have said has been gleaned from boatbuilding practice – I first became interested in wood when I designed and helped to build a transatlantic racing yacht; boatbuilders have centuries of wisdom handed down to them. There are many books on the theory and the practice of building boats in wood that you can apply to building a car of wood. For the practical aspects, I think it's hard to beat Harper and Johnston's *The Repair and Restoration of Wooden Boats* (Batsford, 1980); for the theory, *Wood Handbook: Wood as an Engineering Material* (US Forest Products Laboratory, 1974) is good, with lots of useful tables. Any *Civil Engineer's Reference Book* (mine is edited by Blake and published by Newnes–Butterworth) will have a chapter on wood together with useful references and addresses. As with all the other materials we've discussed, this doesn't absolve you from obtaining from the suppliers or manufacturers of your specific grade of the material the relevant information on the loadability of the material, but it will help you understand what you're dealing with and what to ask for. Most suppliers have a file of spec sheets.

GRP

Glass Reinforced Plastics are the special builder's miracle material; the newer reinforcements and plastics, included here because the principles and processes are similar even if the qualities are superior, will one day be the mass-manufacturer's miracle. Meanwhile, except for very special applications, the special builder will stick to the far more cost-effective if common glass reinforcement, rather than use carbon fibre or Kevlar.

GRP (and the other reinforced plastics) has three main advantages over metals and wood. The first and perhaps most important is that it is rot-free: it does not rust. The second – very important for the special builder – is that its plasticity in the pre-cured in-manufacture state allows virtually any shape to be achieved without expensive tooling and with very modest skills: just enough to watch a wall thermometer and read and follow simple instructions. Though wood is cleaner, GRP may well be marginally easier to work with. Thirdly, GRP has a high strength-to-weight ratio and, while it is down on stiffness, its low density more than compensates and the super plasticity allows local thickening and reinforcement: only a very incompetent design in GRP exceeds 60% of the weight of an equally stiff mild steel structure. GRP also has the minor advantage (though it may entail a large saving) of the ability to make the top, gel-coat, the finished coat without the need for painting.

GRP also has disadvantages. It is messier to work with than wood or metals. The specific capabilities of the finished shell depends on the skill of the operators

---

Table 12.1: Comparative strength and stiffness of steel and various reinforced plastics. Tables 12.1 and 12.2 show how thick plastics reinforced with various glass fibre materials and carbon must be to have the same strength and stiffness as mild steel; also how much the reinforced plastic will weigh. Three points about Table 12.1 are worth noting. It is possible to transpose metric measurements to imperial, as I have done with the density of the different materials. It is unnecessary to make any transpositions if all your figures are compatible with each other even if you have no idea of what MPa and GPa are because you can always compare with the known material, mild steel. It is useful to set out your results as a comparison around unity, using the known material or the most efficient or cheapest as the common denominator. This table takes into account that stiffness increases as the third power of thickness but it deals with representative materials so that you must get specifications for the materials you will actually use and make up your own comparative table as specifications of glass fibre and even mild steel can vary substantially.

	Steel (mild)	Reinforced plastics		
		Chopped strand mat	Woven rovings	40% Carbon reinforcement
Tensile strength, MPa	310	103.4	250	724
Tensile modulus, GPa	200	7	15	193
Density, kg/100mm^3	7.81	1.5	1.6	1.54
Density, lb/ft^3	487	93	100	96
Specific strength	39.7	68.9	156.3	470.1
Weight for equal strength, compared to mild steel	1.00	0.58	0.25	0.08
Thickness for equal strength, compared to mild steel	1.00	3.00	1.24	0.43
Specific stiffness	25.61	4.67	9.38	125.32
Weight for equal stiffness, compared to mild steel	1.00	0.60	0.49	0.20
Thickness for equal stiffness, compared to mild steel	1.00	3.12	2.39	1.01

and on ambient conditions of temperature and moisture. The oft-repeated claim that GRP is fireproof can be disproven by calling your nearest marina; fire-resistant grades of GRP are often less capable in other directions than the grades that will burn; but what burns in most cars is the upholstery, which a GRP car would have too.

But GRP's greatest disadvantage for the special builder, except in very narrow circumstances already discussed (or where the inside should be the finished surface), is that of the cost of manufacture. If the outside surface should be the smooth surface, you will first have to make a plug of, usually, wood, wire, sacking and plaster, finished to the same degree of refinement as required on the moulding. From this take a mould, made of GRP and externally stiffened. Inside this the final-use moulding is made. All this costs materials to the extent that even curved aluminium panels may become cost-effective for a one-off. In this regard, each project must be considered individually on its own merits and the various parameters compromised; we have already commented that eliminating a separate metal chassis in favour of a GRP monocoque taking all the loads may make the latter more cost-effective than a separate chassis and body design.

There are many grades and weaves of GRP and all have different qualities and appearances. In Table 12.1 certain grades of chopped strand mat (CSM) are compared with woven rovings (WR) and 40% carbon fibre reinforcement as well as with mild steel; all the results are reduced to ratios, with mild steel as unity, to make comparison easy. What this table shows is that you can forget about designing for strength: if you design for stiffness, the strength will automatically be

there. It also shows that, unless you have an autoclave or some other method of making really thin skins, you can forget about expensive carbon fibres because you simply cannot make a skin uniformly $\frac{1}{16}$-inch thick in your own garage.

Woven rovings are said to drape better than chopped strand mat but in practice are used mainly for additional stiffness, heat resistance, and for designing in differential crush-zones (for progressive deformation in an accident); WR is good for bulkheads. GRP may be further stiffened by bonding in plywood or metal pieces though the most advanced designers now scorn this kind of reinforcement and prefer merely bonding in zinc-plated doughnuts where through bolts will pierce the skin, locally reinforced or thickened by WR or CSM. Plywood and metal beams may either contribute to the strength or torsional resistance of the design or merely be formers over which to drape the GRP; other internal formers are rope or top-hat sections or shaped foam. *Firet* is a special foam that is bonded and shaped in place and then saturated with resin to become an integral loadbearing part of whatever it is attached to, unlike the kind of foam that merely provides form to drape the GRP over and unlike the self-foaming preparations used to fill hollow members and other cavities in GRP for soundproofing or insulation.

Because the capabilities of a shell is related to the third power of the wall thickness, a useful construction method in GRP is the GRP-foam sandwich which consists of two skins of GRP on either side of a layer of foam. More advanced sandwich materials include all kinds of honeycombs in various materials but the easiest and most effective for the special builder might well be *Coremat*.

Whichever strengthening method is chosen, it must be applied to the inside of the outer shell while the shell is still in the mould but after it has cured enough to prevent the stiffeners distorting or marking the outer skin; lots of people have worked in GRP and it shouldn't be too difficult to get advice.

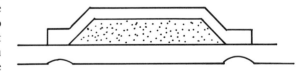

Figure 12.4. If you fit stiffeners to a GRP mould or moulding before it is fully cured, the other – gel – side will develop indentations. Be patient and you won't spoil any mouldings.

The general production procedure for a GRP body is to make the plug around a backbone on which is built the bulkheads – which you want to re-use, covered with chicken wire, sacking and plaster for shaping. When you are satisfied with the shape and finish, give the plug several layers of furane resin, each rubbed smooth, then wax with release agent. The mould is then laid up by painting or spraying on the gel-coat and laying up layers of mat according to the instructions supplied with your materials. When the mould has cured, stiffeners are laminated to the outside and when these have cured, the mould is taken from the plug, cleaned, bolted together along the split lines (see below), waxed with release agent and then the procedure is repeated inside it except that this time the stiffeners are applied to the inside of the moulding, the outer surface being for show. It is usual to put a layer of tissue between the gelcoat and the first layer of mat to prevent the pattern of the mat from showing through the gel.

The thing that troubles the novice most is undercuts. To remove the moulding from the mould without damaging the one or the other, there must be a draft of at least 2° and no undercuts, otherwise the mould must be split. A little thought at the design stage will allow you to put the splits at styling or panel joint lines. The splits are made by cutting ali or thin plastic to shape on the plug, fixing it on with plaster and laying mat up to

Figure 12.5. Splitting a GRP mould in three easy steps: 1. Cut plastic or ali to the shape of the mould and fit with plaster to one side only. 2. Glass up on other side. Remove divider and plaster. 3. After applying separating agent to mould and lip, glass up second side.

Figure 12.6. Chopped strand mat will not fit into or over the smallest styling lines, so build them up or level them up with rovings between the gelcoat and first layer of mat.

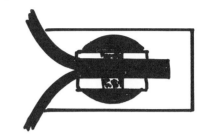

Figure 12.7. GRP joints covered with rubber strips can be used as styling features or rubbing strips.

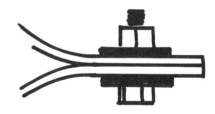

Figure 12.8. GRP mouldings can be glued together or bolted or rivetted if you use large washers each side.

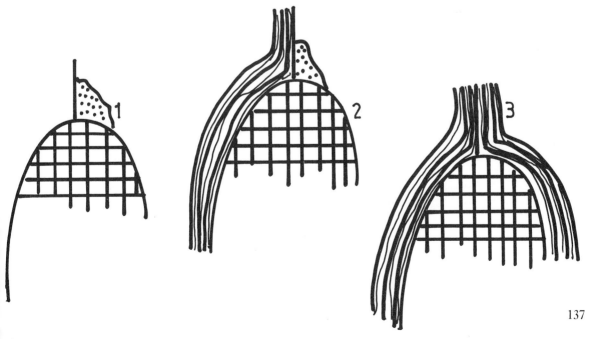

the divider on one side, then removing the divider and laying mat on the other side up the side of GRP already in place. When the GRP has cured, drill the ridge for reassembly after removal from the plug; moulds intended for multiple use should have the holes spigoted. These split lines are natural places for designing-in strength-giving returns. The moulded pieces are bonded and bolted or riveted together, using large washers to spread the load; sometimes, in production GRP parts, you will find screws but I cannot profess to any great enthusiasm for or faith in this practice.

A monocoque in GRP is stiffened against torsion first of all by the boxes formed by its bulkheads and then by the curvature of its skin and then by the longitudinal beams whose main function is to resist bending. The greater and the more complex the skin curvature, the stiffer the whole will be. The bulkheads, which can be of GRP, plywood or metal, give stiffness out of all proportion to their weight as part of the whole; they are best cut a little small, fitted to the shell on slivers of foam and then bonded on both sides to the shell – bulkheads that fit too well raise stress locally.

The novice often thinks in terms of making a complete shell and cutting the apertures for the people and machinery afterwards. Don't. Each of those apertures must have a return to strengthen the edges of the hole and this is best made in unit with the shell rather than tacked on later; it is very easy to build up another

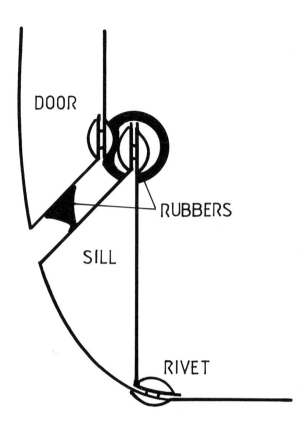

Figure 12.10. GRP door construction and shutface detail from a design by the author. The washers under the rivets are not shown. The triangular rubber seals best.

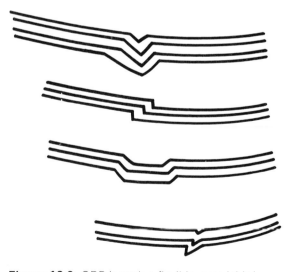

Figure 12.9. GRP is such a flexible material it is easy to make styling lines and complex curvatures, both of which also add strength out of proportion to the material they consume.

small plug in the aperture on the actual moulding to make the aperture closure (door, bonnet, trunk lid) from. These returns should, where possible, each have their own return to form a proper water channel. If you're building a civilized car with wind-up windows and intend using a proprietary doorframe as a moulding fixture, remember that GRP shrinks a little as it cures and make a 2% allowance for shrinking.

Determining where on the inside to place your stiffeners and reinforcements is not difficult if you think of the GRP shell as the stressed panels over a spaceframe, or on a multitube, or even on twin tubes, or a backbone, so that a section through your GRP car will show the skin plus a very large hollow section, or several large hollow sections, or many small hollow sections (the foam in such a section doesn't count for anything, nor the paper rope often used for small stiffeners). It is obvious that suspension and drivetrain mountings will have to be reinforced and here a large bevelled piece of plywood or similarly bevelled metal is the easiest thing to use. Many proprietary parts are fitted by bolts into tapped holes and I suggest that you consider $\frac{1}{4}$ inch of *metal* the minimum depth for this purpose regardless of the thickness of proprietary shell used. Bolts with nuts are better. All metal parts to be bonded in should be zinc-plated; if you're going to have only a few small reinforcements, you could consider stainless steel to specification EN58J which has better corrosion resistance than the more common 18/88. Corners on bonded-in reinforcements and backing plates should be rounded to avoid raising point-stresses.

Depending on the curvature, GRP shells that are not intended to bear suspension and engine loads need be no more than $\frac{1}{10}$-inch thick if suitably stiffened around edges and mounting points; loadbearing monocoques should have shells calculated to bear the expected loads with adequate safety margins. The calculation processes are the same as for metals or wood but the safety margins should be substantially larger. For static short-term loads, a safety factor of 2 is sufficient; for static long-term loads, and variable loads, a safety factor of 4 is indicated; repetitive loads and load reversal call for a safety factor of 5, as does provision for fatigue; impact loads require a safety factor of 10. These are maxima but you would be ill-advised to reduce them unless you're having your body professionally sprayed or laid up by experts under rigidly controlled conditions. The right people – often to be found nearer to hand than the few competent automobile structural layer-uppers – are boatbuilders, whose conditions and workmanship are usually supervised by Lloyd's inspectors. Essentially, a loadbearing shell can also be built to a wall thickness of $\frac{1}{10}$ inch with somewhat heavier bracing and reinforcement than the non-structural shell, but most are $\frac{3}{16}-\frac{3}{8}$ inch because special builders wisely allow for their own deficiencies or inexperience.

A few things to watch for: $\frac{1}{2}$ inch is the practical minimum inside radius in GRP ($\frac{1}{4}$ inch will cause a bridge); watch out for sudden section changes because they are stress raisers; make absolutely sure you bevel all reinforcements round the edges and corners; all loads should be resolved into tension and compression locally and *not* taken out in bending. Finally, a couple of practical tips: the higher the glass-resin ratio, allowing of course that all the glass is thoroughly wetted through, the stronger and the cheaper your shell will be; wear barrier cream *and* gloves – I have yet to meet anyone whose skin isn't sensitive to resin and/ or acetone, the cleaning material associated with working in GRP.

If you're going to be making only a few small parts in GRP, your glass and resin supplier will give you a leaflet containing all the information you need. Strand Glass, who have branches all over England, is particularly good at these instructional leaflets and also run evening classes with demonstrations. If you're going to build a whole car in GRP, you should have a copy of Richard Wood's *Car Bodywork in Glass Reinforced Plastics* (Pentech Press 1980), but note that standards have improved tremendously since he built a GRP special with the rough side out back in the 1950s.

AERODYNAMICS

We have already touched on aerodynamics at the specification stage of the car where it featured in the compromise between style, operating and construction cost, and performance, and briefly at various points since. Now we must consider the detail: how to achieve a low Cd or how to improve the Cd. Aerodynamics is as much an art as a science but unfortunately it has spawned more mathematics (and more *abstruse* math) than any other science but nuclear physics, the majority of it either irrelevant or too deep for the special builder. As always, we will look for shortcuts.

Our basic formula

$$BHP = \frac{Cd\,A\,v^3}{146,600 \times 0.7}$$

to predict the bhp required for a speed v, with a frontal area A (sometimes approximated by height times width times the constant allowing for the curvature of the body and the ground clearance of 0.75–0.85), can also be written

$$Cd\,A = \frac{BHP \times 102,620}{v^3}$$

$$Cd = \frac{BHP \times 102,620}{A\,v^3}$$

and

$$v = \sqrt[3]{\frac{BHP \times 102,620}{Cd\,A}}$$

to tell us what Cd A (the *real* comparison between cars, rather than the simple Cd) the horses of a given engine will allow us with a chosen top speed, what we must reduce the Cd to if we wish to achieve a desired top speed with a known engine and have already reduced

Figure 12.11. Front-engine, V8 powered, rear drive *autobahnfuhrer* – this appealing design was scrapped when, late in the day, a very strict fuel-efficiency parameter was added.

Figure 12.12. This mid-engined, fuel efficient streamliner is a much more radical design, intended to do 120mph on 72bhp and 40mpg at 100mph cruising. The main problem is fitting passengers and luggage into a car only 55"w × 42"h.

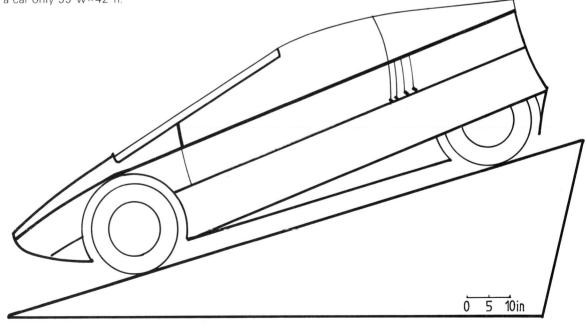

the frontal area to an absolute minimum, and what speed a given design will allow us to attain – Table 12.3 gives the third powers of speeds between 10 and 199mph so you can look up the third roots: the last three digits have been left off but make no difference to the accuracy. Table 12.4 illustrates a series of agonizing decisions to be made regarding a front-engined V8-powered autobahn cruiser; Figure 12.11 shows the general design. This was scrapped as not fuel-effective enough and a series of preliminary studies of mid-engined streamliners done with the results shown in Table 12.5 and the profile in Figure 12.12.

The next question is: How will the designer achieve the aerodynamic efficiency postulated in the preliminary calculations? And, because the special car designer has by now learned to be cautious as well as hopeful, two further questions: Will there be any deleterious side effects? Can I use the side effects to my advantage in any way?

Table 12.3: Third powers and cube roots.
If you know or can guess reasonably accurately the aerodynamic efficiency and frontal area of a car and its bhp, you can calculate its top speed from the formula

$$v = \sqrt[3]{\frac{BHP \times 102{,}620}{Cd\,A}}$$

by looking up in this table the cube root of the number under the root sign. Look up the number in the table, find the tens of miles per hour on the left and the units of miles per hour at the top and that's it. For instance, take $Cd = 0.4$, $A = 20\,ft^2$ and $bhp = 115$, then $V = \sqrt[3]{1{,}468{,}748}$ or, rounded, $\sqrt[3]{1469}$ to which the nearest figure in the table is 1482 which reads off as 114mph. This table also saves calculation for those formulae which use V^3: look up the speed you want, find the figure in the body of the table and add 000 to bring it back up to strength before calculating further with it.

mph	0	1	2	3	4	5	6	7	8	9
					1000					
10	1	1	2	2	3	3	4	5	6	7
20	8	9	11	12	14	16	18	20	22	24
30	27	30	33	36	39	43	47	51	55	59
40	64	69	74	80	85	91	97	104	111	118
50	125	133	141	149	157	166	176	185	195	205
60	216	227	238	250	262	275	288	301	314	329
70	343	358	373	389	405	422	439	457	475	493
80	512	531	551	572	593	614	636	659	681	705
90	729	754	779	804	831	857	885	913	941	970
100	1000	1030	1061	1093	1124	1158	1191	1225	1260	1295
110	1331	1368	1405	1443	1482	1521	1561	1602	1643	1685
120	1728	1772	1816	1861	1907	1953	2000	2046	2097	2146
130	2197	2248	2300	2353	2406	2460	2515	2571	2628	2686
140	2744	2803	2863	2924	2986	3049	3112	3177	3242	3308
150	3375	3443	3512	3582	3652	2724	3796	3870	3944	4020
160	4096	4173	4252	4331	4411	4492	4574	4657	4742	4827
170	4913	5000	5088	5178	5268	5360	5452	5545	5640	5735
180	5832	5930	6029	6128	6230	6332	6435	6539	6645	6751
190	6859	6968	7078	7189	7301	7415	7530	7645	7762	7881

Table 12.4: Aerodynamic efficiency, width and horsepower v. speed.

There is a wealth or information in this table, which relates to the front-engined, rear-drive two seater sports car shown in Figure 12.11. It is assumed that it will be 45 inches high but similar tables should also be prepared for 47 and 49 inches high, just in case … Three track widths from standard Jaguars (first series E-Type, S-Type and XJ sedan) will give the three overall widths indicated. A "normal" car is 67 inches wide, 63.4 inches makes a narrowish car and 58 inches is very narrow indeed. This is only part of a larger table which also showed figures for Cds of 0.31, 0.35, 0.39, since the actual aerodynamic efficiency will not be known until the car is built. The 156 and 190bhp engines are standard Rover V8 SDI items listed by the factory; the 200bhp engine is built by fitting to the 156bhp engine a Crane H214 cam, stronger valve springs (not essential but recommended) and BAF needles to the standard twin SU carburettors; 220bhp is achieved by fitting additionally a Holley 390cfm carb on an Offenhauser inlet manifold; a streetable and perfectly durable 250bhp can be had by supercharging the Rover V8 but would be quite unnecessary in this instance and, in any event, a mildly modified small block Chevy will be both cheaper and more economical. The cheap engines here are the 156 and 200bhp ones. If your top speed parameter is 140mph – this design is for an autobahnfuhrer in a place where the fast lane *average* is 200kph (125mph) – it is quite clear from the table that, if you want to use the cheapest possible engine, the car should be no wider than 63.4 inches and the Cd no worse than 0.37; if you want a car 67 inches wide, you *must* get the Cd down to 0.33

O/A width	CD in	0.33			0.37			0.41		
		58.1	63.4	67.0	58.1	63.4	67.0	58.1	63.4	67.0
BHP	DIN				Speed, mph					
	156	148	145	142	144	140	137	139	135	134
	190	160	155	152	154	149	146	148	144	141
	200	162	158	155	156	152	149	151	147	144
	220	168	163	160	161	157	154	156	151	148
	250	175	170	167	168	163	160	163	158	155

Table 12.5: Choosing an engine for a small streamliner.

The idea here is to choose either a standard engine or an off-the-shelf modified engine. A mid-engined two/three seater is envisaged, 42"h × 55"w with Cd = 0.33 and CdA = 4.27, running on 185 section tires. To stay inside the width, all engines will have to have modified driveshafts, except the BL engines which can use the Mini shafts. Automatic boxes are being considered at this preliminary stage of the design because we don't yet know what, perhaps insuperable, gear linkage problems we're going to run into in moving the engine from the front to the middle of the car. The codes are T for turbo, M for modified, F for factory, and A with those engines which are available with an automatic gearbox – the speeds indicated take no account of the horses the autobox will devour.

BL MG Metro 4-sp			Ford Escort 5-sp			VW Golf 5-sp		
Code	BHP	Speed	Code	BHP	Speed	Code	BHP	Speed
F	72	120	AF	79	124	AF	75	122
TF	93	131	F	105	136	AF	90	129
M	110	138	F	115	140	F	112	139
			T	132	147	M	130	146
						M	150	153

Purpose of streamlining

We streamline our cars to make them go further or faster for the same fuel consumption or to make them go as far or as fast for less fuel consumption. The greater efficiency may also affect the mechanical components: we may be able to fit a smaller or a cheaper engine; mechanical components may last longer because higher gearing means the engine turns slower for the same performance.

Furthermore, we can use the weight of the air to improve the ride, roadholding and handling characteristics of our car without increasing the *actual* weight of the car that has to be lugged around and accelerated and braked.

Cd A

Cd is a dimensionless coefficient, simply an indicator of how efficiently in aerodynamic terms you have designed your car; A is the frontal area of your car, within very wide parameters totally within your control. Together, at any given speed, they will tell you *how efficiently* the car will push *how much* air out of its way. Cd A can therefore be used to make a direct comparison between competing designs whereas one or the other alone may give a misleading result.

Dimension, shape and detail design influence Cd A, with detail design by far the most important, given the constraints functionality puts on shape and dimension. From now on, to simplify matters, the rest of the discussion will assume that the frontal area of the car, A, has been optimized, leaving us to discuss shape and detail design.

Aerodynamic drag

The main components of aerodynamic drag are skin friction, profile drag, and service drag – the drag of the air being conducted to mechanical parts for cooling and to the passengers for ventilation.

Skin friction is related to the area and texture of the surface but can easily account for 15% of aerodynamic drag. Every time you fair something else in, or add bodywork to direct air more advantageously, you also add skin area.

Profile drag is badly named because it makes you think of only the side profile of the car. It relates to the way the *three-dimensional* shape of the car disturbs the air in passing through it.

Service drag (often called radiatior drag but far more important than that) is caused by the air passing through the car to cool the water in the radiator, the oil coolers if fitted, past the engine and gearbox and

brakes for cooling, and through the passenger compartment for ventilation, as well as through the engine and exhaust system for combustion. This air is subject to the same principles of movement as all the other air and careful attention here can improve your Cd hugely.

The ideal shape

It is obvious that some shapes should be aerodynamically superior to others and one superior to all others. Aerodynamicists of yore thought they knew the answer and were surprised when their aircraft knowledge failed to provide all the solutions. The main problem was, and remains, that a car has to be flat or nearly so on the underside and run close to the ground if other desirable characteristics are not to be compromised. This ground effect caused havoc with airfoil-related analogies. An idealized shape was developed – and had a theoretical minimum Cd of 0.12! The work of Kamm showed that the long, impractical tail could be truncated abruptly for greater aerodynamic efficiency than tapering it more sharply (note that this is in direct contradiction to aircraft theory and practice). The ratio of the height of the ideal shape to its pre-truncation length is 1:6 because anything else will increase skin friction disproportionately.

Airflow

There are three kinds of airflow. Laminar airflow follows the body closely, a rough surface less well than a smooth one. This very thin layer of air is totally free of turbulence. Turbulent airflow results when the fluid air laminar layer begins to thicken and, at a certain velocity and viscosity, splits from a now much thinner laminar layer and becomes turbulent; this turbulent layer is still very shallow – nowhere near as deep as often shown for convenience of illustration. The third kind of airflow is called stalled flow and results when the turbulent flow is so much accelerated or disturbed that it can no longer follow the shape of the body at all: it breaks up into whirls, whorls, eddies and a great deal of drag is the inevitable consequence. The laminar flow is most easily maintained by accelerating the air, from a smooth split, around a body of gently but constantly increasing cross-section without bulges or breaks to disturb the flow. A sharply tapering tail will also disturb the flow and Kamm's contribution here was to point out that truncating the tail at the point where the airflow became turbulent or stalled would in fact reduce the drag; note that the true Kamm tail falls in an area of *high* pressure and that, therefore, most of the so-called Kamm tails are no such thing. For a true

Figure 12.13. The Probe IV's shape is almost conventional but the Cd is 0.16! The drag reduction tricks are in the details, including variable ride height and a speed-regulated chin spoiler.

Figure 12.14. Air flow over and under a Midas.

Kamm tail, look to the Citroen GS (a design more than a decade old as I write this) which has the best Cd A in the world, superior even to the Audi. Figure 12.15 shows the pressure variations on a typical car of the three-box variety but note that each car will have its individual pattern.

Kamm's most important contribution – rather than the often-misapplied tail for which his name has gone down in auto-jargon – was to the management of air *through* the car. He showed that, if you lead radiator cooling air in at the high-pressure area at the front of the car and out in the area in front of the windscreen (which is also a high-pressure area with probably over half the pressure at the front of the car, but *relatively* a low-pressure area), this air can be used to energize the flow over the brow of the roof and along the roof, so keeping it laminar till much further over the tail. Here, when separation can no longer be avoided, as an afterthought the tail is simply truncated.

It is to the purpose of maintaining laminar flow that detail design is directed.

Important details

The quick way to find out whether a car on which all the aerodynamic details seem perfect is intended for show or go is to look underneath it. The management of the flow underneath the car is as important – sometimes more important – than the management of the flow across the car. Forget skirts that brush the road: they are illegal in many places, they are impractical in that those that seal properly soon get destroyed on everyday roads and those that don't seal properly are useless, and they are in any event of use only to monstrously powerful and virtually suspension-less Formula One racers. On the other hand, a smooth underside to the car, smoothly blended into the sides, will improve Cd. Even fitting an undertray to the front suspension area will be a large improvement; a complete undertray will be a major improvement.

Let us dispose immediately of spoilers, lips, wings and other such stick-on devices, now being built into econoboxes by wideawake stylists. A spoiler on a special is essentially an admission that its designer

Figure 12.15. Air pressure variations over a moving car.

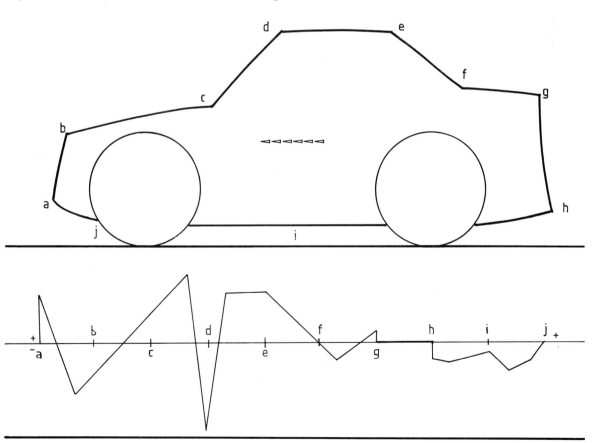

failed to design an aerodynamically stable car and therefore had to resort to a spoiler to correct the problem. This is not to say that they don't have their advantages, to which we shall return, but the perfectly designed car will have all the advantages of air-weight management without the addenda. Even a cursory look at most spoilers will show an increased area for skin friction and that they will disturb rather than promote laminar airflow.

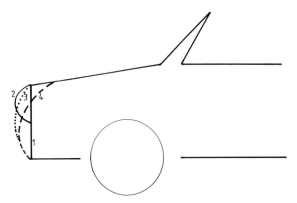

Figure 12.16. A blunt nose shape 1 will do a bad job of dividing the obstreperous fluid air. Shape 2 is worth 8–10% off the Cd of shape 1, shape 3 10–12% and shape 4 around 12–14% – a worthwhile reduction.

The major detail is the shape of the car, in three dimensions. The first essential is that the lines should flow as smoothly as possible in all directions. Next you must pay attention to the body's entry into the air in front of it. The nose must not be too blunt, nor too sharp: an elliptical shape is indicated as shown in Figure 12.16, from there the cross-section should increase gradually and constantly for as far as possible before being gently and constantly reduced to the point where the separation of the laminar airflow can no longer be avoided and the body should then stop. The Audi (and to a lesser extent the Mercedes 190, W201 series) has shown that even a three-box design can give good results but the semi-fastback fits easier into the classical shape. The squareback or hatchback with its tailgate at around 35° to the horizontal is not a particularly aerodynamically efficient design; a slope of about 10–12° will serve far better.

The next important item is to manage the flow of air through the car so that it either aids the laminar retention of airflow as by exhausting radiator cooling air in front of the screen, or causes as little disturbance as possible either at the intake or exhaust point. Low air pressures are created by leading the air the long way around a body and thereby speeding it up; the faster the air moves, the more difficult it is to keep it laminar. It follows that, in general, when you cannot manage the airflow through the car to exit where it will contribute to the equalization of flow speed over the car by energizing relatively low-pressure areas, you should exhaust it in an area where it can do the laminar flow no harm and this will normally be as far to the rear of the car as possible. Also, if you want to control the through-flow of air, don't do it at the inlet end, where it will cause turbulence, but by varying the opening at the exit. An opening one-sixth the area of the radiator will allow entry to sufficient air to cool the engine. I have my doubts about the ram-effect of air taken to the carbs from the front of the car and prefer to have the mouth of the intake in the low-pressure area in front of the windscreen. If you're fairing in engine exhaust units, a heat shield a minimum of ½ inch from the exhaust and the same distance from electrical wiring or bodywork will give adequate insulation if you can manage to guide a good deal of air around it.

Now begins the work with the apparently minor details that can make so much difference. All edges should be rounded, a procedure with important side-effects to which we shall return at some length below when we discuss the centre of pressure; the rounding is subject to the law of diminishing returns but, as a rule of thumb, all edges should be rounded to a radius of not less than ½ inch.

There should obviously be no protruberances – more skin friction, a break in laminar airflow! – but those that are unavoidable should be faired in to the same dimensional relationship as the complete car. Note that gutters are protruberances that can be either eliminated or, with a little thought, sunk into the bodywork. The best treatment for gutters is to incorporate them into the door shutlines.

The side windows are normally inset at least ½ inch and this is a discontinuity that causes considerable turbulence and may need special aids to direct air onto them to keep the rain off – more drag. Do you really need opening windows at all? What about a hatch in the driver's door? Glass bonded in flush with the skin can be worth as much as 12% off your Cd; even just bonding the quarter window flush with the outer skin is usually worth something. Windscreen and rear glass should also be bonded in.

Panel joint and shutlines, especially those lying transversely across the car, are an invitation to turbulence by providing places where the laminar flow can either pile up or unstick. Panels should fit closely (more a construction than a design problem) and be positively sealed; a strip of flat rubber glued around the edge of a shutline on the high-pressure side will seal automatically. The thing to watch is that there are no air inlets or outlets that *you* didn't plan and that won't happen unless you take care to seal all other holes, no matter how small.

Can you bond in the lights rather than fitting them in rubber surrounds? Can you fair in the windscreen wipers? Can you arrange for one screenwiper rather than two to do the job? Can you clean the headlamps with a powerful jet of water or do you really need headlamp wipers as well (Porsche don't)? Is there space to fit number plates front and rear where they will not ruin your carefully contrived aerodynamics?

It's easy to get carried away, so, after doing everything to streamline the car, you must go back and answer a few questions more. Is there provision for *all* the air that comes into the car to get out again? Is there a place for air to get in to *and out from* the radiator? the oil cooler? the induction system? the front brakes? the rear brakes? around any heat shields? around any parts known to run hot – gearbox or final drive unit, for instance? the car interior?

Aerodynamic stability

It was soon found that the perfectly streamlined car had wretched directional stability and very tricky handling at speed – and became lethal in crosswinds. Certain modern streamlined designs also suffer to some extent from these maladies. They are all related through the *centre of pressure* and, to a smaller degree, to differential lift and downforce created by pressure variations over the body travelling at speed which cause weight changes over the driving or steering roadwheels. The latter, which affects all cars, can be used to modify the ride, roadholding, handling and performance of the car and we shall return to it after dealing with the centre of pressure.

The centre of pressure – more correctly the centre of aerodynamic pressure – is that point through which the air pressure against the profile of the car can be said to be concentrated. Since this weight is often said to be one-fifth the all-up weight of the car, it is not negligible. It is not a fixed point but moves about according to the speed of the car and the angle of the wind to its direction of travel. We already know that it is desirable that the centre of pressure (CoP) should be behind the centre of gravity (CoG) because otherwise the car will oversteer terminally in side winds as the CoG tries to attain the more stable position where it leads: the perfectly streamlined car is safer and faster around windblown corners going backwards (and in just about the same proportion as the typical 1930s car was more streamlined going backwards than forwards).

The CoP also has a lateral component: if it is too high, there will be a definite aerodynamically-induced body-roll; if it is down at roughly the same height as the CoG, its effect will be reduced to the lesser complications of side-slip and yaw.

The pressure of the air against the side of the car is largest per unit of area against the front of the car and reduces to almost nothing per unit of area at the rear of the car. Thus, to move it rearwards, you must provide several square feet of rear profile for every square foot at the front. This explains why fastbacks are often more stable than three-box sedans, and station wagons more stable still – and why a boot stuck on a hatchback will make the resulting three-box less twitchy when passing the big hauliers on the motorway. The common three-box saloon and its estate brethren have their CoP between a quarter and a third of the length of the car from the front but the truly well streamlined car will at speed lie entirely behind its CoP. This is the reason for the fins we see sticking out well behind the rear of some sports-racers – to move the CoP back in order to ensure high-speed directional stability. It is also the reason that most designers keep the nose low if they can and take the penalties of a quite sharp angle where the bonnet joins the windscreen because a windscreen running directly from the nose of the car to the roofrail would, disregarding the multitudinous practical problems, entail substantial side area which would move the CoP forward and affect the handling. The perfect "teardrop" car is dangerous because the CoP is too far forward; the mid-engined sports car is tricky to design without handling defects though it does have the advantage of naturally high sides, relative to the rest of it, well to the rear; the movement forward of the CoP with increasing speed accounts for the reputation of mid-engined cars to require expert handling and quick reflexes at speed – a few lead ingots in the nose to move the CoG forward would answer but there are easier and better ways.

With a rear drive car, the alternative of moving the CoG forward to provide aerodynamic stability is a weak answer. On front drive cars moving the CoG forward is not a bad idea at all; you can start by moving the engine from behind the front wheel axis to in front of it.

Other solutions are fin rails on the roof (but keep them small because of the height), tailfins like on 1958 Cadillacs, BMW's 3.0CSL and Batmobile racers (entirely functional), rigid side skirts if you have ground clearance to play with, or redesigning the car as a fastback or sports estate.

By simply changing the radii on the corners of your car, you can move the CoP backwards and forwards. There are two kinds of edges, those lying transversely across the car, and those lying longitudinally along it.

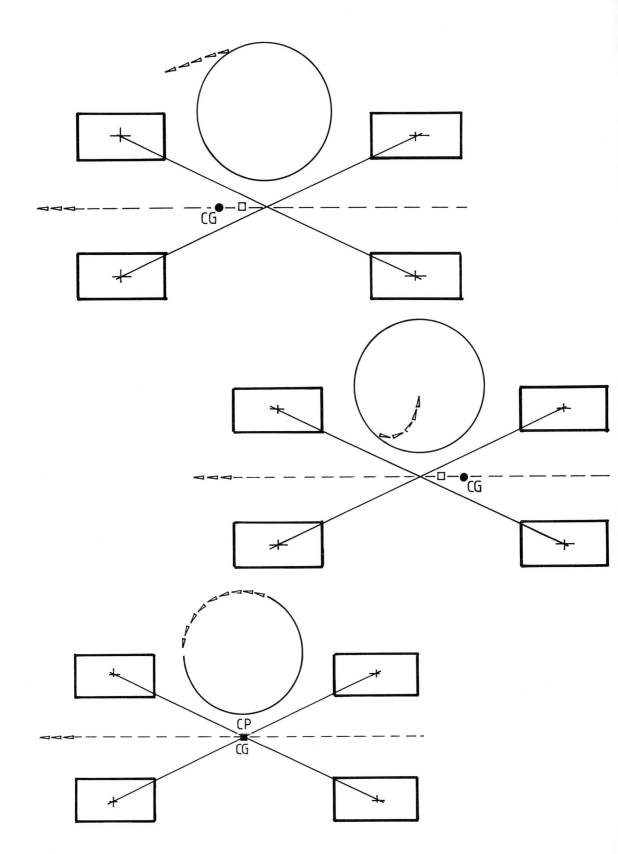

Figures 12.17, 12.18 and 12.19. The placement of the CoG in relation to the Centre of Pressure and the resultant Neutral Steer Line. The squares indicate the CoP and the big circles inset show the resulting over- and under-steer. A car with theoretically neutral steering – CoP and CoG coinciding – would in practice be terminally unpredictable.

The rounding of transverse edges moves the centre of pressure forward: transverse edges should therefore be radiused only enough to keep the airflow attached. Rounding the longitudinal edges will not affect the CoP a great deal.

So why bother? The answer is that rounded edges reduce drag: you must compromise some drag because you don't want to round transverse edges so much that the CoP creeps forward to lurk an inch behind the grille. Furthermore, the actual amount of side force the wind applies can be influenced by edge-rounding.

Specifically, sidewind force will be increased by rounding transverse edges and reduced by rounding longitudinal edges – and the latter do not greatly affect the position of the CoP. In addition, rounding contains the seeds of an argument for narrow bodies against wide, in that the influence of rounding transverse edges is less on a narrow body than on a wide body; also the effect is greater when longitudinal edges are radiused on a narrow body than on a wide one. This is the rationale (or part of it) behind the tall, narrow and very aerodynamically efficient designs from, inter alia, Fiat.

Rounding edges thus has an influence not only on directional stability and Cd, but contains an argument for the result A and through that for the important characteristic Cd A.

Since the special builder is unlikely to have access to a wind tunnel, a careful study of the side area distribution and the edge radii of an Audi 100 or a Ford Sierra will tell you a great deal those companies spent millions to learn.

Downforce

As we have said, the perfectly designed car will need no aerodynamic afterthoughts to keep it doing exactly what the driver orders through the controls. No designer can claim perfection: the automobile is, because of its proximity to the ground, not the perfect aerodynamic tool the aviationists have, and the purposes and functions of the motorcar compromise its design to such an extent that it cannot even metaphorically approach perfection closely.

The design approaching perfection, however distantly, will regulate the flow of air around *and under* the car so well that at any speed there will be no aerodynamic *lift* over either the steering or the driving roadwheels, leaving the weight transfers regulating roadholding and handling entirely to theory and the suspension. Contrariwise, in the state of perfection such a car would, with a Cd A no greater than the part-perfect car, *optimize* through the weight of air at the required time the ride, handling, roadholding, steering, braking and traction of the car, without of course any deleterious side-effects.

The spoiler was re-invented by the American racing driver Ritchie Ginther when he was with Ferrari in the early 1960s, and from a quite modest beginning has sprung an art that may one day entirely negate the wisdom contained in the chapters on suspension design: by managing aerodynamically induced weight distribution, it is possible to make a car behave as desired without much regard for its own weight distribution, now merely of mechanical interest. These aerodynamic "aids" – spoilers, wings, dams at the front and the rear – do not have to weigh a great deal and can be designed to offer only a modicum of additional drag so that Cd and often Cd A can be reduced by fitting them even to already competent mass-produced designs.

Consider the air travelling over a fastback design, say, which through attention to big and little considerations has an impressive Cd A and in addition very nice directional stability – except that at speeds over 130mph the tail goes light, not too much of a bother in the dry but very tricky in conditions of reduced traction. Because of the convex fastback tail, the air is being speeded up and the pressure therefore is reduced: the air pressure underneath the car is greater than over it and all of a sudden (or so it feels from the driving seat on a wet roundabout) there is a few hundred pounds less weight on the rear wheels than there should be. The remedy is to slow the air over the tail down and allow a build-up which will negate the lift – or even add as much weight of air to the downforce as the designer considers necessary for optimum traction. This is easily done by placing either a dam on the lip of the tail or an airfoil (wing) above it, arranged to have a longer air-route and therefore lower pressure on the underside than on top, thereby inducing downforce.

At the front, the weight of air can be damned to negate lift or to increase downforce on the front wheels for greater steering or braking traction or simply to guide and speed up the air for cooling or ventilation.

A lip on the rear end of the roof of a coupe can be used to direct the air to the wing or the dam on the bootlid.

Figure 12.20. That tail found its way onto the Sierra XR4i but whether it works is not something on which I'm prepared to pontificate. That unobtrusive lower lip looks functional.

An airfoil can be used on the rear undershield to guide and smooth the air out from underneath the car, or can be used to generate downforce from the air flowing underneath the car.

The handling characteristics can then be changed simply by altering the effects of the various aerodynamic devices. Since the effects will be related to speed, the cure can be made to operate only at the required speed; the penalty at lower speeds will be modest as aerodynamic drag increases as the square of velocity.

FRANK COSTIN

Costin, who has an aircraft industry upbringing in the same way Bentley had a railway-shed upbringing, and with equally predictable results, is the greatest automobile aerodynamicist of our time. From the aircraft industry he brought with him the principle of reflex camber – seen in many of his own now-classic designs starting with the Lotus Elite (the first all-GRP one) and embodied in some form or another in the majority of sports and many other cars today. Like many other

equally great ideas, it is perfectly simple to grasp but not so easy to apply merely by imitation: you must first study the background theory and make an effort to understand what you're dealing with.

Reflex camber describes the horizontal centreline of a longitudinal body section – the side view of your car – where the centreline curves continually, gradually, from a point lower at the front than at the rear: the body constructed around such a mean centreline will be aerodynamically stable *without ground effect interference* and will have a minimum of induced drag. Since all those years after the first Elite many sports cars still bear a very striking resemblance to it, it is entirely probable that the perfect sports car when – if – we ever set eyes on it, may not startle us at all. It will be the final proof of how much Frank Costin was ahead of his time and almost everyone in it.

13 The Drivetrain

The drivetrain consists of the engine with its ancillaries, the gearbox, the propeller shaft, the final drive unit or differential, and the drive shafts to the wheels. The creator of a special car will of course have considered these essential components of a motorcar many times at various steps in the development of his design. We have made reference to the size of the engine in its external dimensions and by displacement, to the comparative combustion efficiency of engines, and to the bhp and torque required from the engine to satisfy various performance parameters. You now need to bring all these factors together with some other important considerations so that you can choose the logical engine, together with ancillaries, gearbox, propshaft and final drive and drive shafts.

Once the most common entry to special cars was for those who owned a set of good mechanicals clothed by a lace of rust (often an MoT failure) to buy a chassis and/or body to put the car back on the road. I cannot recommend this. The special car, however humble, is too expensive for such a random method of making your choice; in the end it will work out cheaper to sell the rust bucket or to exchange it for a rust bucket with more desirable mechanicals, and then to build your special car.

Many special car builders choose their mechanicals because the shape of kit car they want fits only those mechanicals, e.g. all those VW Beetle kits.

Others choose their mechanicals because they're cheap and plentiful – Cortinas or Pintos or, in Britain at least, rusted MGBs – and this is a good way to go because the more common the base machinery, the easier and cheaper it is to uprate and to maintain in standard form. (I have my doubts about the Cortina Mk III front suspension used on some kits but that's another matter – the drivetrain is a bargain.)

This listing makes it sound simple to choose an engine but that is an entirely false impression. Even if you are designing from scratch and you have followed all the steps which should have, theoretically, described the perfect engine for you, the choice is still likely to be bewildering. Nevertheless it is very important to choose the right drivetrain.

Most people new to special cars would think that the simple Beetle chassis takes the air-cooled flat four VW engine in any of its sizes and that's it. Many would also know that, since the Porsche flat six air-cooled engine was derived from VW engines via a Porsche flat four, there is the possibility of fitting these more potent engines. Just these two choices force a bewildering variety of subsidiary decisions on the size and level of the performance of the engine – from 40hp to over 300hp! But even that's not all. You can buy adaptors off the shelf to match the Beetle chassis with small Ford water-cooled engines, Rover-Buick V8 engines, Corvair engines, Chevrolet V8 engines all the way up to 454cid (7.5 litres) among others. You can turn the VW chassis into a mid-engined configuration with the aid of alterations, adaptors, or a brand-new specially designed chassis to take VW kit bodies.

RELATING PARAMETERS

As I have shown, your choices about the top speed of your car or its acceleration or economy determine what *kind* of an engine you're looking for by specifying its required bhp, torque and efficiency with fuel. We have seen that the bhp is determined by the required top speed for a given aerodynamic efficiency coefficient:

$$\text{BHP required} = \frac{\text{Cd} \times \text{A} \times \text{v}^3}{146,600 \times 0.7}$$

and that this formula can be rearranged to give us the speed an engine of a given bhp will give with Cd and A fixed. We also saw that the acceleration from standstill to 60mph depends for a car of a given weight on the torque so that:

$$t_{0-60mph} = \frac{\text{Kerb weight} \times 0.55}{\text{Torque}}$$

which can be rearranged to tell us how much torque we want in order to achieve, with a given weight of car, a desired acceleration:

$$\text{Torque required} = \frac{\text{Kerb weight} \times 0.55}{t_{0-60mph}}$$

Torque relates to the amount of work done by an engine while its power relates to the rate at which it works so that Power = work done or time for the work to be done. So that we don't buy an engine that turns fantastic revs but does no more work because no more torque is developed, we then compare the brake mean effective pressure of competing engines:

$$\text{bmep} = \frac{\text{hp} \times 13,000}{\text{cubic capacity in litres} \times \text{rpm}}$$

(1 litre is 61 cubic inches).

All these things are related to each other:

$$\text{hp} = \frac{\text{torque} \times \text{rpm}}{5250}$$

$$\text{torque} = \frac{\text{hp} \times 5250}{\text{rpm}}$$

at any particular engine speed – but note that peak power and peak torque will not occur at the same rpm. Also:

$$\text{torque} = \frac{\text{bmep} \times \text{swept volume in cc}}{2473}$$

(61 inches is 1000cc).

All this is fine and well but may well – *will*, in most cases – leave the special builder with a bewildering variety of engines that meet or exceed his requirements for horses, torque and efficiency, and perhaps even the additional parameter of lb/hp – pounds per horsepower.

ENGINE DESIGN

The torque of an engine depends very largely upon its cubic capacity or swept volume. The larger the engine, the greater the torque output, all other things being equal. Other but minor influences on the torque an engine will develop include the type of valve gear, the compression ratio, and the design and execution of engine breathing details, especially those that govern mid-range volumetric efficiency.

Table 13.1.
The brake mean effective pressure of some highly regarded engines makes interesting reading – especially where engines readily available at the scrap yard have crept in unannounced.

Engine	BMEP – psi
Cosworth (quad valve) Mercedes 190	190
Lotus 2.2 (non-turbo)	182
Ferrari 512i BB	166
Jaguar AJ 3.6	165
Porsche 911 Carrera	164
BMW 3.5 CSi	164
Ferrari 308GTB	162
Mercedes 280	158
Lamborghini V12 Countach	157
Ford XR3i	156
VW Golf GTi	156
Porsche 928 S2	150
Jaguar V12 (May Heads) HE	148
Ford Capri 2.8i	141
Jaguar XK4.2	138

More horsepower will come from the engine which has more cubic inches, a higher compression ratio, or which turns more revs. Detail design is much more critical than is the case in determining the torque output of an engine. Both the power per litre of the engine and the engine speed at which maximum power is developed will increase when the induction pressure is increased (this is the case for ram stacks on carbs and for forced induction by either mechanical superchargers or turbos), when the valves are big and open wide ("high lift") in relation to cylinder diameter. All other things being equal, the engine with the longer stroke in relation to its bore will develop the lesser power *and* at lower revs. Also, all other things being equal, the engine with many cylinders will produce more power than the one with few cylinders *for the same capacity*.

There is not space here to go into the theory behind all this but interested readers may follow it through the various editions of Colin Campbell's book. The main point is that the reader should choose, in general and unless there are pressing reasons to the contrary, the engine with the "square" or "oversquare" or at least short stroke over those of long stroke because the big bore engine will not only deliver more power at lower revs but will be more easily developable should you want to increase the power output later.

One more important point lurks here: the higher the compression ratio the more efficiently and economically the engine will work. You should therefore choose the engine with the highest compression ratio compatible with the fuel available in your area. Note that fuel additives may be used to increase the octane rating; in Britain the best one is made by Aldon.

This brings us two steps further towards selecting the ideal engine for your car. Let's look at the choice from a practical rather than a theoretical viewpoint.

POPULAR ENGINES

By far the world's most popular engine ever is the small block Chevrolet of which 35,000,000 were built.

The mouse motor Chevy is a hot rodder's heaven and is, quite simply and without exception, the best engine in terms of horses per dollar (and often per lb and per £ as well) that you can buy or bolt on from Chevrolet part bins. It is an engine so simple that you can take it apart with three spanners, it is designed to be impossible to assemble wrong unless you try very hard indeed, it has fewer parts than many four cylinder engines – and in horses per pound it is a match for many all-ali engines. If you live in the States or Australia, you can't beat a small block Chevy. For European use (and petrol prices) an engine that starts at 265cid and of which the good ones are all over 5 litres and up to 5.7 litres (302–350cid) is a near relative of overkill.

American and European rodders have two popular

Figure 13.1. Straightforward, common and cheap, the small four-in-line engine from a mass manufcturer is a good choice for the novice special builder. This one is a Ford ohv.

Figure 13.2. The American base engine is this Pinto. Two litres – and an overhead cam – is a step up for the Europeans.

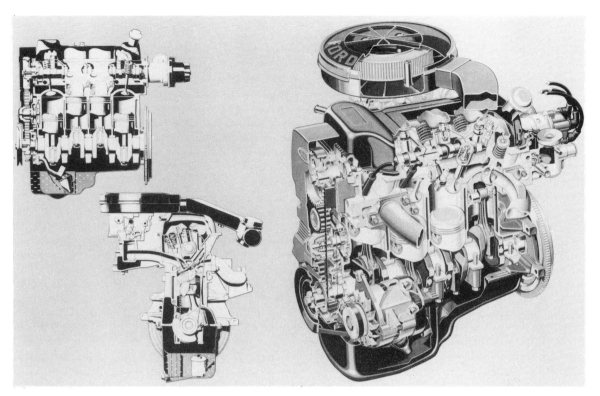

Figure 13.3. The CVH Ford engine from the Escort and Lynx offers the versatility of transverse front or mid-mounting or front-engined rear-drive configuration.

engines in common: the air-cooled flat four VW and the 2.0-litre Pinto/Cortina overhead cam engine. Both of these are good engines with solid aftermarkets. The Ford has, in Europe, smaller brothers of 1.6 and 1.3 litres; a newer sibling, the CVH engine, is available in the States as well as Europe (note that it can be used as a transverse front or mid-engine or mated to various in-line boxes to drive the rear wheels from the front in the traditional manner). These engines are more expensive than the OHC and crossflow (also Europe only) Ford fours.

Europeans who want to go bigger can, as their American counterparts, fit a V6. The European choice is often the Ford of 3.0 or 2.8 litres. Hot rodders are also keen on the Chevrolet V8 or the other American engines from Ford and Chrysler; all three of the big V8 manufacturers have found favour with limited-production special builders in Europe. Those who want a smaller V8 can choose the Rover-Buick 3.5 litre (215cid) and Australians can go all the way up to 4.4 litres; this is my favourite engine but it was only in production in the States for three years in the early

1960s so, if I lived there, availability would probably point me at the small block Chevy.

The other very popular engine in Europe is the British Leyland (Austin and Morris) A and A-plus which can be used transversely at the front or the centre of the car or in-line driving from the front to the rear wheels. From under one litre to just over 1400cc in specialist but still roadable 110bhp trim, this one can be a cheap choice – or it can cost as much as a good pre-loved Chev engine: it depends entirely on what you want the engine to do for you.

The alert reader will notice that I left the straight-sixes right out. There are two reasons for this: size and money. A four cylinder engine installed at the front of a car to drive the rear wheels can virtually always be replaced by a bigger-capacity four, a V6 or a V8 by the simple expedient of measuring carefully; if you're willing to do a very modest amount of alteration work, you can fit any V8 where an in-line rwd four came out. This is simply not true of in-line sixes. They are *very* long motors. On my large nostalgicar design shown in Figure 10.11 (page 120) the bonnet seems to stretch for

155

a mile – but fitting an in-line six would be a shoe-horn operation, some would not fit at all, many of those which would fit would probably run hot for lack of air circulating around them, and the shape of the bonnet might cause induction problems.

Besides, in-line sixes as desirable as a V8 cost more to buy, to rebuild and to keep going – and the choice is really not very large, since most current in-line sixes are left-over truck engines due for redesign at any time. I can think of only four in-line sixes the special car builder should consider on their own merits rather than for the appearance of filling a nostalgicar bonnet. They are: the Jaguar XK engine in the 3.4- or 3.8-litre sizes, the other sizes being inferior in output or too highly stressed (this long-stroke engine which first was conceived during World War II is the ultimate 1930 Grand Prix engine); the BMW straight six in sizes from 2.0 to 3.5 litres (expensive to buy and keep up to scratch but a technical marvel for the engineers, as are both the Jags here discussed); the Mercedes 2800cc twin cam which is a very advanced design (expensive to buy but very durable and 185hp from 2.8 litres makes it a very efficient engine); and, finally, the world's premier in-line six, the 24-valve Jaguar AJ6 engine which offers 225hp in its mildest form and weighs 470lb (the same as the 160hp Ford 2.8 V6). Of these four, I would personally fit only the Merc and AJ6 because the XJ engine has long been outclassed in hp per £ and hp per lb by the Rover V8 or small block Chev suitably breathed-on; the BMW valvegear frightens both me and my bank manager even though it is known to be durable if properly cared for. The two that I would fit are not price-competitive with engines of lesser breeding in initial purchase, in work or parts to extend the performance if necessary, in availability of aftermarket gear, though maintenance and operating costs may be only marginally more expensive for the in-line sixes than the V8s.

Other engines not really worth considering are V4s, rotary engines and V12s – some of these may be cheap to buy but they cost more to fix and there is no aftermarket even if there is a dealer right next door.

So, unless you are stuck with the VW or some other engine because that's what your kit demands, the engines I think you should consider first are: in the States, the small block Chevrolet and the Ford Pinto; in Britain, the Rover V8, the Ford in-line four cylinders up to 2 litres, and the Austin/Morris/BL A series or A-Plus engine. This is not, as seems at first glance, a mere handful of engines: the 3.5-litre Rover V8 for instance has at least two basic designs and five tune levels that were all sold in Britain plus the different Stateside castings, the bigger capacity Australian engine and, just in case you're interested in

exotica, Repco in Australia turned it into a 4.5-litre for Jack Brabham's Grand Prix racers and Techno in the States had their own big bore programme. Besides all this, there is an aftermarket that will allow you to attain any stage of tune you like with or without reason. In addition, Austin-Rover are working on a 2.8-litre version and at least one special builder has been allowed to "borrow" such an engine. To attempt to list all the size and power variants of the small block Chevy or the Ford fours would be futile: the point is there is still, even at this somewhat arbitrary cut-off level, a confusing choice.

In practice, however, you will decide on an engine, read the trade papers and small ads and visit the breaker's yards. All the variants will not be available without extensive search (and probably expense) so that what you can get then limits the choice. Before rushing out and buying a used engine, note that it is often possible to buy a brand-new engine quite cheaply when the big wholesalers find themselves overstocked, but do allow for "dressing" with the necessary ancillaries and auxiliaries. Sometimes kit car manufacturers either include a complete drivetrain in the price (Caterham Seven – and some very desirable drivetrains too) or will sell it to you with your kit cheaper than you can buy the separate parts at retail, i.e. they pass some of the bulk-purchase ex-factory savings on to you.

A HOT ENGINE?

Should you fit a hot engine right from the word go? That depends on what you want to use the car for and your driving style. If you are used to driving an ultra-hot engine all the time, fine. But, in general, my experience is that the most suitable engine is the one that gives the desired performance levels straight out of the box or from the scrapyard. This usually means choosing the larger displacement engine rather than the smaller or, with an existing engine, swapping in a bigger standard engine rather than attempting to increase the performance of the engine-in-place. There are two reasons for following this course. The first is cost. Aftermarket parts and work cost more per additional horse than buying a bigger engine. Since weight is the main determinant of fuel economy, a big engine in a small car, used reasonably, need not be less economical than a small engine in the same car; many's the hot rodder and road racer who will tell you they went one size up and got not only better performance but better mileage and certainly the small block Chevies in my Healeys (but not the big block Chryslers) gave better fuel consumption – and toweringly better performance – than Austin engines half the size. A bigger engine is less highly stressed to produce the

Figure 13.4. Many people, fed up with Econobox Lookalike Marknothings, choose a distinctive appearance before performance. For them, Neville Trickett conceived this VW-based GP Madison.

same horses than a highly modified, high-revving small engine and so will last longer, another cost consideration. The second reason for choosing the higher displacement engine is that, however carefully you set your parameters and work out your requirements, a time will come when you want just a little more from the engine. If the engine is already highly modified, that may be the last straw; if it is even modestly modified, that bit extra may make it impossible to drive with pleasure because it now becomes too high-strung and, besides, may be more expensive than merely modifying the engine because you may have to change the rear axle ratio and/or the gearbox in order to enjoy the little bit extra you want. Fitting the big standard engine first off allows you scope for development at a later date.

The next question is how to choose the standard engine I want to start with, given that there may be two or three or sometimes many more versions of the same engine, all with different hp and torque outputs at different rpm levels? This is relatively simple: choose your final drive and gearbox first and your engine choice will be obvious.

FINAL DRIVE AND GEARBOX

One often hears special car builders ask if the final drive or box they have in mind will be strong enough. This is the wrong question – the answer is, yes, most final drives and transmissions are strong enough to deal with the torque they were designed for together with a very substantial safety margin. As long as you stick with the box and final drive that your engine normally takes, you shouldn't have problems; if you hot the engine up, you can usually find a direct swap from a heavy duty or GT model higher up the range. But, as I say, this is the wrong issue, a subsidiary concern – the last question you should ask about a transmission or final drive (as long, of course, as you aren't being stupid and fitting a box designed for a one-litre car to 5.7 litres of small block Chevy).

The correct and important first question should be: Are the ratios of this box and the ratio of this final drive the correct ones for my application?

The gearbox and the final drive multiply the engine's torque with the aim, ideally, to let the engine work at its most efficient under all driving and road conditions and at all speeds; the final drive also turns

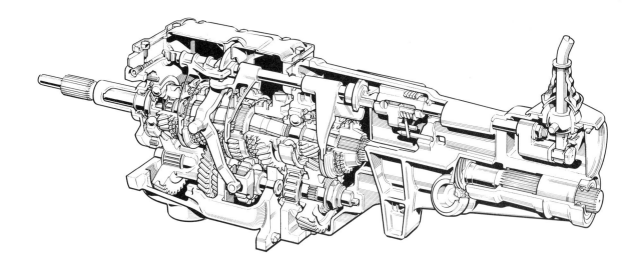

Figure 13.5. Many enthusiasts consider a five-speed box a necessity. Fuel scares have made them common and from the large choice I like those of Ford (illustrated) and Toyota.

the transmitted power through 90°. You will find that both the gearbox ratios (usually three, four or five) and the final drive ratio are quoted as a number such as 2.9:1. For the gearbox ratios, this gives the number of times the engine will turn for each turn of the prop-shaft; for the final drive, the number of times the prop will turn for each turn of the drive shafts (and therefore the wheels). Say that the gearbox ratio is 2.9:1 and the final drive ratio 3.06:1, the rear wheels will then "see" a ratio of $2.9 \times 3.06 = 8.87$:1 – the rear wheels will turn once for each 8.87 revolutions of the engine. There is a bit of confusing nomenclature here as the *higher numbers* represent the *lower ratios*, thus 2.88 is a higher ratio than 4.1. The point is that for the same speed, the 2.88 final drive will require the engine to turn only 2.88/4.1 the revs of a car fitted with the 4.1 final drive – obviously a more economical procedure. On the other hand, the 4.1 ratio multiplies the torque many more times than the 2.88 ratio, so if your rubber can stand it, in theory a car with a suitable torquey engine will accelerate 4.1/2.88 times better with the 4.1 than the 2.88 final drive. This of course assumes a suitable gearbox as well but, while there is ample choice, a gearbox swap is much more involved than a final drive ratio swap or even a complete final drive replacement. For many final drives a number of internal components giving different final drive ratios are available and most often also a "quick change rear-end" which is merely a covering plate that can be quickly removed to replace the gears with which you just burned up the drag strip by the gears that are going to give you 50mpg on the way home. Special car builders – unless they're building rally or racing cars or out and out dragsters – therefore normally stick to the top standard gearboxes, sometimes tweaking the slower types of auto-boxes a bit, that can be fitted directly or via aftermarket adaptors to their engines, and swap the final drive ratios for the desired compromise between acceleration and top speed and economy. An easy formula to use for the top road speed in any gear is:

Road speed mph in any gear

$$= \frac{\text{rpm} \times \text{tire circumference}}{\text{overall gear ratio} \times 1056}$$

where the tire circumference is the distance from the top of the tire to the ground in inches (under load this is different from the dimension horizontally across the tire) multiplied by 3.1416 and the overall gear ratio is the gearbox ratio multiplied by the final drive ratio. In theory, this is a calculation for the maximum rpm the engine can safely pull but in practice the best acceleration, as opposed to merely the top speed in each gear, will be given by changing at the revs where the torque delivered *at the rear wheels* drops least between gear changes.

158

Table 13.2: Axle interchangeability.
The axles in each box are directly interchangeable. Note in particular that all the Jaguars diffs from 2.88:1 to 4.55:1 make straight swaps. The final drives for American cars are not listed as the poss-ible swaps are almost unlimited. The ratio is nor-mally stamped on the casing; if not, you can turn the input shaft and count the turns of the half shafts. Open it up and count the teeth if you want an absolutely exact measurement.

	Ratio	Crownwheel teeth	Pinion teeth	From
FORD	3.9	39	10	Escort, Cortina 1, Cortina 2, Corsair, Zephyr/Zodiac up to 1965
	3.77	34	9	Escort, Cortina 2
	4.125	33	8	Anglia, Classic, Corsair
	4.444	40	9	Anglia, Cortina 1, Cortina 3 1300
	4.111			Cortina 3 1600
	3.89	35	9	Cortina 3 1600
	4.375			Zephyr/Zodiac to 1965
	3.54			Capri (in-line)
	4.444	40	9	Zephyr/Zodiac to 1965
	4.111			Zephyr/Zodiac to 1965
	3.9	39	10	Zephyr/Zodiac to 1965
	4.625			Mk I Consul
	4.556			Mk I Consul
	3.444	40	9	V4 Capri
	3.222			V6 Capri
	3.09			V6 Capri
JAGUAR	2.88			E-type Manual, XJS, XJ12 HE
	3.07	43	14	4.2 Auto, V12 Auto
	3.31	43	13	4.20 Manual, V12 Manual, all XJ12
	3.54	46	13	S-type Manual and Auto, 4.2 XJ Auto & Overdrive
	3.77	49	13	S-type Manual, Auto & Overdrive, Mk 10 Auto & Overdrive
	4.09	54	11	XJ 2.8 Manual & Auto
	4.55	50	11	XJ 2.8 Manual & Overdrive
BMC/BL	5.375	43	8	Minor, Morris 1000
	4.875	39	8	Minor, Morris 1000
	4.555	41	9	Morris 1000, 950 versions of A40, Sprite, Midget, A35
	4.222	38	9	Morris 1000, 1100 versions of A40, Sprite, Midget, A35
	3.9	39	10	Midget, Sprite 1275
	3.727	41	11	Sprite, Midget 1970 onwards
	4.111			Marina 1.3
	3.636			Marina 1.8
	4.111			Spitfire 1.3
	3.89	35	9	Spitfire 1.3

This formula can be rewritten to help you choose your final drive and gearbox top speed ratio, which in overdrive boxes need not be the final or even top two ratios (an overdrive ratio is higher than 1:1, i.e. 0.77:1 meaning that the engine turns less than a full revolution for each revolution of the propshaft – another economy measure):

Top speed gear ratio × Final drive gear ratio

$$= \frac{\text{rpm} \times \text{tire circumference}}{\text{top speed} \times 1056}$$

where the top speed is limited by the bhp for the car's given Cd and frontal area as we determined in earlier chapters. A useful version, if you've run out of gearboxes but still have choices left in final drive ratios, is this one:

$$\frac{\text{Final drive}}{\text{ratio}} = \frac{\text{rpm} \times \text{tire circumference}}{\text{top speed} \times \text{gearbox ratio} \times 1056}$$

In all the best cars, maximum safe rpm is also the maximum aerodynamic speed in one of the gears, and you should try to choose your ratios accordingly.

Note, in all this, that the rolling radius of the wheels increases with speed, so that we are working in approximations; the error is too small to lose sleep over.

It is obvious that you want to choose an engine, gearbox and final drive combination that works

Figure 13.6. Transverse boxes are not as easily swapped between engines as in-line boxes but most are well matched, so there is little call for swaps.

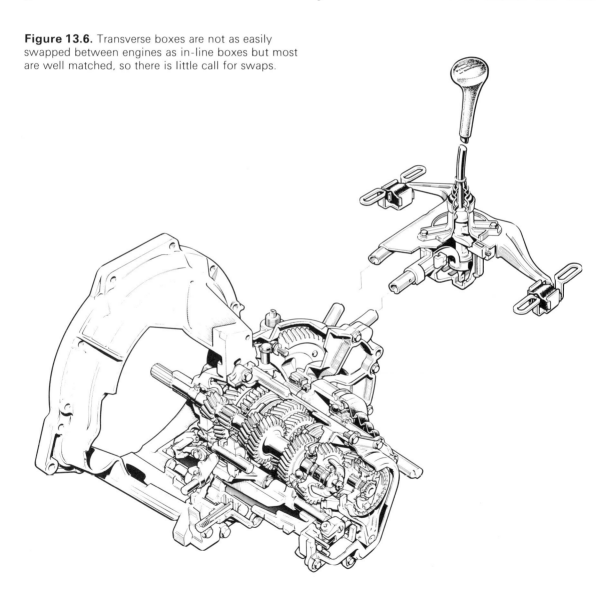

together. It is no good having an engine that makes maximum power at 7000rpm if your car with the given gearbox and final drive will reach maximum speed at 5000rpm because of wind resistance. It is no good having gearbox and final drive ratios that with a given engine will rocket you to 60mph in nothing flat – at which stage the engine runs out of revs and uses huge amounts of fuel just to keep up on the motorway. You must compromise and, generally speaking, since top speed is given for your particular engine and gearboxes are pretty standard items, what you will compromise through your choice of final drive ratio, is acceleration versus touring economy.

To summarise, choose the engine that in standard form will give the bhp and torque for the top speed and acceleration you want, then match it with a gearbox and final drive so that peak power rpm coincides with the top "aerodynamic" road speed, choosing your lower gear ratios (if you can) so that you will at each gear change lose the least amount of torque at the rear wheels at least to 60mph, preferably to 90mph. For best economy, choose a multiple speed box with an overdrive top gear or gears.

OVERTAKING ACCELERATION

Until now we have contented ourselves with a single acceleration parameter, namely the important one of 0–60mph. But we did specify that it is extremely desirable for a "proper" car to be able to accelerate from 60 to 90mph in no more time than from 0 to 60mph and, moreover, that overtaking increments as determined by your driving style and the roads on which you will use the car are also important. This can be calculated quite closely with the aid of Koffman constants to correct the simple Newtonian formula for the polar moment of inertia of the rotating parts of the engine and the polar moment of inertia of the road wheels. The polar moment of inertia of the engine varies from gear to gear and for the road wheels with speed as the rolling radius increases with speed. That is, these correction factors vary with speed, so that the calculations are complex. Besides, the information about the polar moments of inertia of the engine is not available to the special car builder. Campbell shows a set of Koffman calculations for a Jaguar XK150S in an appendix.

There is an alternative which uses information we already have or can easily obtain, plus simple math. Since we have already calculated the bhp required to drive the car to its desired maximum speed against air and road resistance and with an allowance for frictional losses in the drivetrain, it is easy to calculate the bhp required at lower speed, say at 5mph intervals from

standstill to maximum. These hp requirements can then be converted to torque figures with this formula:

$$\text{Torque} = \frac{(5250 \times \text{hp} \times 60 \times \text{rolling diameter of tire in feet})}{(\text{mph} \times \text{overall gear ratio in top} \times 5280)}$$

where mph is the speed at which the hp is required and the overall gear ratio is that of the highest (lowest numerical ratio) gear, i.e. unity in the case of a direct top gear and less than unity in the case of an overdrive top) multiplied by the final drive ratio. The rolling diameter of the tire is tricky, as it varies with speed but measuring from the top of the tire to the ground will give you an approximation; the tire companies supply this information on request.

The table of torque figures so achieved can then be transformed to tell the tractive force required at the rear wheels to maintain the speed at each calculated point:

$$\text{Tractive effort (lbf) required} = \frac{(\text{torque in ftlb} \times \text{overall gear ratio})}{(\text{effective rolling radius of driving wheel tire in feet})}$$

where the rolling radius is the dimension taken from the hub centre to the ground of the loaded tire at operating temperature, either measured or obtained from the manufacturer. You could also calculate the effective rolling radius by taking a car of similar weight on the same tires, running them until they're hot (10 miles at 70mph minimum), making a mark on the circumference, rolling the car forward, measuring on the ground; this measurement divided into the number of feet in a mile, 5280, will also give you the tire revs per mile, which is often useful to know.

The tractive effort required over a range of speeds makes a curve such as the lowest line in Figure 13.7. It curves steeply upwards because the aerodynamic resistance rises as the square of the speed. It is called a tractive resistance curve. It is obvious that at some point, the point where maximum speed is achieved, this tractive resistance will be matched by an equal and opposite force, the tractive effort. It follows from this that at any speed below maximum speed, there must be a surplus of tractive effort – which is what we are interested in because *it can be used for acceleration from that speed.* This surplus tractive effort depends on the tractive resistance at the speed under consideration, which we have already calculated, on the torque curve of the engine, and will vary according to the gear ratios that may feasibly be used at that speed without over-revving the engine. The gear ratios are known (we may be comparing several boxes to see which will give the

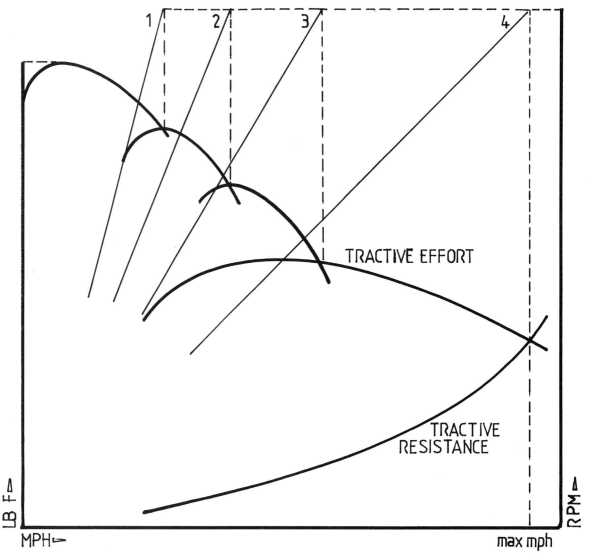

Figure 13.7. Cascades of tractive effort: the difference between what is available and what is required merely to maintain a given speed is then free for acceleration or climbing hills. The gear ratios in this example are perfectly chosen for change points at the same rpm level. A different gearbox would of course have different cascades and change points.

best acceleration). The torque curve can be had from the manufacturer or calculated from an available horsepower curve or from the dyno operator if you've had an engine rebuilt and dynoed* (or, more commonly, if you fit aftermarket parts: reputable parts manufacturers will supply you on request with the new curve) or the tractive effort at the rear wheels in each

gear at each rev level may for complete cars be obtained either directly from the rollling road (correctly, "chassis dynometer") or by calculation from the coast-down method described in Chapter 14.

The tractive effort available at each rpm interval – say every 500rpm – in each gear can then easily be calculated:

Tractive effort at rpm in gear (lbf) =

$$\frac{(\text{torque (ft/lb) at same rpm} \times \text{gear ratio} \times \text{final drive ratio})}{(\text{effective rolling radius of driving wheel tire in feet}}$$

---

*Correct flywheel bhp by ± 2.5% for each pair of gears or each universal joint between the flywheel and the driven wheels before calculating further.

and a table constructed from which the cascades (correctly "curves of tractive effort") in Figure 13.7 can be drawn.

Where the curves cross lies the rpm at which you should change gear for maximum acceleration; if the curves do not cross, change at maximum safe rpm. (If, on an existing car all you want to know is where to change gear for best acceleration, there is no need to go through this whole rigmarole: you can merely determine for each rpm interval for each gear that rear axle torque equals torque at that rpm multiplied by the overall gear ratio in that gear, and construct your cascades from that – your gear changes should still be where the lines intersect.)

The distance between the tractive resistance (i.e. the tractive force required to maintain that speed on level ground without wind) and the total tractive effort available represents the tractive force available for climbing hills or accelerating the car from that speed. If you look at Figure 13.7 closely, you will see that this differential at some speeds in a gear is nearly twice that in the next higher gear.

If you then measure and tabulate (or read from your tables) the maximum tractive force available for acceleration at each speed, you can project the acceleration of your car:

Acceleration in g =
$$\frac{\text{(surplus tractive effort at base speed)}}{\text{(all-up weight including driver and passengers)}}$$

where the base speed is wherever you want to start accelerating and g is $32.2\,\text{ft/s}^2$. Note that the acceleration will be limited to the coefficient of friction between the road and the tires if this is less than the calculated theoretical acceleration; also, with live rear axles, one wheel can lift off the ground and spin around uselessly, a problem that is merely alleviated by a limited slip diff; for good acceleration you must watch your rubber and suspension design.

The formula above is all right for instantaneous acceleration but over speed increments of 20mph, such as the ones we are normally interested in, and the one of 30mph from 60 to 90mph that we are particularly interested in, the surplus tractive force varies too much and we must resort to averages to calculate whether the car will accelerate over the speed increment in the desired time. To find the average surplus tractive effort, merely add up the surplus tractive effort every five miles (or every three or every one mile) over the speed range under consideration and divide by the number of readings. We know that

Average acceleration, ft/sec^2 =

$$\frac{[(\text{higher mph} - \text{lower mph}) \times 5280\,\text{feet per mile}]}{(\text{time in seconds} \times 3600\,\text{seconds per hour})}$$

and this is easily converted to g by further dividing by 32.2. Therefore,

$$\frac{\left(\begin{array}{c}\text{average surplus tractive effort over desired speed}\\ \text{increment}\end{array}\right)}{(\text{all-up weight})}$$

must equal

$$\frac{(\text{higher mph} - \text{lower mph}) \times 5280}{\text{time in seconds} \times 3600 \times 32.2}$$

and by transposition it is then easy to find that

Time to accelerate over speed increment, seconds =

$$\frac{[(\text{higher mph} - \text{lower mph}) \times 5280 \times \text{all-up weight}]}{(\text{average surplus tractive effort over speed increment} \times 3600 \times 32.2)}$$

If this time is too long, you can change the tractive effort at the rear wheels by changing the rear tire diameter, the final drive, the gear ratios, the engine torque curve or any or all of these in combination. Or you could reduce the weight of the car . . .

DON'T

Forget electric overdrives unless you get one free with your engine and box. They're heavy and complicated. A five-speed box is far superior. Forget close ratio boxes for road use. If you need one, you're trying to get too much from too small an engine and you'd do better fitting an engine with more cubes and consequently more torque.

Forget straight cut "racing" gears; you have to learn how to change them, they're noisy and they don't last.

Don't overmatch your differential and gearbox to too big an engine.

Don't mount the prop at too big an angle. The manufacturers will tell you what is safe but as a rule of thumb, don't go over 15° and don't forget that the output shaft from the gearbox and the input shaft to the final drive must lie parallel in side view and (in most cases) in a straight line in the other dimension. Don't forget to line up the universal joints with each other. Don't forget to have a shortened (or lengthened) propshaft balanced.

ENGINE DEVELOPMENT

Until now, we have regarded the engine as a black box with an output shaft about which you need to know absolutely nothing to build special cars. Though many special car builders enter the hobby either with or because of an extensive interest in and knowledge of

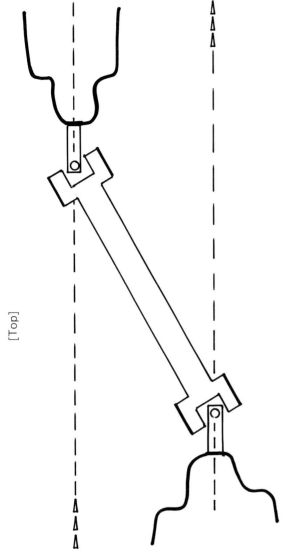

[Top]

Figure 13.8. It is essential that the engine output shaft and the final drive input shaft parallel to each other and, further, that the universal joints do not operate at an angle larger than that specified by the manufacturer.

internal combustion engines, it is not an essential; I built several very fast Healeys by dropping in bigger and bigger engines simply because I did not at the time feel competent to open up and develop whatever engine I had in the latest one. Today, having practised on a number of engines, I know more but the novice must not assume that engine work is easy: that would not be fatal, as incompetent suspension design and work could well be, but it would certainly be expensive.

A book much thicker than this one would be required merely to give you a full understanding of the principles of operation of the internal combustion engine. If you just fit engines, you don't need to know, but if you intend modifying one you *must*; even if you intend having it modified by someone else, you need at least some knowledge in order to judge the merits of his proposals and the quality of his work. That *minimum* I can share with you: for deeper knowledge you must go to a good book about the general practice of engine modification that offers theoretical explanations where necessary. Here I can wholeheartedly recommend A. Graham Bell's *Performance Tuning in Theory and Practice: Four Strokes* (Haynes/Foulis, 1981; there's also a companion *Two Strokes*) as a book that neatly balances all the essential theory with a good deal of blunt common sense. You must at the same time have a handbook or workshop manual for the engine you are fitting; the best ones are published by HP books (who cover the engines I've mentioned), by Haynes and by Autobooks. If you're interested in theory, read Colin Campbell.

Internal combustion

Our interest is in the Otto or four-cycle internal combustion engine, which is best described as a pump, specifically as an air pump. It uses this air, mixed with amounts of fuel regulated by the induction system, to move pistons up and down in a bore sealed by piston rings in a block, by alternately compressing and explosively expanding the fuel–air mixture. We shall return to the most interesting and most important part of an engine's operation, getting the air and fuel in and out, below, when we discuss valve gear and the cylinder head. The spark to ignite and explode the compressed air–fuel mixture is provided, logically enough, by a spark plug which is regulated by a distributor geared to the cam, which is part of the valvegear; the spark is intensified by the coil, or some kind of electronic black box. The pistons are connected by connecting rods (little ends to piston, big ends to crankshaft) to the crankshaft; the crankshaft turns rectilinear bidirectional movement into rotary movement and runs on bearings lubricated by the engine oil. The crank is connected to the flywheel (which smoothes out the pulsating power-delivery) which is connected in turn to the clutch or torque converter (an automatic clutch for automatically shifting gearboxes) which feeds power to the gearbox while allowing disengagement to change gears. The crankshaft is usually held in its bearings between the crankcase and the block and the bottom of the engine is covered by the sump pan, which catches the oil. An oil pump to pump oil to other parts of the engine that need lubrication is usually found either in the sump or on the outside of the engine; it is driven either from the crankshaft or the camshaft; the oil is always filtered though some filters are more efficient than others. The crankshaft also drives the camshaft by gears, chain(s) or belt(s); the cam revolves once for every two revolutions of the crank. The crank may have an internal or external vibration damper and at the front usually protrudes from the block to allow bolting on pulleys for the fan and drives for the alternator, air-conditioning and power-steering pumps, and other hydraulics and mechanical supercharger if fitted. The engine is cooled by either air or water from a liquid-to-air heat exchanger called a radiator; the water runs in water passages cast around the other holes in the block (and cylinder head).

Many horses can be had by attention to the bottom end of your engine. Alterations here are normally made to improve the lubrication, or to strengthen the engine for higher revs and more power, or, most commonly, to reduce frictional losses. The cubic capacity of an engine can be increased by fitting a "stroker" crank, but this is expensive work best reserved for racers; special car builders should fit a bigger engine before even considering one. If you're stripping your engine down anyway, often just painting the interior will result in better lubrication; there are also windage shields that prevent the oil from being flung around by the air disturbance of the crank, and dividers to stop it running around during cornering. Specific engines may need oil passages enlarged (or sometimes closed off) and/or better oil pumps for high-performance duties – ask the specialist who's doing your machining or the specialist you buy your parts from. Most bottom ends are pretty strong these days, so, by the time you need to strengthen it and if the engine is fitted in a road car, you have probably reached the point where it would be cheaper to fit a bigger set of cubes which will in any event be more pleasant to drive. In the small block Chevy (and several other V8s) you have the choice ex-factory or ex-breakers of two- or four-bolt main bearing retention and, if you have a choice, take the four-bolt mains, though it won't make much difference until you're getting well over a horse from every cubic inch. The 327cid Chevy came in two journal sizes – choose the big one if you can (the journal is the part of the crank on which the bearing sits); many other engines had the crankshaft strengthened during the production life and you should ask about this. In addition, many manufacturers offer special cranks, forged or toughened, and these are cheaper than having a one-off job done. For ultra-high-performance applications, a bearing girdle is available for some engines.

Blueprinting an engine simply means assembling it to the manufacturer's blueprints for optimum performance. Engines vary according to the tolerances allowed on the production line. The cycle of morale over a period of years can be important: Jaguar engines were pretty erratic to the nearest 25hp but the position has improved and most engines now give within a couple of per cent of the advertised power which compares favourably with Porsche, from whom you can expect any engine to give 204bhp on the dyno and 163 at the rear wheels on the rolling road. What the specialist builder does is to have his engine painstakingly and patiently machined to the blueprint spec in his handbook and then fit it together so that it is *exactly* as the designer intended it to be, not as some "fitter" passed it off. All of this costs more than you would believe but it is worth a few horses, usually between 5% and 15%, even on an engine from a reputable and consistent manufacturer. Fanatics can of course blueprint the whole drivetrain because what counts is the number of horses you can put on the road: see Table 13.3 to find out what happens to the fuel you burn and where you can make the savings. Racers in restrictive classes of the sport have been known to find as much extra as 20% of the advertised power by blueprinting.

Table 13.3: Automobile fuel energy use.

For each gallon of fuel burnt, only 12% or roughly one pint is used to propel the car forward. Your design should take account of this and attempt to minimize drivetrain energy losses by reducing friction, not overcooling the engine, etc.

	%	%
Engine auxiliaries	2	
Transmission	9	
Engine friction	13	
Exhaust heat loss	22	
Coolant heat loss	42	
DRIVETRAIN ENERGY LOSS		88
Rolling resistance	2.4	
Aerodynamic drag	3.2	
Braking resistance	6.4	
FORWARD PROPULSION		12
		100

The cylinder head and valvegear

For quite modest amounts of work and/or money spent

on aftermarket bolt-on parts, many horses can be discovered here, but as usual, there's a catch; you must thoroughly understand what you're doing. There are also a lot of cowboys and many misconceptions and areas of ignorance even among those who regularly earn their living at the modification of cylinder heads and valvegear; I shudder every time I see beautifully polished ports – they should be reasonably smooth but *not* polished because that helps to separate the drops of fuel out of the air – for which some poor ignorant sacrificed many hours or perhaps half a week's wages at a "specialist". The main thing is to keep in mind that moderation is a virtue; this is one area where biggest is not only *not* best but can actually have an adverse effect. Here again the law of diminishing returns applies: the first ten extra horsepower may not cost much but the next ten could cost twice that, the next ten five or six times as much, and the next ten twenty times as much – by which time you should long ago have swapped in the bigger engine.

As a guide, a standard engine should give you not less than 45bhp per litre, a good roadable sporting engine over 60bhp per litre and a hot engine for road use around 75–80bhp per litre. Any higher and you start worrying about tractability and durability: track racing engines pump out around 110bhp/litre. The precise numbers within these broad bands would depend on the exact breathing arrangements of the engine and the details of valvegear design, i.e. whether there are overhead cams and how many per bank of cylinders, as well as the compression ratio of the engine and the shape of the combustion chamber.

The cylinder head is a casting with waterways for cooling, a combustion chamber to burn the air and fuel in, ports to bring the air–fuel mixture to the combustion chamber, and more ports to guide the residual gasses away into the exhaust manifold and exhaust pipe and silencer. The inlet ports are connected to the inlet manifold which in turn carries carburretor or fuel injection mechanism (the latter could be part-electronic) which mixes the air and fuel in a predetermined ratio. The holes where the ports join the combustion

Figures 13.9, 13.10 and 13.11. Three Ford engines in the Caterham Super Seven: 1599cc standard, 84bhp, 0–60mph 7.5sec; Caterham twin carb, 110bhp, 0–60mph 6.5sec; VTA twin cam, 130bhp, 0–60mph 6.0sec. The oil cooler is in the most efficient spot, in front of the radiator.

chamber have valves in them which are opened by the camshaft either via pushrods or by acting directly on the rockers by which the valves are pivoted to the rocker shaft. The pushrods run on the cam in little buckets called cam followers or tappets. The valves have their own springs which close them again. We shall return below to the sequence in which the valves open and close. The cam can be either in the block or in the head; the latter is called an overhead cam. Many engines have only one cam for all their cylinders no matter how many banks of cylinders there are, e.g. the Rover V8; others may have one cam per *bank* of cylinders like the V12 Jaguar, and yet others may have twin cams per bank (i.e. two cams for an in-line engine and four cams for a V) in which case we talk of twin-cam or double-camshaft engines.

The complete sequence of functions of all the valves in a cylinder is performed every two revolutions (720°) of the crankshaft, i.e. every single revolution of the camshaft. As the piston descends, the inlet valve opens fully and the cylinder is filled with a mixture of air and vaporized fuel. This is the induction stroke. The piston then rises on the compression stroke while yet more air/fuel mixture pours in and part way up the bore the inlet valve closes. As the piston approaches top dead centre (the highest point it will reach) the spark plug sparks to ignite the mixture and the expansion of the exploding air and fuel drives the piston down. This is called the power stroke. When the piston approaches bottom dead centre (the lowest point it will reach) on the power stroke, the exhaust valve opens to let the burnt gasses escape. The piston turns about at bottom dead centre and rises, driving the "dead" gasses into the exhaust port. This is called the exhaust stroke. Before the piston reaches TDC on the exhaust stroke, the inlet begins to open and fresh air–fuel mixture starts entering the combustion chamber and continues to do so while the piston descends on the new induction stroke. The exhaust valve will meanwhile have closed not too long after the piston reached TDC. The average road cam would have a specification something like 20°–50°/50°–20° which you read as "inlet valve opens 20° before TDC and closes 50° after BDC, exhaust valve opens 50° before BDC and closes 50° after TDC". The inlet duration is $20° + 180° + 50° = 250°$ and the exhaust duration is similarly calculated. The greater the performance desired from the engine, the more air/fuel mixture you want to cram in (without supercharging), the greater the duration must be, also the overlap which is the period between inlet opening and exhaust closing, in this case 40°. Over 250° duration, we have sports cams and from about 280° to 290° duration cams are unsuitable for anything but racing.

If that was all there was to it, it would be easy. But the cam is shaped not only to *lift* the valve but to lift it at a certain speed to a certain height, to accelerate it away from its seat as briskly as possible and to seat it as gently as possible on closure. The valves and ports must be shaped to flow the right amount of air with exactly the correct amount of turbulence and in the correct direction. The combustion chamber must be shaped to get the maximum amount of energy from the fuel – and not to send unburnt fuel out of the exhaust or, worse, down the side of the piston to wash the oil from the cylinder walls and dilute and degrade the oil in the sump. All this must be done without overheating or overstressing any part either thermodynamically or mechanically.

Everything must work together: it is no good hogging the port out to the limit if the cam doesn't lift the valves high enough for long enough to flow all that air. It is no good fitting a big carb if the ports and valves won't pass the amount of air–fuel mixture it will flow. It is no good having everything right if the peak power rpm will then be so high that, with the given gearbox and final drive, you will never be able to get there because of the car's aerodynamic limitation.

But, despite these complications – and I'm giving only a brief gloss – there are things that you can do to increase the performance or economy of your engine if you understand what you are doing. Some of these things are free, i.e. they take only the time to understand things and to turn a spanner, and some cost for aftermarket parts or for professional machining.

Before you touch the engine, you should work through your complete drivetrain and mechanical parts to improve efficiency and reduce friction. For instance, cooling the engine is best done by water at a temperature only slightly below the maximum temperature you want to run your engine at but circulating very quickly: are the radiator, thermostat, fan and water pump capacities and speeds consistent with this? Can the friction of the wheel bearings be reduced? Work through the whole car like this asking common-sense questions about each and every component and you might be pleasantly surprised by picking up anything from 3 to 5% extra hp at the rear wheels even in a well-made car, sometimes more if you're using the more common and cheaper proprietary parts.

PERFORMANCE MODIFICATION

When you get a new engine or a rebuilt engine, drop the sump to check that there is no casting flash, shaken loose in transit, lying in it. Also check that at least the main bearing cap and conrod bolts are properly torqued up. If you remove the sump carefully, you may be able to use the gasket again.

The first step in modifying your engine is to put the standard engine in perfect tune and test it, either on a dyno, a rolling road, or an open piece of level road (average of three 0–70 accelerations each way, ditto for top speed in some lower gear) for a comparison.

The next step is economy-oriented but will usually pick up a few horses. This is to disassemble the heads and clean up with a grinder (on a cable attached to your drill – you can buy special grinders if you're going to make a habit of working on cylinder heads) all the casting flash inside the head, to radius sharp corners in the inlet and outlet ports very gently, and to match the inlet ports to the inlet manifold. All this must be done very gently, with the minimum of material taken out, because you only want to ease the airflow, not to increase it largely. If you make a mistake, the people who sell the little grinders will also sell you epoxy with which to build up the damaged areas again. Stay away from the valve seats until you have much more experience. Reassemble and test again, as after every modification.

That is as far as the novice should go in modification though he can confine himself to "bolt-on" parts; contrary to the name, many of them actually "bolt-in" but the concept includes everything you can fit to your engine without actually taking it out of your car, which is pretty wide even for an American term. There is no reason the novice should not do all the assembly of the modified engine himself if he takes care to read the handbook and patience to follow the instructions. The easiest way to describe how even the least mechanically minded of us can pick up some very impressive horses is by citing an example. Here I'm going to use a Chevy 350cid as an exemplar but remember that similar percentage increases can be obtained by treating lesser engines similarly. The engine described will be as from-the-box without even cleaning up the heads: all that is required from the builder is to wield the spanners, yet we're going to do better than double the bhp and add nearly 50% to the torque . . . all without touching any of the engine's internals except the camshaft (which will be a straight swap). But the point is not the enormous power gain, it is that all these things work together. First choose aftermarket parts your supplier tells you work together; alternatively, build your engine exactly like the example in *Hot Rod*

Figure 13.12. The cheap way to get more miles is to buy a good used engine. But if your engine is special like this twin-cam, it must go to a specialist rebuilder.

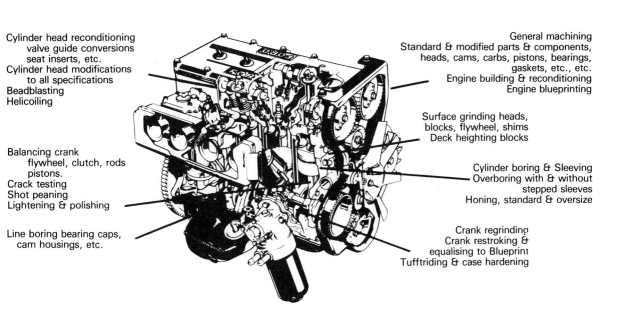

Cylinder head reconditioning
valve guide conversions
seat inserts, etc.
Cylinder head modifications
to all specifications
Beadblasting
Helicoiling

Balancing crank
flywheel, clutch, rods
pistons.
Crack testing
Shot peaning
Lightening & polishing

Line boring bearing caps,
cam housings, etc.

General machining
Standard & modified parts & components,
heads, cams, carbs, pistons, bearings,
gaskets, etc., etc.
Engine building & reconditioning
Engine blueprinting

Surface grinding heads,
blocks, flywheel, shims
Deck heighting blocks

Cylinder boring & Sleeving
Overboring with & without
stepped sleeves
Honing, standard & oversize

Crank regrinding
Crank restroking &
equalising to Blueprint
Tufftriding & case hardening

Magazine or *Cars and Car Conversions* and, if machining is involved, try to use their machinist for your job.

The Chevrolet 350cid 4-bolt-mains replacement engine arrives on its pallet. Take the sump off and shake it out; a new gasket is not required to refit the sump after we retorque every bolt and nut we can see according to the book. This engine is supposed to give a compression ratio of 8.5:1 but the real gen is that it gives 8.2:1, which is going to be useful later. Check the factory spec timing (6° at 650rpm for a total advance of 28° at 4000rpm) and break the engine in gently. With standard cast iron manifolds but freeflow exhausts plus the stock air cleaner, this engine dynoes 185bhp at 4000rpm and 286ft/lb torque at 3000rpm and has an operating range stretching from below 2000rpm to 4500rpm. This is of course better than it will do with the stock silencers (mufflers) but the dyno is not able to accommodate those, so we'll never know . . .

Step one

The first step is almost invariably to improve the engine's breathing and this does *not* mean bigger carbs straight off. First consider getting the gases that go in *out* again to make room for the new incoming fuel/air charge and perhaps to add a little suction. Factory cast-iron mufflers are fitted because they are Adequate (the other partners of the trio are Cheap and Nasty). Tuning the exhaust system is a big science that starts right at the manifold and aftermarket exhaust designers know their science and apply it. Graham

Figure 13.13. Don't match the exhaust port to the manifold (header); there should be an anti-reversionary mismatch, more at the top of the port than the bottom.

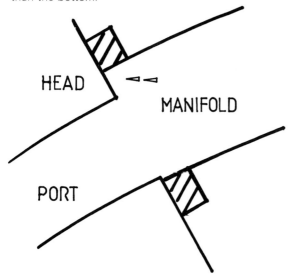

HEAD

MANIFOLD

PORT

Bell, whose book you must have if you're going to do anything more involved than I'm describing here, devotes nine large pages closely packed with sketches, tables and formulae merely to determining the length of the primary pipes and the collector and the effect of the megaphone if any, as well as the other dimensions of these parts. Longer pipes of smaller internal diameter will tend to improve mid-range power and lower the rpm at which peak torque occurs (which is what you want in a road engine), while shorter pipes of greater internal diameter will raise the revs at which you see peak torque and increase top-end power at the expense of mid-range or low-end power. If you go over the top and fit manifolds and piping that suck like Hoover, you might find that your engine runs only between 6500 and 8000rpm – and the rods are only good to 7000rpm.

For this exercise, we'll choose headers with $32 \times 1\frac{3}{4}$-inch primaries running into a 3-inch diameter collector. We'll keep the turbo silencers. A close inspection of any stock air cleaner will show that it will let through a great deal of muck and will restrict the airflow through the carb. Sling it out. Now fit a low-restriction air cleaner (K&N make the best ones): a good brand made to fit to your engine will be sure to flow enough air.

Finally, in this step, we'll advance the initial timing 8° to 14° to take advantage of the better breathing.

Now we see 230 horses at 4250rpm and 322ft/lb torque at 2500rpm and the engine's operating range has been extended by about 400rpm, gaining 45 horses and 36ft/lb (more, really) for a very modest outlay of money and time to buy and fit exhaust manifolds (headers), silencers, and air cleaner, and to reset the advance.

Note that the exhaust manifold must *not* be matched to the exhaust ports; a certain amount of mismatch is in fact beneficial. The port floor and exhaust manifold floor should match and all the mismatch should occur at the top of the port; you may have to trim the gaskets to prevent them hanging into and disturbing the airflow. Good aftermarket headers have this mismatch, so check for it.

Step two

In this step we want to get the full value of the improvement in exhausting the spent gases and we also want to cram in more fuel/air mixture to give the piston a bigger push. For that we want a bigger carburettor, a more effective manifold and a cam that will open the valves faster and hold them open longer. To make sure all the mixture is burnt at the right time, a new ignition may be called for; in this particular case

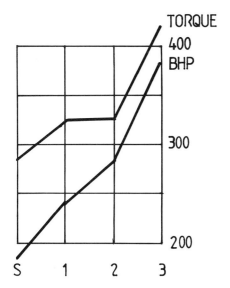

Figure 13.14. Modifying a stock engine in three stages, as described in the text, to nearly 400bhp and over 400ft/lb torque.

the engine came with the GM High Energy Ignition (HEI) which is very good indeed. The carb, the inlet manifold, the cam and the ignition may each in isolation be worth a few horses but it is as a package that they really make the engine come alive. Fitting only one or the other in isolation usually has unwanted side effects, like flat spots in the rev range. Resist the temptation to fit too big a cam or a carb: all the parts must be well matched, not only with the others in this step but also with the exhaust flow capacity achieved in Step One.

In this case the package is the Weiand Team G manifold, the factory L-82 Corvette hydraulic cam number 3896952 (the 929 cam found as standard in Mexican and Canadian assembled replacement 350s is a good cam with super low-end torque, if you want to keep it), a Holley 650cfm spread bore carb, and the HEI ignition package already fitted. Note that, on a used engine, you must fit new cam followers (tappets) when you fit a new cam. You must also check that the pushrods will take the rpm the new package will turn. In this case, since the engine is new, no new tappets are required; since the top revs in the next, most exotic state of tune will be only 5500 and the standard pushrods are good for 6500rpm, these too are okay. The cam grinder will tell you if the pistons need cut-outs to clear the new high valve lift and if stronger valve springs are needed – and will sell you the better springs. You can check for yourself whether the valves clear the pistons by assembling the engine with a piece

of child's play dough stuck to the top of the piston and then turning the engine and measuring carefully the compressed thickness of the dough. The standard Quadrajet carb can be made to give very respectable horses but the Brits don't seem at home with this carb and in the States a Holley is cheap enough to be more cost effective than working over the Quadrajet. The timing remains unchanged, also the spark plugs, because they're matched to the HEI just as the engine came off the pallet.

This step definitely involves more work and expense than the previous step. The power is now 275 horse-power at 5000rpm and the torque 322ft/lb at 3500rpm. Though the peak torque falls at higher rpm, the curve starts off higher than the "smaller" camshaft's curve, so that there is more torque available right off idle.

In Step One we gained 45 horses for a very modest outlay of time and money; this second 45 horses on top has cost three times as much money and five times as much time. The higher you go, the more each additional horse will cost in relation to the last incremental horse. But, for the money and the time – and still without modifying any part of the engine, still merely by bolting in or on pieces of equipment available over the counter at any good speed shop – we now have an engine that, installed in the car, will be torquier than a V-12 Jaguar and put out more ponies than a 5-litre Mercedes engine.

More horses still

To get any more horses with the naturally aspirated engine, the internals of the engine will have to be modified, together with the externals, to provide more flow and higher efficiency in the combustion chamber. The compression ratio will have to be raised and, unless you can get high-test fuel, this may lead to detonation which is, to say the least, not good for your engine. The inevitable result of trying to get more power from a naturally aspirated engine, already developed to this level of performance, by increasing port and valve sizes and associated work is that the rpm for peak revs and peak torque will be raised quite dramatically and that the usable power band of the engine will be narrowed, quite possibly faster than the increase in power. An engine that works only between 5500 and 8000rpm is not pleasant to drive on the road and the chances are that the rev band will be even narrower than that. The answer is forced induction by either mechanical supercharger or turbocharger.

Step three: supercharging

We will return to the relative merits of supercharging

and turbocharging below. Here it is enough to know that kits are available to bolt on to standard low-compression engines (high-compression engines must have the compression lowered, usually by changing the pistons or machining the combustion chambers or compression bumps on piston tops). The novice must buy a kit – don't try to put together your own – and the kit supplier provides instructions on the top compression ratio and the highest boost setting that will not wreck the engine.

In this case we had an already modified engine but kits are available for bolting to low-compression engines straight out of the box and the results should not sacrifice much because the supercharger rpm and consequently the amount of air it will pass can be changed by over- or under-driving it through merely swapping the driving pulleys. Kits are also available for higher-compression engines but these are usually more complicated and expensive.

The supercharger kit that was fitted to the engine on the dyno was underdriven by 11% and came complete with two modified 750cfm carburettors, one of which has a choke for cold-starting, making this a good kit for everyday use. Everything needed for installation is with the kit and set up for street use. The spark is further advanced according to the instructions, the supercharger bolted on – and horsepower jumps to 375 at 5500rpm and torque to 419ft/lb at 4000rpm with more than 300ft/lb of torque all the way from under 2000rpm up to 5500rpm. Many special car builders will consider that the cost of the extra 100hp (the same as the complete engine so far) rules this bolt-on goody right out; high-performance specialists might find the horses essential; hot rodders often give the impression that they find the appearance of a supercharger by itself worth the price of admission to the highest status levels of rodderdom; off-roaders might find the full-range torque essential. I like superchargers because they give such splendid low-end torque even to small engines and because the power is there *instantly*, something that the very best of turbochargers cannot promise.

Turbochargers and superchargers

You do not need a big engine to supercharge or turbocharge it: in fact, the main advantage of forced induction is that it gives a small engine the same low-end and mid-range torque as a big engine; forced induction is a viable alternative to additional cubic inches or the more normal modifications to the engine's breathing that increase the mass of air flowing through it by making it run faster. A high output naturally aspirated engine with a narrow powerband will require a multi-ratio gearbox or one with different ratio-spacing than a more flexible engine – and good gearboxes cost more new than turbo- or supercharger kits. The machining for a hi-po engine, together with its associated parts, costs about the same as a turbocharger or supercharger installation and within a few years forced induction will be cheaper than labour-intensive modification work. And for road use a hi-po engine that needs very high revs to work is not much fun.

Until quite recently, it was thought that forced induction required special preparation and machining, especially of the engine's bottom end. But careful consideration will show that the mechanical stresses in an engine with forced induction are no greater than in a similar engine that is naturally aspirated; forced induction may in fact be beneficial in evening up the pressures inside the combustion chamber and so making stress reversals less strenuous. This assumes that you force the induction within reason. In Step Three above, $9\frac{1}{2}$lb of boost was used, but in practice the engine would rarely see more than 6lb of boost; there are many superchargers on the market that will compete with turbo kits, most limited to about 6lb of boost which is enough to *double* the power output of a low-compression engine; turbo kits for unmodified engines of reasonable compression are normally wastegated to around $8\,\text{lb\,in}^2$ boost. The exact boost level will vary from engine to engine and kit to kit. It is important to buy a reputable kit and follow the assembly and use instructions, especially with regard to the maximum permissible boost, unwaveringly; you must also rigorously adhere to the service instructions, especially with regard to lubrication.

The mechanical reliability of properly designed and installed forced induction is not in question: I know of one supercharger installation that's done 60,000 miles and of more than one turbo with more than 100,000. As a rule of thumb, the supercharger or turbocharger should last the life of the engine. On road cars such as we've been discussing, I would expect that to be 60,000 miles minimum and normally at least 80,000. A truly strongly and meticulously engineered and built normally aspirated engine of the same power would have to be rebuilt at least twice and perhaps as many as four times during the same period and the cost would have to include brand-new heads each time, as the valve seats would have to be cut so narrow, to provide the great pressure that allows for the maximum transfer of heat from the valve to the head, that there would be no metal left for recutting the seats.

Together with the kits, information on forced induction is becoming generally available. If you're thinking of fitting this, you should read Hugh MacInnes's *Turbochargers* (HP Books, 1978); if you're going

Table 13.4: Supercharger over- and underdrives.

If you have the right pulleys, you can tailor your supercharger installation to give exactly the boost you want. The figures in normal type are overdrive percentages, normally of interest only to racers. For street use, you want the combinations of pulleys that result in the underdriven percentages shown in bold.

TOP PULLEY

BOTTOM PULLEY		32	33	34	35	36	37	38	39	40	41	42	43
	32	0	3%	6%	9%	13%	16%	19%	22%	25%	28%	31%	34%
	33	3%	0	3%	6%	9%	12%	15%	18%	21%	24%	27%	30%
	34	6%	3%	0	3%	6%	9%	12%	15%	18%	21%	24%	26%
	35	9%	6%	3%	0	3%	6%	9%	11%	14%	17%	20%	23%
	36	13%	9%	6%	3%	0	3%	6%	8%	11%	14%	17%	19%
	37	16%	12%	9%	6%	3%	0	3%	5%	8%	11%	14%	16%
	38	19%	15%	12%	9%	6%	3%	0	3%	5%	8%	11%	13%
	39	22%	18%	15%	11%	8%	5%	3%	0	3%	5%	8%	10%
	40	25%	21%	18%	14%	11%	8%	5%	3%	0	3%	5%	8%
	41	28%	24%	21%	17%	14%	11%	8%	5%	3%	0	2%	5%
	42	31%	27%	24%	20%	17%	14%	11%	8%	5%	2%	0	2%
	43	34%	30%	26%	23%	19%	16%	13%	10%	8%	5%	2%	0

to take the risky road of making up your own kit, you *must* study this seminal book very carefully indeed.

How do you choose between turbochargers and superchargers? Turbochargers give high specific outputs at high constant engine revolutions and are efficient even when lightly loaded. Superchargers are less efficient at light loads and take part of the extra power developed to drive the mechanical rotors whereas the turbo uses "waste" exhaust gases (don't let anyone tell you turbocharging is "free" — it can never be that but it can be very cheap in that you can minimize the backpressure). Superchargers offer instant response; turbochargers first have to pick up rotor speed, causing the dreaded turbo lag. All of these considerations used to lead to the use of turbochargers for applications where more or less constant high speeds were required and superchargers where instant response off the line or out of a corner was required (i.e. in competition). It really depends what you want to use the car for. For driving in traffic, for the traffic light grand prix, for cutting in and out of heavy traffic, the supercharger is best but you will pay in petrol consumption. For high-speed transcontinental journeys, the turbocharger is ideal and can be more economical than a naturally aspirated engine, especially when coupled to fuel injection. (If fuel injection doesn't come standard on your engine, forget it: it is too complicated to tailor a one-off roadable application.)

It used to be that you chose between superchargers and turbochargers by size and weight. Turbo installation had an advantage of being compact and fitting with stock hood clearance. They also had the advantage of weight. This no longer applies. The once universal "Jimmy" (GMC Roots-type supercharger) weighed about 110lb with ancillary equipment when installed and rose a minimum of 12 inches through the bonnet (hood) of most modern cars. Most turbo-

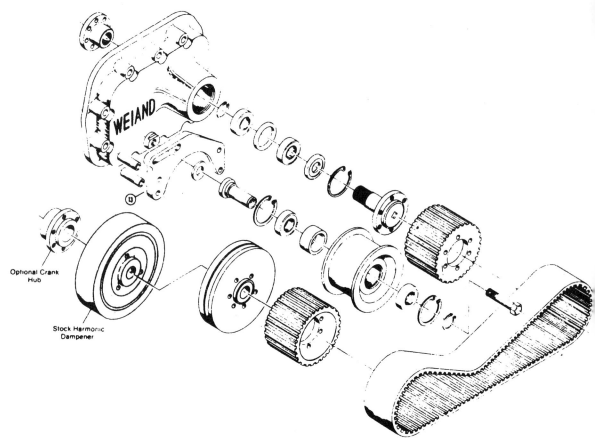

Figure 13.15. The secret of a good supercharger installation resides in buying the proper kit or, if you're doing it yourself, the right drive set-up.

Optional Crank
Hub

Stock Harmonic
Dampener

charger installations, by contrast, fitted under the bonnet and weighed, despite the somewhat less-than-aesthetic plethora of pipes, under 15lb fully fitted. While today's turbocharger installations are down to about 11lb, the supercharger has shed weight and size in a much more convincing manner: the latest Paxton, installed, weighs only 33lb. The Penco weighs 60lb and the B&M 50lb; both of these will boost a standard smogger 350cid Chevy to double its out-of-the-box horses and torque without detonation. Of particular interest are Jerry Magnusson's straight-rotor Magna-chargers which come in a variety of sizes and include a siamesed twin-supercharger version that fits under a stock Corvette hood – and therefore shouldn't have clearance problems anywhere else.

In the end, on a road car, your choice will be determined by the driveability of the car under *your* driving conditions and looking at torque curves is not a realistic or sensible way of deciding on such a major investment. My best advice is to find a purveyor who

fits both superchargers and turbochargers, explain your requirements to him very carefully indeed and get his agreement that, if he advises you wrong and you aren't satisfied with what he has fitted, he must then fit the alternative free of any charge (except the price difference between the two). The problem with this is that, while many suppliers will agree to the arrangement, they will insist on fitting the equipment in their own shop which can add a labour bill of between 10 and 20% of the equipment cost: you must decide for yourself whether it is worth that much for the "insurance".

Initial choice

In summary: Choose your standard, naturally aspirated engine with enough cubes to drive the car to the expected top speed and to accelerate it as briskly as you wish; in this form the engine should give between 45 and 55hp/litre. If you want more horses, improve the breathing with bolt-on and -in parts to 55–65hp/litre (or up to 70hp/litre with a good five-speed box). If you want still more power, turbocharge or supercharge either the bog-stock engine, or the mildly modified engine described, to put out 65–75hp/litre. Choose between supercharging and turbocharging by careful assessment of your road requirements and driving style with particular reference to your need for instant response versus operating economy, the first favouring supercharging, the latter turbocharging.

Don't

For a road car, don't tune it any nearer than 500rpm to the safe speed of the connecting rods, the pushrods or the onset of valve float, whichever is lower (and if you're having trouble with valve float, it's no longer a road engine in the definition we're using here). Don't fit an expensive new crankshaft, rods and pistons just because someone tells you they're the "performance option" – tell them firmly you're building a road car; responsible people won't try to sell you anything you don't really need. Don't switch from hydraulic to solid tappets because they're the "performance option" – in most engines hydraulic tappets are good well over the revs you would normally modify a road car to; they work and work and work with minimal attention. Don't buy gas-flowed heads from any but the most reputable modifiers and *do* buy the rest of your modification gear from the same people after explaining your requirements and securing their assurance (preferably in writing) that all the gear works together; don't buy anything they can't or won't show you an airflow diagram *and* a dyno power curve for (anybody can get massive airflow – it's *control* that separates the artists from the cowboys). Don't buy anything at all from a modifier who proudly displays highly polished ports as evidence of his craftsmanship – they're good only for separating out drops of fuel you'd rather have vaporized in air. Don't rush any assembly job: if it is worth doing, it is worth doing right. Above all, don't lie to yourself or any supplier about what you want from the engine: be conservative rather than radical and you'll improve the chances of being satisfied for a good long time.

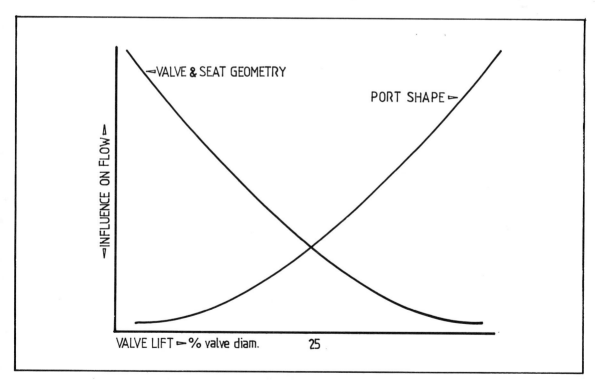

Figure 13.16. Anything more than a modest cleanup in the ports is wasted on road and even quite hot cars, as most roadable cams never lift the valves more than 25–30% of their diameter. Anyway, the valve is at half-lift twice for every time at full lift. (After a drawing by David Vizard.)

Figure 13.17. (Pages 176–180) The better engine specialists *specialize*. Oselli, whose services are listed here, once refused to work on my Bentley engine on the entirely sensible ground that they know nothing about Bentleys.

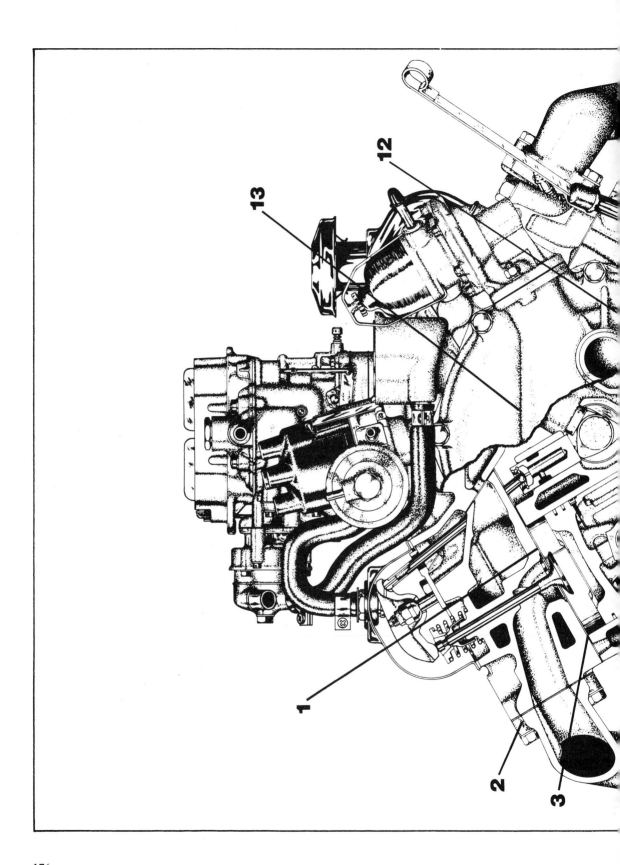

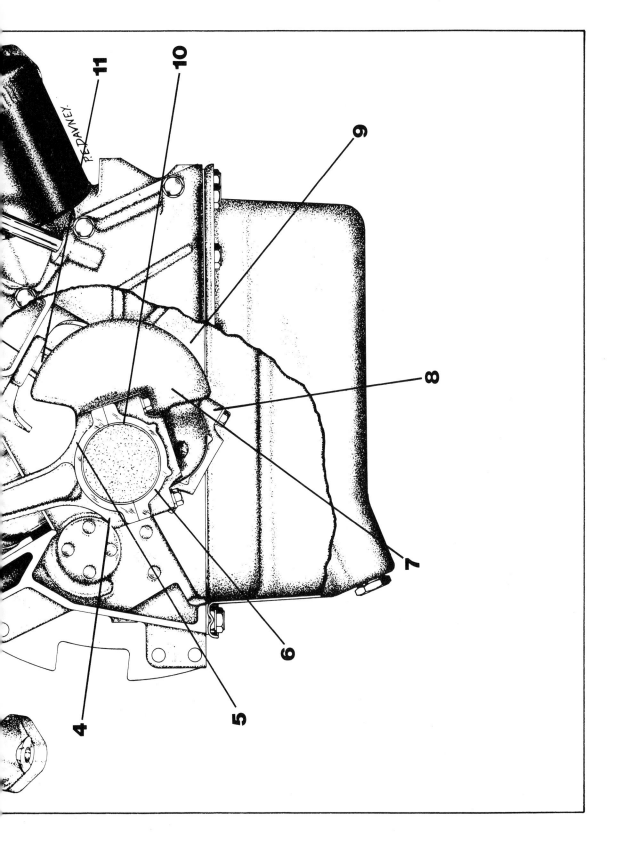

P.E. DAVNEY.

Cylinder Head Reconditioning and Modifying 1

We have recently invested a great deal of money in the latest American equipment for our Headshop and can now complete virtually any job on any cylinder head. Many Vee engines use complicated valve seat forms and compound valve angles and these present no problems to us. Cast iron heads with integral guides can also be reclaimed by machining and fitting guide sleeves, and three angle valve seats are one of our many specialities. Other operations include the manufacture of special alloy-bronze valve seats for aluminium heads, argon-arc welding to repair corroded aluminium waterways, buretting and grinding to cc chambers, replacement of bucket guides on O.H.C. heads, plus all the normal reconditioning processes. Additionally we offer a full gasflowing and modification service on all types, with a great deal of care and attention going into several hours' handwork on each head. Combustion chambers are balanced for equal volumes, and after assembly valves are vacuum tested to ensure correct seating. Inlet manifolds can also be matched and polished, and this should always be done when modifying the cylinder heads. Remember that the cylinder heads are the most important item when looking for power and tractability and money spent wisely here is a first-class investment.

Beadblasting and Helicoiling 2

If you are faced with a heavily carboned or rusted component, don't spend hours with a wire brush when our glass beadblasting service will bring parts up almost better than new at a very reasonable cost. Aluminium in particular comes out with a pleasant matt finish, and since there is no surface damage even machined parts such as pistons and valves can be treated. Heavily soiled components have to be degreased first, but the end result is a base metal finish ideal for the application of your "concours" paint finish.

Stripped threads or broken studs can be permanently repaired with steel helicoil inserts, and when used in conjunction with our alloy and cast iron welding services, there are few components which cannot be reclaimed. NOTE: Do not attempt to drill out broken studs yourself, it is much safer to let us to it properly on a pillar drill or milling machine.

Surface Grinding 3

Always check block and cylinder head faces during an engine rebuild, the extra work and parts required to carry out this job when a head gasket blows later can add up to a considerable sum. Remember also that many engines in standard form have the pistons much further down the bore than is desirable for maximum efficiency and compression ratio, and the block should therefore be surface ground to correct this. Cylinder heads come in for similar treatment, and once the chambers have been buretted the face is ground to give the correct volume. Vee blocks with unusual face angles are accommodated on a universal milling machine, and aluminium heads and blocks are also normally milled with a flycutter to give a very fine finish. We have a total of four machines at our disposal and can also resurface flywheels, discs, shims, cam buckets etc.

Crack Testing 4

There is nothing more frustrating than to spend a great deal of time and money rebuilding an engine unit only to have a rod or crank break and destroy all your hard work. For the sake of a few pounds invested in crack testing all the vital components, you can be assured of their condition and suitability for re-use. We can treat virtually any component, ferrous materials by magnetic detection, and other types by dye penetration, and in a highly stressed or competition unit we would normally recommend the testing of crank, rods, pistons, valves, springs and caps as being the basic essentials.

Lightening and Polishing 5

The forces operating on reciprocating components at high rpm are quite enormous and any weight saved on components can be beneficial to the performance and longevity of the engine unit. Conrods in particular benefit from the removal of surplus metal and great care is taken not to weaken the design of the rod. In fact many standard rods have inherent weak points, particularly around the big end bolt, and careful re-shaping of this area will reduce the risk of failure. Once the lightening process has been carried out the flanks of the rod are ground and polished to a mirror finish to remove all the casting flaws from which a fatigue failure can start, and the rods are finally shot peaned. Valve rockers will benefit from similar treatment and depending on the design of the individual engine several other components such as pistons, cam followers, pushrods, flywheels etc. can also be lightened by varying degrees. Remember that once any component has been machined to remove substantial weight, it is essential that the engine is rebalanced, and this applies particularly to Vee engines where the rod and piston weights directly affect the balance of the crankshaft assembly.

Tufftriding 6

(Low temperature liquid nitriding) This process revolutionized heat treatment of engine components when it was introduced about twenty years ago, as the low temperature used meant minimal distortion and the ability to treat finish machined parts. All ferrous materials can be treated, and the advantages are many, primarily, (a) increased wear resistance, (b) increased fatigue resistance, (c) corrosion resistant, and (d) very good self-lubricating properties. These features make the process highly desirable for any engine, and a virtual necessity for a modified unit if any degree of reliability is to be attained. Crankshafts are the most common component treated by us, but other items such as conrods, camshafts, followers, rockers, rocker shafts, pump drives etc. can also benefit. Prices are based on the weight of the component, therefore when enquiring for quotes please try to give the weight and type of material concerned.

Balancing 7
For many years we have offered a specialist dynamic balancing service, handling all types of engine units for several of the country's leading motor manufacturers and tuning firms as well as private individuals. In the mid-1970s we began to receive regular enquiries for the balancing of Ford V6 and Rover V8 engines, a service virtually unobtainable elsewhere due to the complexity of the operation, as the disposition of the big ends does not allow the crankshaft assembly to be in natural balance. It is therefore necessary to know the "balance factor" of the engine, and from this we can calculate the mass of the bob-weight required to simulate the reciprocating weight of the rods and pistons and enable the assembly to be balanced on our machine. We have now built up a wide range of standard bob-weights to suit virtually all common Vee engines and will also be pleased to advise on unusual applications. It is most important to remember that ANY modification or weight change of components such as crankshaft, conrods, pistons, flywheel and damper pulleys will affect the balance of a Vee engine and rebalancing is therefore essential. Even when the specification remains unchanged our experiences have shown that in many cases the production balancing leaves a lot to be desired and careful balancing can make a significant difference to the smoothness of the unit.

Cross-Drilling 8
In most production engines the position of the crankshaft bearing oil feed holes is a compromise, dictated by simplicity of production machining, and whilst these drillings are adequate for normal usage they will often be unsuitable for a modified or highly-stressed unit. In these applications the combined effects of increased bearing loads and of centrifugal force acting on the oil spray at high RPM, can lead to premature bearing failure, the remedy being to plug off the original feed hole and cross-drill the journal to divert the oilway to the point of maximum load. Please bear in mind that this work must be done BEFORE any hardening or balancing work is carried out.

Line Boring 9
Any misalignment or ovality on main bearing housings is detrimental to engine performance and reliability,

causing excessive friction on the crankshaft and possible bearing failure. It is important therefore to carefully check the housings for out-of-true and out-of-round and small irregularities can be corrected by line honing to correct. However, if the housings are badly out, or replacement main caps are being fitted, it is necessary to line bore the housings, and we are able to carry out this operation on most crankshaft and camshaft housings up to 3" diameter.

Crankshaft Regrinding and Restroking 10
There is much more to preparing a top-class crankshaft than meets the eye! On many occasions we have seen crankshafts up to 0.015" out of stroke due to either substandard original manufacture or subsequent incorrect regrinding, and this can have a very marked effect upon the engine. On a unit with 4" diameter 500cc bores and 9.5:1 compression ratio, a big end which is 0.015" out of stroke will cause a variation of half a ratio in C.R. (i.e. from 9:1 to 10:1 depending on whether it is longer or shorter), as well as giving a considerable out of balance force. Our grinding machine will handle crankshafts of up to 72" in length, and can operate to tolerances of 0.00015" on diameter and 0.002" on stroke. The operators are well aware of the necessity to grind the journal slowly to prevent surface burning, and great care is taken to ensure a good fillet radius is retained to give maximum strength. We can also rectify badly damaged journals by building up with submerged arc weld, a process far superior to the more widely used metal spraying method.

Shot Peaning 11
As a simple cost-effective means of surface strengthening this process takes a lot of beating, the principle being that the component is bombarded with shot at high pressure, giving a thin compressed surface layer which imparts a higher tensile strength. Conrods are the most popular item treated, but many other parts such as crankshafts and valve rockers can also benefit.

Reboring – Honing – Overboring – Step Sleeving 12
All our reboring and sleeving operations are carried out on a Danish Schou machine, generally acknowledged as among the best in the world. Due to the complicated angles of Vee blocks many firms use a small lightweight machine which clamps to the top of the block, but the Schou is equipped with a very rigid swinging fixture which locates through the main bearing housings. The advantages are several, primarily that the bores are assured of being vertical to the crankshaft centreline, and as the machine is also fitted with a sophisticated centreing device to accurately position the tool in the bore the finished result is as near perfect as can be attained. This same device also allows us to offset the bores to close tolerances when

necessary during an overbore operation. If you are faced with a block having a damaged bore or already at maximum oversize, do not despair, our step-sleeving service will restore it. Many people are discouraged from sleeving by stories of liners moving or dropping, but our method is to bore the block not quite right down the bore, leaving a step at the bottom, and the depth of this is controlled by an automatic cut-out on the machine. The liner is then pressed against the step and faced to the top of the block and once the cylinder head is fitted it is impossible for the liner to move. This method is infinitely more satisfactory than conventional straight linering or even flange linering, as the flange can crack off under extreme usage, and allow the liner to drop as if it were the straight type.

All boring work is automatically hone finished with a 45° cross-hatch pattern and we are quite happy to individually hone each bore to a precise piston skirt clearance if required.

Engine Blueprinting, Building, and Reconditioning 13

Our workshop is able to handle all aspects of fitting and assembly work on engine units, from straightforward removal and refitting of engine units to diagnostic tuning, blueprinting, race engine building, and high-quality standard reconditioning. The term "engine blueprinting" means the preparation of every individual component to the most beneficial specification within the tolerances laid down on the manufacturers' original design drawings, and is really only cost effective when the engine is being prepared for use in a restricted motor sport formula. For road use a slightly less rigorous job will give better value for money, and would normally involve checking and adjusting of all running clearances, complete balancing, piston and deck heighting, and tidying up of the cylinder heads. Manual and automatic gearbox work can also be undertaken, giving customers the peace of mind of being able to leave the whole job up to one firm rather than having to carry parts all over the country to be worked upon.

Miscellaneous Services

With an extremely wide range of machinery at our disposal there are few operations we are not able to handle, and other than those specifically detailed in this brochure the following will be of assistance to Vee engine rebuilders:

Reaming and honing of bushes etc.
Brake Drum and Disc refacing
Starter ring gear replacement
Small end rebushing
Piston valve cut-out machining
Cylinder block valve cut-out machining
Valve spring seat recessing
Press fit piston removing and refitting
Oil restrictor replacement
Conrod alignment and ovality measurement
Conrod straightening and housing reclamation
Crankshaft straightening
Ultrasonic cylinder wall measurement
Drilling and tapping
Milling
Turning
Grinding
Welding
Small component manufacture.

14 Test and Rectify

Once your car is built – or if you are modifying an existing car – you will need procedures to determine facts not available to you, to substantiate guesses you've taken in the construction about the aerodynamic efficiency and road friction, and to make and test modifications. There are three main areas of interest: setting up the suspension for the desired handling, roadholding and ride; minimizing road and wind resistance in so far as is compatible with the desired style and passenger capacity and performance of the car; maximizing engine and drivetrain efficiency.

The first thing to do is to set up the drivetrain. You will already have minimized friction in the drivetrain and other moving parts. Now set the engine up by

Figure 14.1. Don't forget you need lights and, most places, seatbelts too before your car is road-legal for road-testing.

tuning it very carefully. If the engine is out of the car for any reason, there will be at least another 5 horses you can find by tuning it on a dyno and fiddling around with the carburettor jets, the ignition timing, the dwell angle, the spark plug types and gap, the cam advance, air cleaners, etc. The 5 extra horses apply to very experienced tuners; for us lesser humans the difference between tuning by ear and tuning on the dyno can be as much as 10% – which comes to 20bhp on a medium-sized mildly tweaked Rover V8. Since dyno time is expensive, you must decide for yourself whether you really need the last ounce of efficiency out of your engine and whether the pleasure of a crisper engine and the fuel saving over your annual mileage will be worth it. You can't get the same state of fine tune on a rolling road. Whichever dyno or rolling road you choose, stick to it (none of those available to you is likely to be very accurate but what you're interested in is comparisons from some baseline, not super-accurate figures), make one change at a time and keep accurate records for comparisons against earlier and later tests.

The rolling road will tell you how many horses you have at the driving wheels. From this you can construct a horsepower and a torque curve at various rpm. The rolling road is also good to give you an indication of the increased power liberated from your engine by such big changes in breathing as we discussed in the previous chapter. Don't waste time trying fine tuning on a rolling road. In the main, you want two things from the rolling road: the torque and hp curves already mentioned (noting that these are at the wheels not at the flywheel), and an indication of the power band of your engine. If it is too narrow or too high, lower and broaden it by restricting the airflow through fitting smaller jets and/or carbs or a restrictor plate between the carb and the manifold.

The dyno and the rolling road are both steady-state devices (excepting some very expensive dynoes used by performance parts developers you're not likely to get access to) and so ideally suited to developing engines for steady-state applications like boat and truck and plane engines. Car engines are not steady-state devices. There is no substitute for the feel of the car driving on the road and in particular it is impossible to test the crispness of response on the dyno. For engine tuning, you want a section of little-used road about a mile long with wide curves and rising constantly and gently, together with a good run-up so that you hit the timed section at a good speed every time, say 70mph or the legal limit. The timed section should not be shorter than half a mile. Try to drive as consistently as possible and change only one thing at a time, keeping very accurate records including the temperature, the barometer pressure, the humidity,

the relative air density, the changes you have made and for each change the time averaged over three to five runs to accelerate over the measured stretch from your base speed. Obviously you should change gears at the same rpm to get consistent results. After the test at full throttle, repeat at half-throttle: this shows whether the improvement, if any, will be good in everyday driving. If you don't have access to a dyno or rolling road, this is the procedure to follow if you're tuning your engine for the last ounce of efficiency; it could take days but it is usually worth it.

Next you must set up the suspension. I am assuming that your suspension was designed and constructed so competently that there is nothing wrong with it, that it needs only fine-tuning. The reason I advise fine-tuning the engine first is that we don't want an expensive piece of equipment to detonate and blow itself apart while you're fine-tuning the suspension. However, if the roadholding or handling is obviously not right, you'd better stop and fix it before you kill yourself and then return to the engine.

To set up the suspension you need several roads, preferably little used with a variety of curves and surfaces. First find a fairly long piece of straight but very badly surfaced road. By driving across it at various speeds you will be able to judge whether the spring and damper rates and settings are to your taste. Major changes you will have to effect by changing springs and dampers. Don't forget the link ratio: unless the damper is mounted directly on the hub and travels absolutely parallel to the wheel (virtually impossible to arrange), the damper – and the spring around it – will move a distance different from that of the wheel. The required resistance in the damper rises as the square of the link ratio so that a change from 1.2:1 link ratio to one of 1.8:1 requires only 36% greater damping strength for the same damping (rather than the 50% apparent at first sight) and any change, softer or harder, without changing the link ratio, must be factored by the square of the link ratio. Minor changes can be brought about by changing the link ratio if you have adjustable inboard mountings which need be no more than a long bracket with a row of holes for mounting the inboard end of the damper. Soft long-travel springs and firm dampers give, in my opinion, the best compromise of ride and handling; if you can afford it, adjustable dampers together with variable rate springs give the best control, the variability of the springs ensuring a soft ride under most normal conditions without excessive wheel travel. You use the same piece of road to judge whether the car is properly insulated from road noise and vibration, again a matter of taste and personal preference, this time as a compromise between comfort and weight as proper

Figure 14.2. First the cost accountants make the car so soft it pleases even your Aunt Emily, then they sell you the goodies to make it handle again.

insulation (including thermal insulation) can weigh up to 400 lb on a big car; rubber bushed suspension and driving components will transmit less disturbance from road irregularities but also less "feel", so there is another compromise though not a very big one: no one except racers needs rose joints.

Next you want a mile-long stretch of level or rising road with wide sweeping curves. Drive through them at a constant speed (start with 30 mph and work your way up to the legal limit or 70 mph) and note the handling of the car. Do not do this test if there is any wind at all. Repeat the test several times at each speed, trying to drive consistently. What we want to observe here and correct if necessary, is body roll and over- or under-steer. If the car rolls too much, we can install a stiffer front roll bar but, if the roll bar has been

integrated in the design from the start, we must then also install a rear roll bar to re-establish the front/rear roll stiffness which governs weight transfer from rear to front. In general, though not invariably, a stiffer (i.e. thicker) front roll bar will result in more understeer and a rear roll bar added or increased in size will reduce the understeering tendency. You may also have to compromise some more with the spring and damper rates and therefore the ride. However, if your chassis is stiff enough and your suspension designed and built according to the guidelines in this book, no major changes will be needed. Instead you will be able to fine-tune the suspension merely by fiddling with the built-in adjustments for castor, camber and toe-in, and by choosing your tire sizes and inflation rates correctly. Bigger tires at the rear than at the front increase

183

Figure 14.3. Bad roads are everywhere but French pavé is surely the most destructive. Fast roads are fewer every year but the German autobahns hold out hope.

understeer or increasing the rear tire pressures relative to the front tire pressures will increase understeer or reduce oversteer. As always, change only one thing at a time, then re-test across the same road under the same conditions.

When the car has been set up to handle properly and the engine has been tuned, you should do the various acceleration tests (0–60mph, 60–90mph, whichever 20mph overtaking increments are of interest to you), and test the top speed some safe place where you won't be breaking the law (some race tracks and drag strips have "open days" but check before you turn up whether they require a competitions licence before they'll let you use the facility). Note all these results carefully and compare them with your desired parameters set out before you started designing your car.

You're now ready to check out the car's aerodyna-

mics, but the method we'll be using can be applied to determining the power and torque curves.

ACCELERATE AND COASTDOWN

First have the speedometer and tachometer accurately calibrated; do not just assume they are correct. Next weigh the car and the occupants – driver, recorder-assistant, camera operator for example – with the utmost accuracy. Next find a flat, level stretch of good smooth road and mark your start point clearly. You will need a notebook, a stopwatch and a tape recorder; if you need truly objective and accurate results, a video camera or 16mm camera with operator should also be carried to photograph the dials. If you can borrow an accelerometer reading in divisions smaller than 0.1g up to about 0.3 g (i.e. not the aircraft type which don't have divisions small enough to be of any use here) you'll save yourself a lot of work with the calculator and/or headscratching. Finally, choose a dry windless day for your testing and re-test only on windless, sunny days so that friction between your tires and the road is not a variable unless you want it to be, i.e. when you're trying out different tire widths, patterns or compounds. The average of six tests, three in each direction, is the minimum requirement for consistent results; it's very time-consuming.

If you don't have access to a rolling road or dyno and you want to build a horsepower and torque curve, this is easy with an accelerometer. For each rpm at set intervals (say at 200rpm intervals), calculate a speed necessary to give that rpm in top. Then drive along your chosen road at full throttle and when that rpm (or speed if you don't have a tacho) is reached, call "Now" at which your assistant records the reading of the acceleration on the accelerometer. About five miles or so over the speed, lift your foot from the accelerator, put the gear level in neutral and let the car coast. When you again reach the rpm or mph you are testing for, have the deceleration on the accelerometer read and recorded again. Now add the acceleration reading to the deceleration reading (adding the deceleration reading is by way of allowing for road and wind drag) and proceed to calculate the hp and torque by the straight-forward formula

$$\text{Force} = \text{Mass} \times \text{Acceleration}$$

where

$$\text{Mass} = \frac{\text{Weight with passengers}}{\text{Acceleration of Gravity}}$$

and the acceleration of gravity is $32.2\,\text{ft}\,\text{sec}^2$. Since the accelerometer readings are in g which is

$$\frac{\text{Acceleration of vehicle}}{\text{Acceleration of Gravity}}$$

it follows that

$$\text{Force} = \text{Weight} \times \text{Accelerometer readings (summed)}$$

This force drives the tires at so many mph which can easily be converted to comparable ft/sec:

Velocity (ft/sec)

$$= \frac{\text{Velocity mph} \times 5280 \text{ feet per mile}}{3600 \text{ seconds per hour}}$$

and, because we also know that one horsepower equals 550 ft lb/sec, we can calculate

$$\text{HP} = \frac{\text{Force} \times \text{Velocity}}{550}$$

To put it all together: HP at chosen rpm =

$$\frac{\text{Gross weight of vehicle} \times [\text{acceleration (g)} + \text{deceleration (g)}] \times g}{g}$$

$$\times \frac{(\text{Velocity in mph} \times 5280)}{(3600 \times 550)}$$

and the torque is found from the hp:

$$\text{Torque in lb ft} = \frac{\text{hp} \times 5250}{\text{rpm}}$$

When repeated at intervals throughout the rev range, the results will give you a horsepower and torque curve at the rear wheels. You can then construct curves of tractive effort (cascades) as in the previous chapter.

If you take deceleration readings every 5mph you can build a curve of road and air resistance – together, tractive resistance – and then test aerodynamic alterations or tire changes against it.

If you cannot borrow an accelerometer, you can use exactly the method described above but, instead of instantaneous acceleration/deceleration readings, you will have to use average acceleration and deceleration over, say, a five-mile segment, calculated as explained in Chapter 13.

The curve of tractive resistance is not so easy. You need a long, straight road on a good, windless day. Do several runs in each direction and average the results. From a speed that is as high as you feel is safe or legal on that particular road (the higher the speed the more accurate your curve), put the car in neutral and let it coast to a standstill, recording at each 5mph interval how long the car took to slow through that interval. Then, using the same formula from the previous chapter to calculate the average deceleration and convert it to feet per second per second, you can apply this formula:

Tractive resistance in lb f

$$= \frac{\text{deceleration} \times \text{gross weight}}{g}$$

where the deceleration is in ft/sec^2 and the gross weight of the vehicle is in lb. This ignores the inertia of the rotating wheels but the result will be accurate enough. The resulting curve represents the tractive resistance of your car which is the total of air and road friction against the body and the tires. Changing the weight of the car, the tires or the aerodynamics will move this curve or alter its shape.

The stage you are now at allows you to make comparisons against a baseline. You should have a complete set of cascades showing the tractive resistance throughout the speed range of the car, the tractive effort in each gear, the gear change points. Compare this with your calculations at the planning stage; compare this with your tested acceleration times. If there are differences, what causes them?

With your engine and suspension perfect, you can now afford to spend a lot of time on aerodynamic details such as the mass manufacturers determine very expensively in the wind tunnel. Tape tufts of wool or nylon to the body of the car and see how they behave at various speeds. Try various shapes of air inlets and wheel opening shapes. Air dams, spoilers and other major items are obvious but it is my experience that attention to the many small details pays off best in higher top speed and better mpg. For instance, if the windscreen wipers at rest are hidden behind a cowling merely for the sake of appearances, will bringing them

out into the airstream energize the relatively dead air in front of the lower windscreen or merely cause more drag? Alternatively, if they're in the airstream, does taking them off improve the tractive resistance curve? Rear screen wipers, it seems to me, are invariably wrongly situated at the bottom of the rear screen: at the top, since you can't keep the air attached any more, the vortex that the wiper mounting will cause were it mounted there will aid instant breakaway and so lower the aerodynamic drag.

Aerodynamics has enough hard math and theory surrounding it to be a science. Drag reduction is a craft and like all crafts it is perfected by hard graft on the actual goods rather than by sitting in front of a drawing board or a computer. You must – if you want the lowest possible Cd – pay attention to every detail on and under the car. Do you really need gutters; can they be covered with a rubber strip? Do you really need a large mirror each side? I approve of two outside mirrors, certainly, but small curved mirrors are more aerodynamic. Once you've attended to the size and shape of the mirrors, watch their *position*: can you integrate them better? Can you arrange for the radio aerial to be flush with the bodywork when retracted;

Figure 14.4. Setting up the suspension on this Sud-based Cheetah prototype has taken all day on this rising road with its treacherous righthander. Note on the return trip a milk run is taken to give everything time to cool down and the observer a moment to write up his notes.

can you wire it up to retract automatically when you switch from radio to tape?

Check the airflow through the engine compartment and the interior of the car as carefully. The oddest things happen when you get serious about drag reduction. I once picked up top speed equivalent to another 13hp merely by tilting the radiator of a car a couple of inches forward so that the air passages through it lay more in line with the air ducted to it. Neither I nor any of a number of engineer-friends have ever been able to offer a satisfactory theoretical explanation for even as much as half those phantom 13 "aerodynamic" horses (the engine ran no cooler and put no more horses down at the rear wheels). Check the effect of shorter and longer exhaust tail pipes. Duct the air as carefully under the back of the car as over the top. The opening or closing of interior air vents (not windows) should not cause any difference in the top speed of your car.

Here, regretfully, I must leave you before this book becomes the size and price of a small car! We have said nothing, or very little and then merely in passing, about the interior trim, the painting, and electrics of your car: information on these things is easily available to the enthusiast in books and the monthly regurgitations of the specialist magazines. Instead I have concentrated on an exhaustive analysis of the information and skills the would-be car designer and builder requires to start his car from the blank sheet — and that is available nowhere else. It was partly my irritation at the lack of a suitably compact handbook that led me to writing this one; additionally I don't like trusting my life (or my money) to memory on a formula last used three years ago, so that the shelf over my drawing board groaned under more than a hundred reference books plus a card file of notes on short-cuts laboriously worked out over the years, all for the first time gathered here.

The design and construction of an object as large and complex as a motorcar cannot be summarized in a few aphorisms but I think it fair to say that the outstanding characteristics of the successful special car designer and builder are neither aesthetic nor mathematical genius but the much more valuable plain common sense and perspiring perseverance.

I hope you will find this book useful in designing and building your own special dream car.

Good luck!

Publisher's Note

While the text of this book was written with an international readership in mind, a choice had to be made between English and American English usage for certain words. The list below is of words and phrases where the difference is more marked, with the English version in the first column.

baulk ring	: synchro cone	set off	: touch dry
body sill	: body rocker panel	set screw	: set bolt
bonnet	: hood	spanner	: wrench
boot	: trunk	spigot	: pilot
breaker's yard	: auto-salvage yard	split pin	: split cotter
bush	: bushing	swivel axle	: stub axle
choke tube	: venturi	trolley	: dolly
circlip	: snap ring	windscreen	: windshield
clutch release bearing	: throwout bearing	wing	: fender
coach bolt	: carriage bolt	withdrawal arm/fork	: throwout arm
control box	: regulator (box)		
crown wheel	: ring gear ('ring gear' in English is starter only)		
decoke	: decarbonize		
dynamo	: generator		
earth, chassis earth	: ground, chassis ground		
estate car	: station wagon		
float chamber	: carburetor bowl		
gearbox	: transmission		
grub screw	: dog screw		
gudgeon pin	: wrist pin		
layshaft	: countershaft		
methylated spirit	: denatured alcohol		
Mole wrench	: self-gripping wrench		
overrider	: bumper guard, bumperette		
panel beating	: body repair		
paraffin	: kerosene		
quarter light	: vent window (if it opens)		
	: quarter window (if it does not open)		
saloon	: sedan		
scuttle	: cowl		

Index

Numbers in bold type indicate reference to illustrations.